THE AMERICAN JOURNAL OF HYGIENE
MONOGRAPHIC SERIES

No. 20

THE SARDINIAN PROJECT:

AN EXPERIMENT IN THE ERADICATION OF AN INDIGENOUS MALARIOUS VECTOR

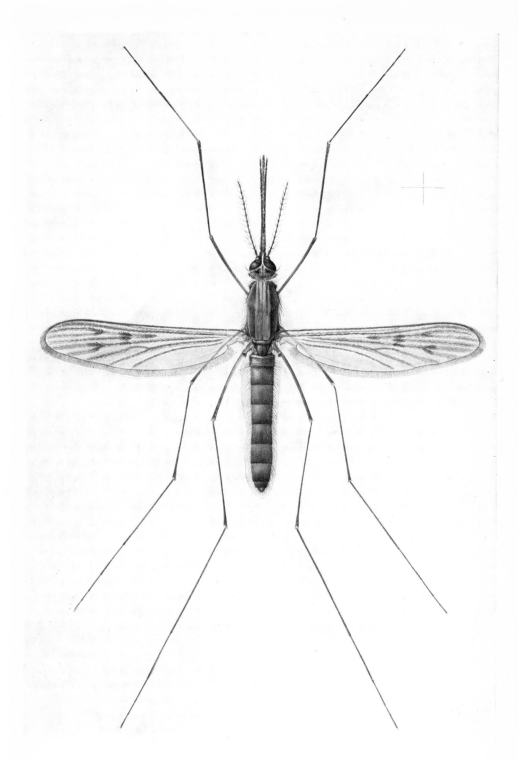

ANOPHELES LABRANCHIAE Falleroni ♀

THE SARDINIAN PROJECT:

*An Experiment in the Eradication
of an Indigenous Malarious Vector*

BY

JOHN A. LOGAN

with the collaboration of

THOMAS H. G. AITKEN
GUIDO U. CASINI
FREDERICK W. KNIPE
JOHN MAIER
ATHOL J. PATTERSON

1953

Baltimore: The Johns Hopkins Press

Copyright 1953, The Johns Hopkins Press.
Distributed in Great Britain, India, and
Pakistan by Geoffrey Cumberlege: Oxford
University Press, London, Bombay, and Karachi.
Printed in the U. S. A. by J. H. Furst Co.

Library of Congress Card Catalog Number: 53-11176

FOREWORD

This volume presents a report on a large-scale effort to eradicate the *Anopheles labranchiae* mosquito in Sardinia during the years 1946-50. Scientific interest centers on the attempt to determine whether it was feasible to eradicate totally an indigenous species of mosquito from a selected but considerable area. It had already been demonstrated in northeast Brazil (1939-40) and in the Nile Valley (1944-45) that the eradication of a non-indigenous species was practicable. The complete eradication of *Anopheles labranchiae* in Sardinia, as shown in this report, was not accomplished. In one sense, this negative result represented a " failure "; in a more fundamental sense, the negative result and the accompanying development of useful experience and information made an important contribution to knowledge in the field. This volume is published to make this experience and knowledge available to others.

Despite the " failure " of the experiment, the effort produced by-products of great value. Malaria in Sardinia was brought under control, substantial amounts of land were recovered for agricultural production, the entire island became a significantly more agreeable place in which to live, and large numbers of people were given employment during a critical phase of Italy's postwar period. Apart from valuable experience in eradication techniques, the Sardinian project presented interesting organizational and management problems involving, in addition to The Rockefeller Foundation, various agencies of the Government of Italy, the local government in Sardinia, UNRRA, ECA, and a number of private agencies. The manner in which these procedural problems were solved, or left unsolved, has some bearing on the organization of technical assistance programs elsewhere. In publishing this report, The Rockefeller Foundation considers that those involved in Operation ERLAAS are entitled to feel that their investment of time and money was worthwhile.

DEAN RUSK

The Rockefeller Foundation
New York, N. Y.

February 1953

vii

PREFACE

This report seems to me an important document. It describes a large-scale effort, carried out over a five-year period, to exterminate a mosquito, *Anopheles labranchiae*, on the island of Sardinia. At the end of the period the mosquito was still there —exceedingly rare and very hard to find, but definitely persisting. Malaria had been eliminated from the island rapidly and thoroughly, so that the operation, as a public health measure, was clearly successful. But in terms of its direct objective, the eradication of an indigenous insect, it failed. To me, as a biologist, this experimental failure is more interesting than the public health success.

There is frequent joking discussion among scientists of the need for a " Journal of Negative Results." No one has yet figured out how to arrange for such a journal, but the discussion emphasizes a real defect in our habits of scientific publication. The defect arises not so much from the nature of science as from the nature of man. We like to have things come out the way we plan them; and if something does not work out according to plan, and particularly if the deviation from plan is of a disappointing sort, we like to put it out of our minds as soon as possible or gloss it over by some process of rationalization. Yet, from the point of view of the advancement of science, the most interesting things may often be those that fail to come out according to plan; and when disappointment leads us to throw experimental data into the wastebasket instead of taking time to find out what we can learn from the failure to meet expectations, we are being human but not scientific.

The Sardinian project failed as a mosquito eradication measure; but this is quite different from saying that it failed as an experiment. It is the essence of the experimental method that the results are the consequence of the materials and procedures. Failure of the results to meet expectations or hopes, then, has nothing to do with the failure of the experiment. The results of an experiment cannot be wrong. The experiment may be badly planned, so that it fails to illustrate the point intended; it may be badly carried out, with mistakes in procedure and errors in record or observation; or it may be badly interpreted. But the experiment does not fail because the results differ from expectation.

The Sardinian project was, of course, a very special sort of an experiment, if only in terms of scale of operation. The participants, I suspect, were sometimes uncertain as to whether they were conducting an experiment or implementing a public health measure, and this uncertainty often seems reflected in the planning. The results, too, must be judged in contexts that are not experimental. After all, malaria did disappear from the island even though *Anopheles labranchiae* managed to hang on, and this must be taken into account in judging the expenditures of energy and money. Mosquito eradication looks like a sledge hammer approach to malaria control; but this too must be viewed in the context of postwar economy. Large funds for economic rehabilitation were available for immediate expenditure, and there was a generally felt desire to use some of these for public health measures of more than transitory value. Since malaria had long been judged the primary environmental handicap to Sardinian development, and since new techniques for mosquito control were available, this seemed an ideal point for mass attack on a public health problem. The expenditures, then, were made possible by these unusual circumstances; and the results must be judged not only in terms of public health accomplishment, but also in terms of the effect of the immediate expenditures on the economic rehabilitation of Sardinia.

The report, however, should be read as the record of an experiment. It has been written from this point of view, and the authors have consequently tended to emphasize their mistakes, their false starts and their uncertainties. This should give the record interest and utility to everyone involved in insect control. Beyond that, the report brings out clearly many deficiencies in our knowledge of insect biology, and consequently gives forceful documentation to the need for biological research. It contains, then, matter of value to all biologists, and to all people interested in the relationships between biological research and the solution of human social problems. Each reader will probably draw his own moral from the tale; but that is the beauty of it. The facts are here, for the thoughtful reader to ponder in terms of his own interests, prejudices and developing plans.

MARSTON BATES

TABLE OF CONTENTS

LIST OF ILLUSTRATIONS

LIST OF TABLES

LIST OF FIGURES

INTRODUCTION

Dr. Fred L. Soper, Director of the Pan American Sanitary Bureau and a leading exponent of the eradication technique for insect control, has said that in eradication projects you either have success or failure, you eradicate or you fail to eradicate. Since after an intensive effort which lasted for almost five years and which cost several million dollars, the indigenous malaria vector *Anopheles labranchiae* still persists in small numbers in isolated parts of Sardinia, eradication was not achieved and the ERLAAS [1] project, from this point of view, must be considered as a failure. However, while this failure has been most disappointing, ERLAAS was basically an experimental project and the final result was never predictable. Success or failure was, in this respect, therefore, incidental to the experiment itself.

As a result of ERLAAS operations, malaria as a public health problem has been banished from Sardinia, and for the first time in recorded history it is possible to live or work anywhere on the island in freedom from this age-old affliction. To the people of Sardinia, this is undoubtedly one of the most significant events in its long history. The bar sinister has, in effect, been removed from the Sardinian coat of arms, and the island has in the short space of five years found its status completely changed.

Besides, ERLAAS has meant more to Sardinia than an eradication project, an experiment or a malaria control campaign. Extensive ditching and drainage work have made available considerable areas of new farm land, and, of greater importance, ERLAAS's experience in every corner of the island has demonstrated the extent of its unused and potentially valuable agricultural, mineral and other natural resources. This

[1] Ente Regionale per la Lotta Anti-Anofelica in Sardegna.

has provided Sardinia with a unique opportunity, as at present it is underpopulated and can, on the basis of broad social-economic planning, decide how best to conserve or develop and utilize these resources for the future. A new Italian frontier has been established which is capable, not only of internal development, but also of absorbing large numbers of excess population from the mainland of Italy, thus making a twofold contribution to the life of the nation.

The report which follows describes the project in considerable detail. But it is very difficult, either narratively or through the use of statistics, to give a true picture of the difficulties and problems which were faced or the complexity of incidents which lie behind the bare figures. The reader can only infer these, but it would be remiss, in a report of this nature, not to record the whole-hearted cooperation which the project received from the people of Sardinia. This was true of everyone, from the High Commissioner and the President to the humblest peasant and shepherd. While it is impossible to list the names of the many people and institutions who should rightly receive recognition of ERLAAS's indebtedness to them, particular thanks and credit are gratefully acknowledged to the following:

The Italian High Commission for Hygiene and Public Health, in particular His Excellency Professor Gino Bergami, H. E. Professor N. Perrotti, H. E. Professor Mario Cottellessa, Senator Aldo Spallicci and Professor Saladino Cramarossa.

Mr. S. M. Keeny, Chief of the former United Nations Relief and Rehabilitation Administration (UNRRA) Mission to Italy.

Mr. James Zellerbach and Mr. Leon M. Dayton, Chiefs of the Economic Cooperation Administration (ECA) Mission to Italy.

H. E. Professor Antonio Segni, former Minister of Agriculture, now Minister of Education in the Italian Cabinet.

Professor Domenico Marotta, Director General of the Istituto Superiore di Sanità.

Professor Alberto Missiroli, the late Director of the Department of Parasitology of the Istituto Superiore di Sanità.

General of the Air Force, H. E. Pietro Pinna, former High Commissioner for Sardinia.

The Hon. Luigi Crespellani, President of the Autonomous Region of Sardinia.

H. E. Dr. Stanislao Caboni, Italian Government Representative in Sardinia.

The Prefects of the Provinces of Cagliari, H. E. Dr. Federico Solimena; Sassari, H. E. Dr. Speciale Gerolamo; and Nuoro, H. E. Dr. Volpes Goffredo.

General Carlo Cassini and General Alfredo D'Andrea, the Military Commanders of Sardinia.

Admiral Alberto Parmigiano, Naval Commander of Sardinia.

General Augusto Bacchiani and General Giuseppe Sgarlati, Commanders of the Air Forces in Sardinia.

Colonel Umberto Calderari, Commander of the Sardinian Carabinieri.

The Hon. Professor Giuseppe Brotzu, Minister of Health and Education for the Region of Sardinia.

Dr. Eng. Giovanni Zanfarino, the Director, and Dr. Aurelio Pisano, the Chief Medical Officer, of the Italian State Railways in Sardinia.

Dr. Eng. Giacimo Pellegrini, Director of the Sardinian Highway Department.

Dr. Eng. Faustino Martelli and Dr. Eng. Federico Visioli, the Directors of the Public Works Department in Sardinia.

Dr. Eng. Manfredo Manfredi, the Chief Engineer of the Cagliari Division of the Public Works Department.

The Hon. Professor Antonio D'Angelo, Rector of the University of Cagliari, and Dr. Euco Atzeni, the Director of the Department of Education in Sardinia.

Professor Francesco Passino, Chief Inspector of the Department of Agriculture in Sardinia.

The Sardinian Veterinary Research Station and, in particular, Professor Giuseppe Pegreffi and Dr. Antonio Medda.

Dr. Francesco Boselli, Director of the Sardinian Institute of Phytopathology.

Avv. Mario Palomba, State Attorney.

The Provincial Medical Officers of Cagliari, Dr. Aldo Duce; Sassari, Professor Antonio Canalis; and Nuoro, Dr. Michele Muzzetto.

The Presidents of the Anti-Malaria Committees of Cagliari, Avv. Aldo Palmas; Sassari, Avv. Nino Campus; and Nuoro, Avv. Pietro Monni.

The members of the ERLAAS Advisory Committee.

The members of the ERLAAS Special Technical Committee on Property Damage, in particular, Dr. Eng. Ruggero de Angelis.

Count Aristide Arrighi, late Director of the Sardinian UNRRA Delegation and of the Sardinian Delegation for International Aid.

Professor Mario Floris, Chief Malaria Inspector for the Province of Cagliari.

The Hon. Antonio Maxia, Legal Advisor to ERLAAS and his colleagues Avv. Tullio Mancaleoni and Avv. Attilio Chirico.

Cav. Michele Tufani and Comm. Antonio Deidda of the Italian Customs and Excise Department.

Avv. Gian Battista Benedetti and his colleagues in the Italian Court of Audit.

The Mayors of the Sardinian Communes, in particular, the Mayors of Cagliari, Dr. Pietro Leo and of Sassari, Comm. Oreste Pieroni.

Comm. Dr. Francesco Spano, President of the Sassari Law Courts.

Professor Giuseppe Martinoli, Director of the Botanical Institute of the University of Cagliari.

Professor Alberto Stefanelli and Professor Celso Guareschi, Directors of the Biological Institute of the University of Cagliari.

Most of the photographs which have been used to illustrate the report were taken by Mr. Wolfgang Suschitzky, of the Data Film Unit, of London, England. The only exceptions are plates 16, 51, 56 and 61, taken by Mar. Uda of the Italian Air Force, plates 39, 60, 67 and 68, taken by T. H. G. Aitken and plate 30, taken by Harold Trapido. The frontispiece, Terzi's drawing of *Anopheles labranchiae*, originally appeared in Marshall's *The British Mosquitoes*, and is reproduced through the courtesy of the British Museum of Natural History.

THE SARDINIAN PROJECT:

AN EXPERIMENT IN THE ERADICATION OF AN INDIGENOUS MALARIOUS VECTOR

CHAPTER I

THE BACKGROUND

The eradication of a malaria vector can be considered as a development of the theory, first proposed by Sir Ronald Ross, that malaria and other insect-borne diseases could be controlled by controlling the vectors. General William Crawford Gorgas demonstrated the validity of this theory at the beginning of the present century when he achieved control of yellow fever in Cuba through measures directed against the vector, *Aedes aegypti*. Gorgas also reduced the malaria rates in Havana through anopheline control, and subsequently gave a dramatic demonstration of the possibilities of this new type of sanitation in connection with the construction of the Panama Canal.

In Malaya, at the same time, Sir Malcolm Watson was demonstrating on a smaller scale the effect of anopheline control in the reduction of malarial morbidity and mortality and, indirectly, of all morbidity in a malarious area. Watson showed that only certain species of anophelines were responsible for malaria transmission in any given area, thus developing the idea of " species sanitation."

In the 1930's, while working on the control of yellow fever in Brazil, Dr. F. L. Soper and his colleagues developed the technique of species sanitation to a point where it became possible not only to break the transmission cycle, but to eliminate the vector, *Aedes aegypti*, entirely (Soper *et al.*, 1943). When the African malaria vector, *Anopheles gambiae*, was found to be firmly established in northeastern Brazil, and to be the cause of a disastrous epidemic of malaria, it proved possible to eradicate the mosquito by adapting the organization and techniques that had been developed in the course of the campaign against *aegypti* (Soper and Wilson, 1943).

This dramatic work in Brazil brought malaria control through vector eradication from the stage of theory to that of accomplished fact. The success was repeated in Upper Egypt, where an invasion of *Anopheles gambiae* was stopped, and the species eradicated (Shousha, 1948).

Many people believed that the success of the Brazilian and Egyptian campaigns was due to the fact that they were directed against an introduced, rather than an indigenous, species. It was felt that an introduced species might be in delicate and unsettled balance in the new environment, while an indigenous species would be protected by complex survival mechanisms resulting from the evolutionary process of environmental adaptation. The project in Sardinia developed from this background of controversy; the next logical step in the development of the eradication technique was an attempt to eliminate an indigenous vector species, in this case *Anopheles labranchiae*, from a region with a long history of malaria.

Before describing this project it may be well to give some background of the developments in Italy that gave rise to the idea, and of the geographical, climatic and social conditions on the island where the idea was carried out. Following this background material, the second chapter will be devoted to a narrative account of the history of the project. Details of methods and organization will then be discussed in chapters on the residual spray operations, on antilarval operations, and on the entomological and scouting service. The epidemiology of malaria in the island will form a separate chapter. This will be followed by a discussion of the administrative and the quarantine services and by a chapter on housefly control—a subject which became involved in the mosquito work because of its importance in public relations. The final chapter will be devoted to a critical review and evaluation of the whole experiment.

This general report will be followed by a supplement (appendix 2) by Dr. Harold Trapido in which the eradication experiment is viewed from the standpoint of a biologist, and a

supplement by Dr. T. H. G. Aitken summarizing the entomological knowledge gained in Sardinia. Finally, there are
included a few documentary appendixes of historical and operational interest.

ORIGINS OF THE PROJECT

The Ente Regionale per la Lotta Anti-Anofelica in Sardegna
(ERLAAS) was established by government decree on April 12,
1946 as a special agency of the Italian High Commission for
Hygiene and Public Health, to carry out an anti-anopheline
campaign in Sardinia. The project was financed by United
Nations Relief and Rehabilitation Administration (UNRRA)
and Economic Cooperation Administration (ECA) lire funds
and by The Rockefeller Foundation; the Foundation also
supplied technical direction through its International Health
Division. The project was begun on May 13, 1946 with an
entomological survey of the island and continued until late in
1950.

Sardinia was abandoned by the Germans in September 1943,
as their armies were being driven northward on the Italian
mainland. The problem of malaria control in Italy, which
had plagued the Germans throughout their occupation, now
became one of the major difficulties facing the Italian Government and the Allied authorities. The situation was aggravated
by the retreating Germans who deliberately flooded parts of
the mainland, an action that gave rise to a major malaria
epidemic. With the disease spreading at an alarming rate,
with no civilian transportation facilities and with serious
shortages of supplies, the situation was extremely dangerous.
Control had been practiced before the war by land reclamation,
drug therapy and the use of Paris green as a larvicide, but these
measures had broken down during the war years.

The martial law imposed in combat areas by the advancing
Allies was soon replaced by that of the Allied Military Government. As soon as an area was declared " noncombat " it was
taken over by the Allied Control Commission, a special division

of the Allied Military Government. This group, later known as the Allied Commission, controlled public health activities through a Public Health Sub-Commission.

With the incoming Allied forces came DDT. One of the new "wonder" chemicals of the Second World War, its use was originally restricted to military operations, and considerable quantities were used for malaria control in the vicinity of army camps and as a routine insect prophylactic by the troops. Civilians in Naples first saw the potentialities of this new insecticide demonstrated during an outbreak of typhus fever in 1943 (Soper *et al.*, 1947a). The epidemic, a by-product of the destruction of normal housing and sanitary facilities, threatened to put the city, which was then the principal Italian Allied port, out of action and menaced the entire Mediterranean area. In December 1943 a Rockefeller Foundation Health Commission [1] team working in cooperation with the Allied Military Government and the United States Army Typhus Commission began a systematic delousing of the Naples area, using DDT insect powder. The trend of the epidemic was reversed by the end of January 1944 and by April it was completely stopped. The results of this work attracted national and international attention.

In view of the outstanding success achieved in Naples, and on the basis of preliminary reports received from the United States, Colonel Paul F. Russell, Chief Malariologist of the Public Health Sub-Commission, requested permission from Brigadier George S. Parkinson, Director of the Sub-Commission, to undertake studies on the use of DDT as a residual insecticide for the control of *Anopheles labranchiae*, the principal malaria vector in Italy. Permission was obtained, and the project was approved by Colonel William S. Stone, Chief of the Preventive Medicine Section, and General M. C. Stayer, Chief of the Surgeon's Office of the Mediterranean Theatre of Operations of the United States Army.

---

[1] A special agency established by the International Health Division in 1940 to render public health services to war-afflicted regions.

The Rockefeller Foundation Health Commission was asked to undertake the studies. Residual spraying operations were carried out during 1944 and 1945 in the Castel Volturno coastal region north of Naples (Aitken, 1946) and in the Tiber Delta (Soper *et al.*, 1947b) with the cooperation of the malaria control groups of the British and United States armies. This work laid the technical groundwork for a nation-wide malaria control program for Italy, using DDT as a residual insecticide.

The national program was proposed by the late Professor Alberto Missiroli, of the Istituto Superiore di Sanità, in November 1945 (Missiroli, 1946). It was initiated the following year under the direction of the Health Division of the Italian UNRRA Mission, which began its activities early in 1945 under the energetic leadership of Mr. S. M. Keeny. The program was supplied and equipped with UNRRA imports and was financed by the UNRRA Lire Fund, which was established by the Italian Government with counterpart funds obtained from the sale of UNRRA relief supplies.

While much of the Lire Fund was used for current operations of an emergency nature, such as the malaria program, the mission was anxious to invest part of its funds in permanent projects. Dr. Fred L. Soper, Director of The Rockefeller Foundation Health Commission staff in Italy, was consulted in this regard and proposed to Mr. Keeny that, in addition to the national malaria control program, an experimental project be developed to investigate the possibility of using the species eradication technique as a permanent solution to the malaria problem in Italy.

Following a series of conferences between Mr. Keeny, Dr. Soper, Professor Missiroli and Professor Gino Bergami, Italian High Commissioner for Hygiene and Public Health, it was decided, despite the experimental nature of such a campaign and the doubts as to the possibility of its success, to establish an UNRRA Lire Fund project to attempt anopheline eradication. Both Sicily and Sardinia were suggested as suitable locations for the experiment, and Sardinia was finally selected.

Because of the temporary nature of UNRRA and the need to utilize UNRRA funds, transport and supplies, it was felt that the project should be set up as quickly as possible and completed while UNRRA existed. The International Health Division of The Rockefeller Foundation, under the leadership of Dr. George K. Strode, was impressed with the urgency of the situation and the opportunity it presented. On Dr. Strode's recommendation the Board of Scientific Directors of the International Health Division formally approved Foundation participation in the project on October 2, 1945.

Sardinia had always been considered the most malarious region of Italy and one of the most notorious in the Mediterranean. As it was believed to form a part of the epicenter of *labranchiae* (Missiroli, 1944), it was an especially challenging location for a demonstration of the value of the eradication technique against an indigenous vector species. Although the island provided adequate natural boundaries for an eradication project, it presented a particularly severe trial for the eradication technique because of its topography, its considerable area and its primitive state of development.

GEOGRAPHY

Sardinia (Sardegna in modern Italian) was called Cardossene (holy sandal) by the Phoenicians, and Ichnusa and Sandaliotis by the Greeks, because of its resemblance to a human foot or sandal. Other names have been Sardò, Sardon, Sardonos, Sardonia, Sardania and Sardenia (Fermi, 1934).

The island, with an area of 24,086 square kilometers, is the second largest island in the Mediterranean, being exceeded only by Sicily. It is slightly smaller than New Hampshire, and larger than Massachusetts. Its greatest length is 270 kilometers, and greatest width, 145 kilometers. It lies more or less in the center of the western Mediterranean, 186 kilometers from the African coast (Tunisia) and 231 kilometers from the Italian mainland. It is separated from Corsica to the north by the

Straits of Bonifacio, some 12 kilometers wide; Sicily lies 282 kilometers to the southeast, across the Tyrrhenian Sea.

Sardinia is a rough and primitive land of hills and mountains with scattered villages and large sections not served by either road or railway. From the standpoint of topography, the island can be divided into an eastern and a western division. While the western division comprises some flat land, rolling hills and moderately high mountains, the eastern division is almost entirely mountainous. In this latter area lies the Gennargentu Range, a granitic mass, which has the highest elevations of the island, with Punta La Marmora, which reaches 1,834 meters and Bruncu Spina, 1,829 meters.

A considerable portion of the coastal area is flat and fringed with swamps and salt or brackish water lagoons. The river systems have shallow tortuous beds, choked with vegetation. The mountain streams also contain heavy growths of vegetation and upland mountain swamps are common. While a number of land reclamation projects have been developed, many of these have been abandoned or neglected, and overgrown canals form a prominent feature of the coastal area.

Because of Sardinia's relative isolation from the rest of the world and the lack of internal communications, there developed, over the centuries, a subdivision of the island into regions whose boundaries were established by topography. Each of these regions tended to develop its own dialect, its own costumes and customs and, although the introduction of roads and railways has taken away a good deal of their individuality, the regions remain as important subdivisions, both culturally and geographically (figure 1).

HISTORY

Everywhere in the Mediterranean the traveler is aware of the time dimension in human affairs, from the monuments of the past that form such a notable feature of the landscape, and from the way of life of the people which reflects not only present needs and circumstances but also the vicissitudes of

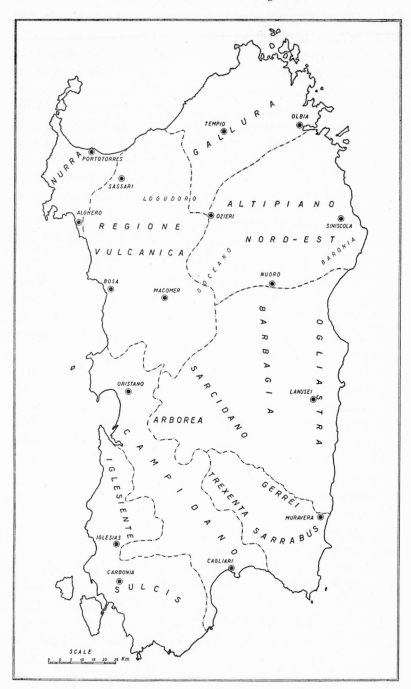

FIGURE 1. Geographical regions of Sardinia.

history. Sardinia is no exception. Centuries of raiding and pillaging have driven the inhabitants away from the coastline and into isolated villages, whose location was determined by defense rather than convenience. The stone, tower-like *nuraghi*, fortresses and watch-towers from the Bronze Age, some three thousand of them scattered at strategic points over the island, form a conspicuous feature peculiar to Sardinia—reminders of an industrious and populous past that has somehow slipped from the direct records of history.

As no signs of Paleolithic man have been found on the island, it may not have been inhabited until the late Neolithic, when the Mediterranean peoples had adopted agriculture and started working metals. Copper artifacts, as well as stone and obsidian tools, have been found in the earliest archaeological deposits, tombs cut into rock cliffs—the so-called *domus de janas* or " Houses of the Fairies." These may date from about 2000 B. C., when the Mediterranean was dominated by the maritime Cretans and when Mycenaean civilization was flourishing on the mainland of Greece. The tower fortresses, the *nuraghi*, are considered to date from the late Bronze Age, perhaps 1000 B. C. (Childe, 1925).

The Carthaginians controlled the island from about 500 B. C. to 238 B. C. and for a short time during this period the Greeks also maintained colonies. The Romans seized Sardinia after the Punic Wars and dominated it from the second century B. C. to the sixth century A. D. At the time of its conquest, it became an important source of slaves for Rome and later, as a Roman province, an important source of grain for the city. With the disintegration of the Roman Empire, Sardinia established itself as a separate kingdom. There followed periods when the island was successively under the domination of the Saracens, Pisans, Genoese and Aragonese. In 1713 Sardinia passed from Spain to Austria, and in 1720 the island was ceded to the House of Savoy. In 1841 it was merged with the Kingdom of Piedmont, which came to an end in 1861 with the establishment of the unified Kingdom of Italy. In 1949 Sardinia was granted the status of a semiautonomous region of the Republic of Italy.

The present-day inhabitants are a mixture of various Mediterranean peoples. While the official language is Italian, the language of the rural villagers, particularly in the mountain districts, is one of several Sard dialects, which have a common root in late Latin. In the vicinity of Alghero, on the northwest coast, where a Spanish colony once flourished, the dialect is a form of Catalan. In the Gallura, one of the eastern divisions, the influence of nearby Corsica is to be found in the speech of the inhabitants.

CLIMATE

The climate of Sardinia is typically Mediterranean, with relatively mild temperatures and moderate to scarce rainfall marked by pronounced seasonal contrast between summer droughts and winter rains.

The average annual rainfall for the island as a whole is about 800 mm. The driest region is the southwestern coast around Carloforte, where the annual rainfall during the years of ERLAAS operations varied from 220 mm. in 1947 to 420 mm. in 1950. The highest rainfall is in the mountains, and the station at Desulo, at an elevation of 920 meters in the Gennargentu Range, recorded rainfalls varying from 1,033 mm. in 1949 to 1,248 mm. in 1948.

From the point of view of mosquito control, the most important rainfall datum is the amount falling during the breeding season. To illustrate this, the averages for the seven principal weather stations on the island are plotted by season in figure 2. From this it will be seen that, although the summers are dry, some rainfall does occur—sometimes as much as 40 mm. in valley and coastal areas, and 80 mm. or more in the mountains.

Annual and seasonal mean temperatures are plotted in figure 3. Temperature conditions, of course, vary with altitude. The annual mean at coastal stations varies from 17° C. to 18° C., and at mountain stations, from 13° C. to 14° C. Means for the

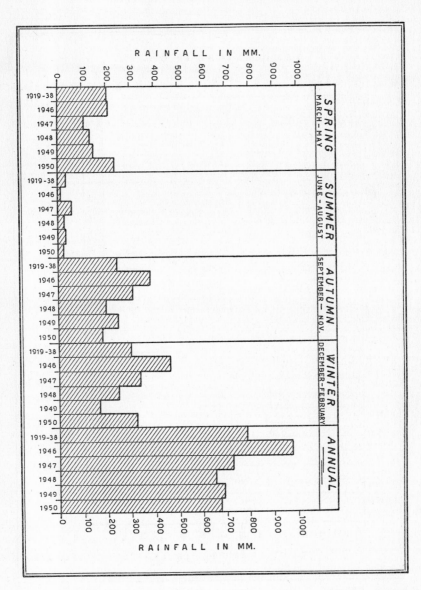

FIGURE 2. Rainfall by seasons, and total annual rainfall in Sardinia, averaged for seven weather stations; annual mean for 1919-38, and seasonal and annual totals for 1946-50.

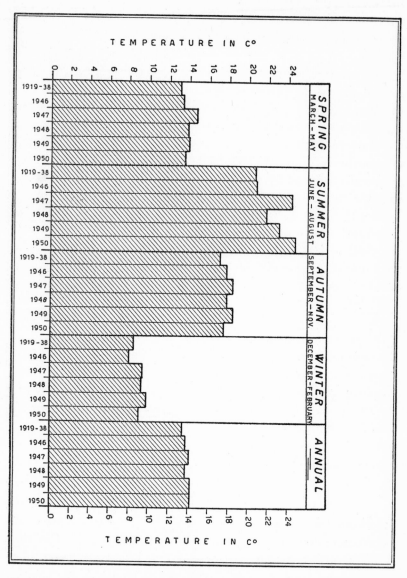

FIGURE 3. Mean seasonal and mean annual temperatures in Sardinia, averaged for seven weather stations, 1919-38 and 1946-50.

summer months range from 24° C. to 26° C. on the coast, and from 20° C. to 22° C. in the mountains. The winter months are cold enough to inhibit mosquito activity everywhere on the island.

The winter weather is particularly changeable, being controlled to a great extent by disturbances which bring periods of strong winds and bad weather. Depressions frequently originate in the southern Alps, but may move from any part of the western Mediterranean. In general, the prevailing winds are northerly or northwesterly throughout the year, but they are greatly affected by local topography. They tend to be more variable, but stronger, in winter than in summer, and sometimes blow with gale force towards the north and west coasts. The south and southeast coasts are more sheltered, except for the Gulf of Cagliari which is exposed to the northwest winds sweeping through the Campidano. The majority of winds are of force 3 or less, except in winter; winds of force 7 blow about 4 to 5 per cent of the time in winter and about 1 to 2 per cent of the time in summer. Winds of force 8 or more blow about 2 to 3 per cent of the time in winter, but rarely in summer.

Evaporation rates at four stations on the Campidano plain during the year 1950 were obtained from the companies operating the salt pans. These show high evaporation rates, varying from 2,617 mm. to 3,107 mm. for the year—to be compared with a rainfall of 249 mm. in the same region for that year. The evaporation rates in June, July and August averaged about 500 mm. per month.

VEGETATION

Although woods are nowhere extensive in the island, they are more common in the eastern mountains than they are in the west. Strong west and northwest winds along the west coast of the island tend to restrict the woods in these districts to sheltered valleys and hollows.

Among the few indigenous conifers are three species of

juniper: *oxycedrus* and *phoenicea* in the lowlands, and *communis* in the higher mountains. The yew also grows at higher altitudes. Alders frequently thrive along water courses; their bright green foliage contrasted against the otherwise parched summer countryside is almost always a certain indication of water. Cork oak grows rather generally at low elevations in mountainous areas. At higher altitudes one sees the common European deciduous oak and the fairly widespread ilex or holm oak. Chestnut trees are found over considerable areas in the mountains of the Barbagia. Some of the other common hardwoods are ash, carob, willow, laurel, fig, pear, olive and tamarisk. The Barbagia is the principal wooded area of the eastern mountains, but there are also extensive stands of cork oak in some sections of the northeast region, the Gallura.

There are now about 125,000 hectares of woodland in Sardinia, about one-twentieth of the total area of the island. One hundred years ago, one-fifth of the island's area was woodland, but due to poor forest management and to frequent fires, Sardinia's forest resources have diminished. The extensive overcutting of hillside cover for charcoal production is a common practice. The annual systematic burning, to supply forage for sheep and goats, is the principal cause of fires. By reducing the quantity of surface cover these practices have caused considerable erosion in many places. Flash floods take place in the winter and spring, and the streams have little flow during the dry summer months. To replenish the damaged forest resources some reforestation projects, largely pine, have been started in the southern mountains in the Sulcis, in the Senalonga Plateau and in the Limbara Range of the Gallura.

Perhaps the most noteworthy characteristic of the Sardinian hillsides is the extensive cover of brush and small trees known as *macchia*. This is comparable to the chaparral of western North America. It consists of a variety of shrubs, small trees and plants, the most common of which are: pistachia or lentischio, myrtle, strawberry bush or corbezzola (*Arbutus unedo*), heather and rock rose or cistus, philaria, buckthorn, rosemary, euphorbia, lavender.

In the cultivated areas, such as the Campidano and the Trexenta and around Sassari, the *macchia* has disappeared. Above 650 meters the low scrub merges into a high scrub that is difficult to distinguish from woodland. Permanent grassland is largely made up of rough mountain pasture but little meadowland.

Along parts of the western and northern coasts the fan palm (*Chamaerops*) is found. The common cane, cattails and oleander grow along many watercourses. Prickly pear or Indian fig (*Opuntia*) is commonly planted for hedge purposes, particularly in the southern portion of the island.

POPULATION AND HOUSING

The population of Sardinia, as of January 1, 1951, was estimated at 1,250,000, or 2.7 per cent of the total population of Italy. The island is divided into the three provinces of Cagliari, Nuoro and Sassari. The population and the density of population by provinces, according to the census of December 31, 1949, are given in table I. With the exception of Val d'Aosta (Piemonte), which has only 27 inhabitants per square kilometer, Sardinia, with 51 inhabitants per square kilometer, has the lowest population density of any of the regions of Italy.

TABLE I

POPULATION DISTRIBUTION AND DENSITY BY PROVINCES IN SARDINIA
(CENSUS OF DECEMBER 31, 1949)

Province	Area (square kilometers)	Population (to nearest thousand)	Population per square kilometer
Cagliari	9,297	640,000	69
Sassari	7,518	351,000	47
Nuoro	7,271	249,000	34
All Sardinia	24,086	1,240,000	51

The average for Italy as a whole is 152 inhabitants per square kilometer.

The zones of lowest population density in Sardinia are the Nurra, the Gallura, the Sulcis and the Sarrabus. Of the island's 326 communes, 272 or 83.5 per cent have populations of less than 5,000. There are 13 cities with over 10,000 inhabitants: Cagliari (129,000), Carbonia (48,000), Iglesias (23,000), Oristano (17,000), Quartu Sant'Elena (16,000) and Guspini (13,000) in Cagliari Province; Nuoro (18,000) in Nuoro Province; and Sassari (71,000), Alghero (21,000), Tempio (17,000), Olbia (13,000), Ozieri (12,000) and La Maddalena (11,000) in Sassari Province (Istituto Centrale di Statistica, 1950 a, b).

A striking feature of the distribution of the Sardinian population stems from the general absence of farmhouses and isolated rural dwellings. It has been estimated that 92 per cent of the population live in towns and villages. Only in a few areas are there numbers of scattered rural houses, as in the region around Alghero and in the Gallura. In many parts of the island it is possible to travel for miles without encountering a single dwelling. Another characteristic is that, apart from Cagliari and a few small ports, the coastal regions of the island are practically deserted.

In the rural villages of the southern part of the island, particularly in the Campidano, houses are generally constructed of adobe bricks made of mud mixed with straw; roofs are of cane covered with clay tile. The adobe is occasionally whitewashed or covered with coarse plaster. Stone houses are usual in the northern mountain areas.

The social and economic pattern of the island is largely rural. With the exception of the principal towns, the workers can be divided into two classes, shepherds and farmers. Shepherds and their families often live in isolated pasture areas for weeks at a time, sleeping on the bare ground in small huts made of reeds and branches known as *capanne*. The farmer normally lives in his village, and daily walks to and from his small plot of ground, which may be as many as 15 kilometers from the village.

Education

Illiteracy is fairly common in Sardinia. In 1939, 12.9 per cent of the persons married were unable to sign their names in the register, as compared with 5.5 per cent in all Italy (Allied Military Government, 1943). It is estimated that approximately 45 per cent of persons over six years of age are unable to read and write.

This situation is due to a variety of causes. School buildings are often inadequate or too few, especially in the sparsely inhabited mountainous districts remote from the larger centers. A survey made in 1949 by the provincial education officers indicated that 217 communes (67 per cent of the island's 326 communes) were without school buildings, and 92 communes (28 per cent) had inadequate buildings. Poverty keeps many children from school, either because they are forced to work or else because they do not have sufficient clothing and school equipment. A 1949 survey showed that approximately 66 per cent of the children were consistently absent from school. Although school attendance is compulsory, a considerable proportion evade the law by enrolling and then attending very irregularly. In the country districts especially, children may attend school for a few months in the winter and then leave school to help on the farm or with the flocks. Frequent illness has been another factor contributing to absenteeism.

Public Health and Vital Statistics

The crude live birth and death rates for Sardinia for 1949 were, respectively, 26.4 and 9.6 per 1,000 of population, compared with rates for Italy of 20 and 10.4. Infant mortality for the same year was 83.5 per 1,000 live births for Sardinia, and 74.1 for Italy (Istituto Centrale di Statistica, 1950 a, b).

The most important health problems, apart from malaria, have been tuberculosis, typhoid fever and trachoma. Paratyphoid fever, bacillary dysentery and brucellosis exist, but their true incidence is difficult to determine, since reporting of these diseases is far from complete. Reported rates for 1948 were 17.9 per 100,000 of population for brucellosis; 92.4 for typhoid fever; 35.8 for paratyphoid fever; and 4.7 for bacillary dysentery. While pulmonary tuberculosis is not a reportable disease, and its incidence cannot be established, it is without doubt the principal public health problem since the disappearance of malaria. The death rate from tuberculosis in 1948 was 84 per 100,000, as compared with 62 for all of Italy (Commission for the Study of the Reorganization of the Health Care Services, 1949). Morbidity data are not available for trachoma, which also is not reportable.

AGRICULTURE

Of the total area of Sardinia, only 3.6 per cent is classified as nonproductive land. Of the productive area, capable of producing some return from agriculture or forestry, 48.8 per cent is made up of permanent pasture; 25.3 per cent is cropland; 5.2 per cent is woodland and forest; 2.7 per cent is given over to olive groves and other fruit and nut trees; 0.3 per cent is grassland. The uncultivated but potentially cultivatable land represents 17.7 per cent of the total productive area.

The great majority of land holdings are small in size. In 1946, 71.4 per cent of the total number of holdings were less than two hectares in size, while 84.3 per cent were less than five hectares (table II). Less than 0.1 per cent of the total number of holdings were larger than 500 hectares; these holdings, however, comprised 26.2 per cent of the total area of the island. Only 32 per cent of the area of these large holdings was privately owned, the balance being owned by the communes. About 23 per cent of the island area was owned by the state, by the communes and by ecclesiastical administrations or commercial concerns (Istituto Nazionale di Economia Agraria, 1947 a, b).

Agriculture is made difficult by the climate. The possibility of irrigation is limited by the mountainous terrain. The

TABLE II

LAND TENURE IN SARDINIA IN 1946 (Istituto Nazionale di Economia
Agraria, 1947a)

Size of holdings, in hectares	Per cent of island area	Per cent of total number of holdings
Less than	5.5	71.4
2–5	6.4	12.9
5–10	7.3	6.5
10–50	24.6	7.5
50–100	20.6	1.5
100–500	9.4	0.2
500–1,000	4.8	< 0.1
Over 1,000	21.4	< 0.1
All holdings	100.0	100.0

destruction of most of the island's forests during the past
hundred years has denuded much of the mountain area, destroying a great deal of topsoil. The erosion of the hillsides is
accelerated because of overgrazing by goats and the constant
overcutting of brush and trees for charcoal.

The principal crops are wheat, oats, barley, broad beans
(*Vicia faba*), olives and grapes. The cereal crops are largely
produced in the plains of the Campidano and in the rolling
foothill country of the Trexenta, Arborea and Logudoro. Although much of the island, even in the mountain areas, appears
to be under grain cultivation during the growing season, the
yield in these marginal zones is considerably lower than in
the more fertile lowland areas. Most of the grain crop is
harvested by sickle and threshed by heavy stones dragged by
horses or oxen around a threshing floor of hard-packed earth.

Vineyards flourish largely in the Campidano, the Ogliastra
around Tortolì, the region around Sassari and in the neighbor-
hoods of Oliena in the Barbagia and Bosa on the west coast.
Olives are grown in the Gallura and the Iglesiente and in the
districts around Sassari, Alghero, Bosa and Oristano.

Fruit culture and vegetable gardening are also important.

These crops are usually irrigated from wells, using the primitive system of a donkey-operated, noria-type waterwheel. Windmills are rare. Citrus fruit orchards are principally found northwest of Oristano and around Tortolì and Muravera on the east coast. Peaches, apricots, cherries, apples, loquats, figs, pomegranates, walnuts and almonds are produced in small quantities in various parts of the island. Some rice is grown in the *Bonifica di Arborea*, which is irrigated by water from the Tirso River.

Cork is a leading export item, and production averages around 5,000 tons per year. The most important cork forests are near Sorgono, on the Senalonga Plateau and in the Gallura.

Both in numbers and by their contribution to the Sardinian agricultural economy, sheep are by far the most important animals (Casini, 1949). Goats rank second to sheep in importance. For the year 1948, Sardinia had 25 per cent of the total number of sheep and 21 per cent of the total number of goats in all of Italy (Istituto Nazionale di Economia Agraria, 1947 a, b).

Fishing

Fishing is not a leading industry, in spite of the fact that the waters around the island abound in sardines, tuna, red mullet, sole, anchovies and lobsters. Continental Italy has 18.5 fishermen per kilometer of coast, and Sicily has 28, but Sardinia has only four. This lack of development may be attributed again to the long history of coastal raids by hostile powers, which depopulated the coastal regions and forced the inhabitants to seek their livelihood in the interior.

Fishing methods are in general primitive. Of the 1,530 fishing craft registered, only 240 are power-driven or have auxiliary engines, and only 25 are of the trawler type. Most of the fishermen use lines, hand nets and pots.

Coastal water fishing production appears to be around 6,000 metric tons annually, while a further 1,500 tons is obtained from coastal lagoons. River fishing is negligible and no attempt has been made to stock the artificial mountain lakes. Tuna fishing, once important, has fallen off, but in 1949 Sardinia still provided one-third (about 550 metric tons) of the total Italian production. Beds for the cultivation of mussels and clams are concentrated principally in the Olbia Channel. The production of shellfish in 1949 was about 340 metric tons, or approximately one-sixth of the prewar average.

MINERAL RESOURCES

Mining constitutes the most important industry in Sardinia. Coal is the principal product, and the island is responsible for 80 per cent of Italian coal production. There are deposits of lignite in the western portion of the Sulcis, at Carbonia and Gonnesa, and small anthracite fields in the Ogliastra region. In 1942 Sardinia supplied two million tons of bituminous coal and lignite, out of a total production of 2.5 million tons for the whole of Italy.

Lead and zinc are next to coal in importance. They are mined in the mountains of the Iglesiente near Iglesias. Sardinia produces approximately 90 per cent and 75 per cent, respectively, of the Italian lead and zinc. The island also possesses deposits of cadmium, antimony, manganese, copper, nickel, iron, cobalt, molybdenum, tin and silver. Some of the metal workings were first exploited in pre-Roman times. The average annual production of the more important metals for the period 1936 to 1940 is shown in table III.

Salt pans at Cagliari and at Carloforte in the island of San Pietro are also of considerable importance. The annual production averages about 350,000 tons (ISIS, 1942).

COMMUNICATIONS

There are more than 4,500 kilometers of roads in Sardinia. Of these, 1,444 kilometers are national highways. Part of the national highways are asphalt-surfaced, but the rest are earth-surfaced on a stone foundation. Communal roads are either earth or cobblestone-surfaced, and are frequently in disrepair.

TABLE III

Average annual production of metal ores in Sardinia and in all Italy, for the period 1936 to 1940 (Inter-Service Intelligence Series, 1942)

Ore	Average annual production 1936–1940 (metric tons)	
	Sardinia	Italy
Lead	60,461	65,727
Zinc	147,400	195,935
Antimony	3,300	4,070
Iron	114,482	990,779
Manganese	2,296	40,065
Copper	5,109	13,325

There are few roads in the less inhabited parts of the island. With only 141 kilometers of national and provincial roads and 50 kilometers of communal roads per 1,000 square kilometers, Sardinia is the lowest of the Italian regions in length of road network (Istituto Centrale di Statistica, 1950 b).

The Italian State Railways operate a standard-gauge railroad network in the island, and a narrow-gauge network is run by private companies.

CHAPTER II

THE CAMPAIGN

It is surprising that, in spite of the importance of malaria in Sardinia, there was only a limited amount of information available, prior to the ERLAAS campaign, regarding the vector. Until 1925 malaria control was limited to the use of quinine and there was little interest in the identification or distribution of the anophelines on the island. However, a field station of the newly created Italian Malaria Experiment Station was opened in Portotorres in 1925 to study new control methods, and the first reliable information about anophelism in Sardinia was obtained. This work clearly demonstrated that *Anopheles maculipennis (labranchiae)* was the most important vector (Hackett, 1929; Missiroli, 1939). In addition to the work of Missiroli and Hackett, investigations had been carried out in the Loiri area by Pampana and Casini (1940) and in Cagliari Province by Spanedda (1940).

As the knowledge of the vector in Sardinia was based on these limited studies, the first ERLAAS plans were made with some doubt as to the number of anopheline species and where they would be found. Although it was generally agreed that *labranchiae* was the principal vector, no precise information was available as to its geographical range. Elsewhere it was considered to be a lowland species normally associated with brackish water. Thus Svensson (1940) stated that *labranchiae* preferred brackish water, and Hackett (1937, p. 61) that it was normally a brackish-water breeder. Missiroli (1944) noted that, although it could breed in either fresh or brackish water, it could not compete with other anopheline species in fresh water and was therefore a borderline species normally associated with brackish water. In Sicily, however, where *labranchiae*

25

was the only species of the *maculipennis* group found, it occurred in a wide variety of fresh-water habitats (Hackett and Missiroli, 1935). Of the other possible malaria vectors in Sardinia, *A. sacharovi* was also classified as a swamp or plains mosquito occurring only in the lowlands. It was surmised that *A. superpictus* might exist in the mountains but that it would be present in only very limited numbers.

Both *labranchiae* and *sacharovi*, as members of the *maculipennis* group, were thought to be highly domestic. Hackett (1937, p. 80) states that "*A. maculipennis* is a domestic mosquito, which means that it will enter any man-made structure without hesitation, and, in fact, almost all of its fundamental instincts for nourishment, for protection from the light and weather, for egg-ripening, and for hibernation cause it to shelter somewhere. Only the necessities of procreation and oviposition, and at times the impulse to invade new territories, take it out of doors. Most of its life is spent under a roof." Although malaria was known to be present over the entire island, it was thought that the disease was transmitted in the lowlands and that people in the mountains became infected only when they went into river valleys or near the seacoast.

Although the information about Sardinian anophelines was limited, it was not considered necessary to make further investigations. Dr. F. L. Soper, in a letter written to Dr. G. K. Strode early in 1946, stated: "The proposal to do ecological studies before undertaking antilarval work overlooks the fact that the *maculipennis* group has had more ecological study than any other *Anopheles*. Also, one really begins to learn the important ecological facts, that is those which render eradication difficult, only when the great bulk of the species density has been removed and points of resistance begin to appear. Sometimes ecological facts learned in study prove unimportant in the field."

Eradication was regarded as an objective which could be attained only through a complete concentration of effort. The end result was to be either success or failure, eradication or failure to eradicate, and any additional objectives would weaken the principal one. Even the study of malaria statistics as part of the project was not originally considered advisable as, again quoting from Dr. Soper's letter to Dr. Strode, "Malaria is entirely too coarse and insensitive an index to be used as a check on . . . antimosquito measures."

The early plans for the ERLAAS project were therefore drawn up without special provision for either entomological or epidemiological investigations. A temporary opportunity existed to obtain UNRRA materials and financial support to carry out a large-scale experiment, and, in the light of the existing information, it was believed advisable to proceed immediately rather than to jeopardize by delay the possibility of being able to start at all.

THE FIRST PLANS

On October 2, 1945, The Rockefeller Foundation agreed to cooperate in an "all-out attempt to eradicate *Anopheles* mosquitoes from the island . . . to determine whether or not the species eradication technique is applicable to the problem of malaria control in the Mediterranean region" (The Rockefeller Foundation Health Commission, 1945). On October 29, UNRRA agreed in principle to a malaria control project for Sardinia, to be carried out jointly by the Italian Government, UNRRA and The Rockefeller Foundation, and on November 26 designated the sums of $400,000 and 15,000,000 lire [1] to obtain transport and supplies for the project. It was hoped to get operations under way in the course of the following month. It was agreed that the project should be carried out by a special agency under the Italian High Commissioner for Hygiene and Public Health. While the legal arrangements for organizing this agency were proceeding, UNRRA technicians produced the first estimate for supplies and personnel (see appendix 4).

---

[1] At this time the official value of the lira was 225 per dollar. During the life of the project the official valuation was changed several times and finally stabilized in 1949 at 625 per dollar.

As they lacked specific knowledge of the topographical, organizational and logistical problems inherent in such a project in Sardinia, their calculations could be only approximate. The essential features of this first estimate were that the operations would comprise a combination of DDT residual spraying against overwintering anophelines and larviciding with Paris green during the breeding season. It was estimated that the entire project could be completed within a year at a cost of $2,766,019. No provision was made for a scouting service either during the treatment period or to check on the results of the campaign on the completion of the project.

It proved impossible to obtain either the supplies or the transport in time to begin operations in 1945. The official decree setting up the project was also delayed. With further delays continuing into 1946, it was decided to carry out an entomological survey of the island. A Foundation entomologist, Dr. T. H. G. Aitken, assisted by Dr. G. U. Casini of the Marchiafava Institute of Malariology, started work on May 13, 1946. In the meantime, on April 12, the official decree (see appendix 3) establishing ERLAAS was published, and on May 2 Dr. D. B. Wilson and Dr. Aitken were nominated as interim superintendent and vice-superintendent of the newly created organization. On May 14 the first meeting of the ERLAAS Advisory Committee (established by the decree) was held in Cagliari with the superintendent as chairman. In discussing general policy, he stated that "we have taken the stand that the campaign will not start until supplies sufficient for six months are at hand, and transport sufficient for two years is in the island."

Dr. J. A. Kerr, who had played a prominent part in the Egyptian *gambiae* campaign, attended this first meeting and afterward made a short tour of the island. Dr. Kerr noted in his diary that Sardinia would be a much more difficult region to work in than Egypt. He was particularly interested in defining the area occupied by *labranchiae* and emphasized that the survey should establish this. He also raised the question of whether *labranchiae* was able to maintain itself independently of man, for " even if eradication work is to be limited to *labranchiae*, it is essential to know how extensively it is able to maintain itself in the hills. What I have seen of the island convinces me that if *labranchiae* occurs at altitudes of above 500 meters, its eradication is not feasible, or even possible. The reason is that the organization of the necessary antilarval work would be so difficult and expensive as to be administratively impossible . . . it would be manifestly impossible to have the larvicider live in his zone as was required routinely in Brazil and Egypt." Before the end of the month, however, the survey reported *labranchiae* larvae up to 1,000 meters.

During the summer a serious infestation of grasshoppers threatened to cause disastrous crop damage and a resultant food shortage in the island. UNRRA flew in plane loads of benzene hexachloride insecticide from the United Kingdom and turned over all of the available ERLAAS transport to the Italian Department of Agriculture. The anti-grasshopper campaign was successfully carried through, but a number of trucks were lost and the transport as a whole received heavy wear.

The anopheline survey was gradually extended to cover the entire island. While the general nature of this work made it impractical to obtain detailed information on the mosquito populations, a number of essential facts were established:

(a) Five species of anophelines were found: *labranchiae, claviger, algeriensis, melanoon* and *marteri*.

(b) *Labranchiae* was by far the most prevalent species, accounting for 88 per cent of all anopheline collections made during the survey. Larvae were found up to altitudes of 1,000 meters.

(c) No *labranchiae* or other anophelines were found in brackish water.

(d) *Labranchiae* were found in large numbers at considerable distances from any human habitation.

Up to the conclusion of the survey there had been some discussion about eliminating the larviciding phase of the eradication campaign. This last finding, however, indicated that eradication could not be achieved by residual spraying alone.

In the meantime the Foundation proposed Dr. Kerr as superintendent of ERLAAS and, at a meeting in New York prior to taking up his new assignment, he recommended that:

    (a) The original one-year program be modified and extended to two years.

    (b) The new program include two residual spraying campaigns, the first during the winter of 1946-47 and the second during the winter of 1947-48.

    (c) Instead of an island-wide larviciding program in 1947, only the southwestern one-fifth of the island be treated at that time for test purposes.

    (d) The island-wide larviciding be carried out during the summer of 1948.

    (e) DDT be used as the larvicide instead of Paris green.

On September 12, Dr. Kerr arrived in Italy, and on September 16 he was named as the new superintendent of ERLAAS; Mr. F. W. Knipe was named vice-superintendent. At the second meeting of the ERLAAS Advisory Committee, held in Cagliari on October 2, Dr. Kerr's recommendations were approved in principle, and it was agreed that a new budget would be drawn up for submission to UNRRA and the Italian High Commission for Hygiene and Public Health.

WINTER 1946-47 — FIRST RESIDUAL SPRAYING

During the summer of 1946, materials, including transport, pumps, office supplies and DDT, were stockpiled in the ERLAAS warehouse. With the arrival of Dr. Kerr field work was begun, and on November 6, 1946, a full year after it had originally been hoped to start operations, the winter residual spraying campaign got under way.

Despite widespread unemployment, the project was immediately plagued with a shortage of capable administrative personnel. The High Commissioner for Sardinia, General Pietro

Pinna, was, however, most cooperative. He placed his entire staff and facilities at ERLAAS's disposal, particularly to help in the complex job of setting up accounting, supply, personnel and transport procedures. ERLAAS, although a semigovernment agency, was allowed considerable freedom in internal wage and accounting policies, but, in general, Italian governmental procedures were adopted as, in the final analysis, ERLAAS was accountable to the central authorities in Rome. Special regulations governing ERLAAS administrative policies, including those pertaining to salary and insurance scales, were drawn up and submitted to the Italian High Commissioner for Hygiene and Public Health.

The planning and operations of the first residual spraying campaign were, of necessity, carried out under pressure, without sufficient time for careful organization. The spraying was incompletely done, and although it was effective in bringing malaria under control, it did not contribute materially to the eradication of *labranchiae*. Instead of developing an over-all plan and estimate for the entire island, valuable time was lost in an attempt to build up the field staff by a process of selection from field crews in the Cagliari area. If a serious attempt had been made soon enough to find and train the dozen or so field directors needed, the work could have started out on an island-wide basis with authority delegated to the areas concerned. Instead, by the time enough foremen had been trained in Cagliari to extend the work to the provinces, it was too late to complete the campaign against the overwintering adults. In addition, for public relations purposes, most of the winter was used for spraying Cagliari and the other large centers where malaria was not a serious problem.

A difference of opinion existed as to the amount of DDT to be used. Since there was no satisfactory method for obtaining an accurate estimate of the surface area to be covered, the original estimate was based on 100 grams of DDT per inhabitant. This amount had proved more than sufficient to control malaria on the mainland, and it was assumed that the same quantity would be equally satisfactory in Sardinia. Instructions were given to spray at the rate of one gram per square meter but to omit the lower one and one-half meters of the wall and all ceilings over four meters in height in order to confine the total consumption to the estimated amount. The fact that no spraying was permitted behind pictures or furniture added to the considerable wall areas left untreated.

As the winter passed, it became apparent that the spraying could not be completed in time, and in March qualitative spraying was initiated. This limited the spraying to sleeping and dining rooms, kitchens and animal shelters. Although it was recommended that priority be given to rural areas, which building for building harbored more *labranchiae*, this proved difficult to follow. In April orders were given to omit certain of the mountain communes altogether and to omit more and more parts of the buildings to be sprayed. By June, when this phase of the campaign was ended, all but 42 of Sardinia's 326 communes had received some treatment.

During the winter months so much time was taken up with organizational matters and residual spraying that little time was left for planning the 1947 trial larviciding campaign. The possibility of postponing this trial from 1947 to 1948 and the island-wide larviciding from 1948 to 1949 was considered but not approved. In February 1947, a revised budget estimate was proposed to the High Commissioner for Hygiene and Public Health. The amount requested was 1,294,338,925 lire, and the plan was as follows:

1946-1947	Completion of residual spray campaign
1947	Trial larviciding
1947-1948	Second residual spray campaign
1948	Island-wide larviciding
1948-1949	Third residual spray campaign
1949	Entomological test for eradication

SUMMER 1947 — EXPERIMENTAL LARVICIDING

At the second meeting of the ERLAAS Advisory Committee there had been some objection to the trial larviciding plan on the grounds that eradication could not be accomplished in Sardinia by one season of island-wide larviciding. The need for a trial period had been demonstrated, however, and it was agreed to proceed on that basis. In April 1947, a larviciding service was organized and the experimental program started.

The original plan for the larviciding combined treatment and inspection. The smallest geographical unit for treatment and scouting purposes was called a sector. It covered an area in which all breeding places could be treated by one workman during a week. Again, however, instead of defining the total area to be treated, subdividing it on maps in the office into the required administrative and operational units and calculating supply and personnel needs on an over-all basis, a policy of delimiting the various sector, district, section and divisional units by field reconnaissance was adopted.

The training of field personnel was again carried out by the apprentice system used in the residual spraying campaign. It was hoped that there would be leaders among the new employees who could direct new zones and that the process of selection could be repeated. This system did not take into account the over-all needs of the campaign and overlooked the basic weakness of selecting key men by trial and error at the apprentice level.

The larvicide used was a solution of DDT in fuel oil with the addition of Triton X-100 as a spreading agent. A certain amount of data on this material was available in the technical literature, but it was felt that further investigations were needed under Sardinian conditions. Trials during the summer appeared to confirm the efficiency of DDT as a larvicide and the spreading power of the oil-Triton mixture. Specific data regarding the speed of kill were not obtained and the efficiency of the larvicide in difficult field operations, such as heavily overgrown swamps, was not fully investigated.

The lack of adequate preliminary area-planning left to field personnel the responsibility for defining the sectors, and in many instances difficult areas were overlooked, intentionally or otherwise. Following the precedent established in Brazil and Egypt, drainage and clearing operations were rarely permitted. The conditions that made treatment difficult in overgrown areas also made scouting difficult, with the result that most of these areas remained " blind spots " for both treatment and scouting.

By May 1, two districts had been organized, and during the summer this number was expanded until by July 1 two divisions (Cagliari and Oristano) with ten sections were in operation. Early in September it was decided to stop work in all except the three southwestern sections and to attempt to obtain larval negativity in these by the end of the summer. Larviciding was continued here until the third week of October, but scouting continued until the end of the month. No anopheline larvae (and only one adult) were reported during the last three weeks of the month.

Although the scouting service improved as the season advanced, it was relatively ineffective and the results obtained were of doubtful value for the following reasons:

(a) The scouts were inadequately prepared and poorly organized. The section chiefs were too busy with eradication activities to remedy this situation, and the chief scouts, who originally were paid by the day and were less capable, could not.

(b) Complete coverage within the sectors was not attained. The emphasis was placed on the total number of examinations instead of on the inspection of all breeding places.

(c) The scouts did not work hard enough. Scouting was considered easier than larviciding, and the standard of what constituted a day's work was far too low.

(d) The district chiefs and their assistants did little or no scouting, although this was supposed to be part of their duties.

(e) Because of unsatisfactory planning certain areas were neither treated nor inspected.

1. Goni, a typical mountain village in central Sardinia.

2. The Flumendosa River delta, a typical coastal plain.

3. Typical mountain terrain in the eastern part of the island near Muravera.

4. A section of the Port of Cagliari, through which most of the ERLAAS supplies were received.

5. A typical plains village, Ortacesus in the Campidano.

(f) Scouting was not done impartially by a group independent of the larviciding service.

(g) The number of scouts required was underestimated.

As the summer program drew to a close, personnel were transferred to a special department of the service known as the logistical group, which had the responsibility for delimiting in the field the operational units for the 1948 island-wide campaign. Again, it was a mistake not to do the over-all planning in the office on the basis of maps; it was thought, however, that field workers, advancing from the existing divisions of Cagliari and Oristano, could do the planning on the ground. Progress was slow, and again no check could be made on areas included or omitted. The basic planning for the future larviciding campaign was being entrusted to a large number of untrained personnel in the field, instead of being centrally controlled by experienced directors.

In order to facilitate the hiring and training of personnel for the future, the larviciding service started training schools in August. Instructions in larviciding, entomology, scouting, map reading, office and supply procedures and statistics were given. From these courses a number of the key field personnel used in later ERLAAS operations were selected.

During the summer, entomological investigations throughout the island, together with intensive scouting in the southwestern corner, failed to disclose either *sacharovi* or *superpictus*. The widespread distribution of *labranchiae*, however, as evidenced by both adult and larval captures, confirmed the view that this species was the important malaria vector in Sardinia. It was evident that *labranchiae* could be expected to develop in any fresh-water collection from sea level to the upper reaches of the highest mountain range. In any island-wide larviciding program, therefore, all collections of fresh water would have to be given treatment as potential breeding places. This eliminated any selective treatment, such as was possible in Brazil and Egypt, or such as could be obtained by omitting treatment above a certain altitude.

Investigations on *labranchiae* indicated that, because of its marked drop in reproductive activity in October and November, larval inspections could safely be stopped in October. It was confirmed that *labranchiae* did not go into a true hibernation during the winter but carried on a considerable amount of flying and feeding. These activities, however, appeared to be confined to the location where the mosquito was overwintering. The seasonal cycle of the species was observed at different altitudes and at different locations with particular reference to preferred habitats at different times of the year. During the winter isolated rural houses harbored a much greater number of adults than houses in villages. The seasonal incidence of adult *labranchiae* in uninhabited shelters varied from 1 to 29 per cent of the monthly collections, and both larvae and adults were commonly found in uninhabited areas miles from human habitation.

The investigations on the effect of the 1946-47 residual spraying program on *labranchiae* larvae were also significant. It appeared to have little effect on larval development, in spite of the general opinion that, because of *labranchiae*'s house-haunting affinities, it would fly long distances to find this type of shelter.

Nevertheless, 1947 saw the first definite break in the number of malaria cases in Sardinia. Beginning before the war, the incidence of the disease had mounted steadily until a maximum of 78,173 cases was reported in 1944. There were 75,447 cases in 1946, but in 1947 the number dropped to 39,303.

As the trial larviciding campaign drew to an end, some of the staff became increasingly pessimistic about the success of eradication under Sardinian conditions. The principal difficulties appeared to be the shortage of administrative personnel and the extent of the logistical problem. It was concluded that it would be extremely difficult to organize, staff and supply an island-wide larviciding program such as had been planned for 1948. In addition, costs were running considerably higher than those originally estimated (wage rates had increased almost

50 per cent in less than a year), and the revised budget approved in February was no longer sufficient. An additional 1,000,000,000 lire, at least, would be needed.

After a careful review it was decided that, although the task was undoubtedly much more difficult than originally believed, the objective of determining whether or not the species eradication technique was applicable to malaria control in the Mediterranean region had not been adequately tested. The difficulties appeared to be administrative rather than technical. It seemed advisable, therefore, particularly in view of UNRRA's desire to bring the project to a successful conclusion, to obtain additional UNRRA lire funds and continue as planned.

REPLANNING PHASE AND 1947-48 RESIDUAL SPRAYING

A request for an additional billion lire was presented to the Italian High Commissioner for Hygiene and Public Health in September 1947. The Rockefeller Foundation approved additional dollar funds. Dr. Kerr requested a reassignment and was replaced on September 24 by J. A. Logan. Through the cooperation of Professor Missiroli of the Istituto Superiore di Sanità, arrangements were made to borrow members of his department to strengthen the field and administrative staffs.

Owing to the uncertainty about future plans no provision had been made, during the summer, for further operations. It was decided in October to reorganize the administration and to replan the field operations, profiting from the mistakes made and the lessons learned (figure 4). The essential features of the new plan were as follows:

(a) Separate departments were established for larviciding and residual spraying.
(b) Basic geographical divisions of the island were agreed upon. Using these as a framework, a rational method of subdividing the entire island into sectors, districts, sections and divisions was developed. This work was carried out in three regional centers, one in Cagliari (southern), one in Nuoro (central) and one in Sassari (northern). The logistical group was eliminated.

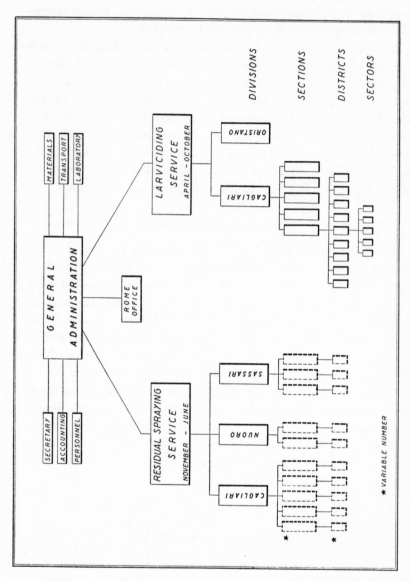

FIGURE 4. Organization chart, November 1946 to October 1947.

(c) The newly designed sector system was checked in the field, and when approved the sector and district boundaries were blazed, using distinct markings to identify the areas. On the basis of the newly planned sectors it was possible to draw up accurate personnel and supply estimates, to select district, section and division centers and to locate offices and warehouses.

(d) Deadlines, based on the time of the first spring ovipositions, were established for the completion of residual spraying against overwintering *labranchiae* and for the initiation of spring larviciding.

(e) A complete residual spray program was initiated with the aim of treating every man-built structure in the island with two grams of DDT per square meter. Pumps and equipment were overhauled, a DDT mixing plant was erected and seven field headquarters were set up in strategic parts of the island.

(f) An independent scouting service was established.

(g) An epidemiological section was organized and spleen and parasite surveys were started.

(h) A public relations office was established. Among other duties this office was given the responsibility of preparing monthly operation reports in both English and Italian.

(i) An office manager was appointed to take charge of supplies, transport, accounts, personnel, statistics and the legal department.

(j) New equipment was ordered, including seven Stinson aircraft for larviciding, Todd Insecticidal Fog Applicators (TIFA) for treating large buildings, ditching dynamite, additional transport, shoes, clothing and a variety of miscellaneous materials.

The residual spray campaign was initiated on October 7. In preparation, a refresher course was held in Cagliari for the men who were to be in charge of field operations in the seven zones. The treatment was designed to eliminate as many overwintering *labranchiae* as possible and to continue the suppression of malaria transmission. In addition to houses, barns, schools, public buildings, stores and factories, the interior surfaces of bridges, culverts, military entrenchments, mine shafts and many caves and grottoes were sprayed. TIFA machines or DDT smoke canisters were employed where the height of buildings made residual spraying impossible. The only areas omitted were the centers of the larger cities.

The spray teams were composed of local labor in most instances, but for rural areas and small villages special teams were selected. Animal transport was used wherever possible, motor transport being reserved for the transfer of supplies from village to village, for flying squads and for inspection purposes. The treatment was controlled primarily by scouting for mosquitoes and by chemical analyses of wall scrapings.

The campaign was finished by the deadline of February 15. With the inclusion of bridges, culverts and similar structures, the quantity of DDT per inhabitant rose to more than double the 100 grams originally estimated. All treated structures were given a stenciled reference number, and these ERLAAS markings became a characteristic feature of the island. By the end of the program, it was impossible to find a single structure untreated or unmarked.

As the residual spray operations continued, the larviciding service concentrated on marking field boundaries, selecting offices, recruiting and training personnel and stockpiling materials in order to meet the deadlines established for the commencement of antilarval operations. To facilitate treatment and inspection, section maps were blueprinted to indicate sector and district boundaries. A total of 3,400 sectors, 448 districts, 57 sections and 11 divisions were established under the three regional offices.

During this period preliminary studies were initiated in the development of a quarantine service to prevent the reimportation of malaria vectors into Sardinia once eradication was accomplished. A study of existing regulations showed that they were not applicable to Sardinian conditions. New regulations were drafted for submission, through the Italian Government, to the World Health Organization.

SUMMER 1948 — ISLAND-WIDE LARVICIDING CAMPAIGN

On the conclusion of winter residual spraying, all field operations were transferred to the regional directors (see figure 5),

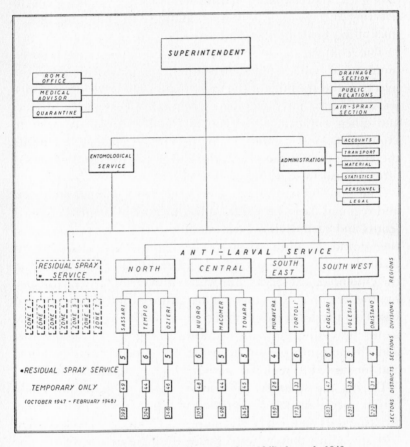

FIGURE 5. Organization chart, October 1947 through 1948.

but technical and administrative control was retained in Cagliari. To avoid misunderstanding and to expedite the dispatch of information to the field, weekly service orders were sent out to the regional, divisional and sectional offices.

The date established by the entomological service for the

start of larviciding in the greater part of the southern region was February 15; the dates for other areas, depending on their location, extended to the middle of April. The first two and one-half months of operations, until the end of April, were mostly of a preparatory nature as time had to be spent in selecting and training personnel, finding and equipping offices, stockpiling field supplies and actually getting work under way.

The completion of residual spraying operations released numbers of badly needed personnel, but even with these the selection and training of the more than 5,000 larviciders, scouts, section chiefs, microscopists, accountants, secretaries, drivers and other workers proved a major undertaking. In order to avoid bias, local committees of prominent citizens, including the village doctor, the priest, the mayor and the chief of police, often helped in selecting field workers.

The scouting service was developed on a sectional, divisional and regional basis, each section having a mobile squad of larval scouts and each division two mobile squads, one of larval and the second of adult scouts. The regions had small, highly trained squads of scouts who were technically responsible to the entomological service but whose itineraries were established by the regional directors. The entire scouting system was based on a series of checks and counterchecks, with the sectional scouts providing the basic scouting strength. All anophelines and all mosquito pupae (regardless of genera) were collected and forwarded to regional laboratories for identification.

During the summer, the concentration on mosquito eradication operations left little time for research and investigation. Routine tests on the larvicide, however, both as to DDT content and spreading power, were made throughout the year. The Adam method (1945) was employed for measuring the spreading power, based on standards supplied by Imperial Chemical Industries Limited. DDT determinations were run in the laboratories of the Istituto Superiore di Sanità in Rome. Field tests carried out in swamp areas to evaluate the mist technique of larviciding, with either benzene hexachloride or DDT, were disappointing. For eradication purposes, it was evident that the larvicider could not count on a larvicide mist to achieve general coverage of an area but had to give individual attention to every water collection.

Larviciding was routinely done with the small continuous-spray hand pump, but shoulder pumps proved more effective for large bodies of water and were distributed in a ratio of about one to every four hand pumps. Persuading the larviciders to get into the water was a serious problem. The Sard's dislike of water originated partly in the superstition that malaria was contracted by wading in cold water. It was aggravated by the discomfort of alternate wetting and drying, and especially by the damage done to boots and clothing. The quality of the field work often suffered because workers had bad shoes or no shoes at all. The nature of the terrain made good footwear essential. This led ERLAAS to issue boots and uniforms, but the problem of keeping these materials in supply and in repair was a difficult one.

Because *labranchiae* did not have a specific habitat, treatment could not be limited to any particular type of water collection or to any special area. All fresh water had to be treated, which affected not only *labranchiae* but all anopheline species. This gave a margin of safety for the eradication of *labranchiae*, and the difficulty of distinguishing one anopheline species from another in the field led to the decision, early in 1948, to attempt the eradication of all anophelines. This was not expected to add materially to the cost of the project and would assist, rather than jeopardize, the primary objective of *labranchiae* eradication.

By May 1, larviciding and scouting were under way all over the island, except for a few mountain districts where work was delayed by the severe winter. The shepherds and farm laborers who formed the backbone of the field staff turned out to be particularly adept at both larviciding and scouting, and their ability to live and work long distances from village centers under rigorous conditions was a pleasant surprise. It was necessary to establish over 100 district and subdistrict offices in uninhabited areas where various types of temporary structures were built. These centers usually received supplies by pack animal or oxcart.

The original intention was to list all breeding places in a given sector on special forms which could serve as guides for both the treatment and scouting. As this system proved unsatisfactory, the practice of numbering the breeding places in the field was adopted. The use of a numbering system helped to solve the problem of unknown breeding places, and special methods were developed in different areas to search out and number these.

Sectors that were too large were subdivided. In zones where running water was a problem, twice-weekly treatment was introduced. Paris green was sometimes used in sectors where beekeepers complained that the oil larvicide was destroying their hives. Special DDT bombs, or bubblers, were developed for use in wells and other places that were hard to treat by normal means. Areas where larvae were found were sometimes given residual-spray treatment for adult control, but this technique was not routinely adopted. It was believed that, in the final analysis, eradication depended on larviciding and that although residual treatment undoubtedly helped, its effect was not conclusive and the time and money involved could be better spent in larviciding. In addition, residual spraying interfered with adult scouting, which, according to Brazilian and Egyptian experience, was a more precise method of verifying eradication than larval scouting.

The air treatment section, using Stinson monoplanes piloted and maintained by the Italian Air Force, operated over much of the island, particularly in the coastal areas and in river valleys. A solution of 20 per cent DDT in Velsicol was used. Unfortunately, even repeated applications by this method did not achieve the percentage of kills needed for eradication, except in those areas where the water surfaces were prepared by large-scale clearing operations.

For drainage and stream-clearing, originally planned as routine measures to facilitate the work of larviciding, 25 tons of ditching dynamite were used. Pretreatment preparations were especially important because of the condition of water surfaces. The extensive coastal swamp areas were heavily overgrown with dense vegetation; many old land-reclamation projects which had been abandoned were choked with growth; streams and rivers in the mountains were covered with blackberry thorns or in the plains were filled with various types of aquatic plants. The extent of this need for preparing water surfaces had not been foreseen. In June, when the work planned in the budget was completed, positivity began to increase alarmingly. It became obvious that further large-scale clearing and drainage operations were unavoidable. Their extent taxed the ERLAAS resources of funds, transport, materials and supervisors. By September, instead of the total of some 5,000 employees originally provided for, the number reached more than 30,000, over 24,000 of whom were engaged in drainage and clearing alone.

The problem of employee morale was considered as particularly important because the final success or failure of the project depended on individuals operating independently and often under difficult and discouraging conditions. Posters, honor awards, special bonuses and an ERLAAS monthly bulletin were all used to stimulate the natural pride of the Sardinian in doing a good job. The Governor of Cyprus and the High Commissioner for Sardinia made a wager on the outcome of the eradication projects in their islands, which helped to promote a competitive spirit in the organization. These factors, together with repeated visits and inspections by administrative personnel, helped to build an ERLAAS *esprit de corps*. Delegation of individual responsibility for a given area, implying dismissal in case of positivity, proved relatively ineffective. Willingness to put in overtime and to carry out extra treatments and the intense loyalty to ERLAAS which were common in the summer of 1948 were due much more to team spirit than to any other factor. The press and radio were used for general publicity, and the people of Sardinia gave their whole-hearted cooperation to the project.

Unexpected problems developed in connection with labor unions. Regardless of the serious unemployment situation, the unions attempted to call strikes on several occasions in an effort to increase wages and allowances. ERLAAS wages were maintained at rates slightly higher than official rates, but one of the principal contentions of the unions was that our field workers (scouts and larviciders) should be paid as industrial and not as agricultural workers. This point could not be conceded and eventually agreements were reached.

Banditry was a more difficult problem. Armed holdups were a hazard, and bandits hiding out in a number of mountain areas threatened to fire on anyone who approached, thus endangering the scouts and larviciders. In spite of the obvious complications in reaching an understanding, matters were settled satisfactorily. Workers were sometimes threatened by property owners who did not want their wells or drinking ponds treated, but most of these difficulties were settled amicably and in only a few cases was it necessary to appeal to the police.

With the advance of the campaign the anopheline population was drastically reduced. As it became more and more difficult to find larvae, special attention was paid to the scouting service. To prevent collusion and to increase the spirit of competition, scouting squads were transferred from one zone to another and urged even more strongly to achieve complete coverage of every sector in the island. Since adult scouting did not prove efficient it was largely abandoned.

While from July onwards the anopheline curve fell sharply, it did not approach zero, as had been the case in Brazil and Egypt, but flattened out. Sectors which had remained negative for months and in which eradication was believed to have been attained suddenly were found to be positive. The cause could not be attributed to any large undiscovered infestation for usually the scouts found only a small number of larvae, and not infrequently just one. Unfortunately no direct comparison could be made with the anopheline population prior to ERLAAS operations. However, the original population was so large that 66 per cent of all water collections examined in 1946 were infected with anophelines, often in high numbers. By the end of 1948 it took hundreds of trained scouts working for weeks at a time to find a single positive breeding place. Nevertheless, these small numbers persisted and it was evident that eradication had not been attained.

Malaria continued its downward trend. The total number of cases for 1948 was reduced to 15,121, or less than half of the number reported in 1947. The spleen and parasite surveys initiated during the previous year also indicated substantial reductions.

During the summer DDT-resistant flies became a problem. The reappearance of flies in large numbers not only raised a serious public relations problem but also affected the morale of the organization. The inability to control flies raised doubts about the possibility of eradicating anophelines. A limited fly control program, using chlordane, was carried out, and it proved possible to obtain control as good as that originally obtained with DDT.

The new ERLAAS quarantine regulations were completed and approved by the Italian Government, the WHO Expert Committee on Quarantine and the First World Health Assembly. Following a detailed study of the sea and airports of Sardinia, the search for anophelines in incoming ships and airplanes was begun, and a number of experimental ship and airplane treatment procedures were carried out.

As the summer campaign proceeded, the task facing the organization was more fully understood, and it again became obvious that the funds available would not be sufficient. ERLAAS had adopted the generally accepted criteria for eradication as proposed by Soper and Wilson (1942): "No reappearance of the species, in the absence of reimportation . . . following the discontinuation of all control measures." Since it seemed certain that some foci would still exist in 1949, an additional year (1950) would therefore be needed in which to apply the test for eradication. In July the entire campaign was reviewed. The essential question was whether to confine operations to those possible under the time and financial limits imposed by the budget (although it was obvious that with these limitations eradication could not be attained), or to obtain more funds so as to continue operations into 1950. It was believed that the eradication of *labranchiae* was possible and that the project should be continued.

During the summer, while on an official visit to Sardinia, Mr. J. Zellerbach, Chief of the ECA Italian Mission, had expressed the opinion that ERLAAS operations were essential to any future development of the island. He stated that Italy had, on her doorstep, an undeveloped area which could absorb more population and produce relatively greater benefits for the homeland than any of the former Italian colonies. He thought that the ERLAAS project should be completed, not only as a public health measure but in the interests of rehabilitation. ECA financing was promised for this purpose.

The recommendation to continue the project was supported by the High Commissioner for Sardinia and confirmed by the ERLAAS Advisory Committee at a meeting held on July 17. A revised budget was drawn up requesting an additional 3,386,485,545 lire from the ECA Lire Fund and proposing that the future program allow for selective residual spraying in 1948-49, mop-up operations in 1949 and a test for eradication in 1950.

The High Commissioner for Hygiene and Public Health appointed a committee of leading Italian scientists to discuss the advisability of continuing the experiment, and on December 29, 1948 the following were invited to a meeting in Rome:

Professor M. Cottellessa	High Commissioner for Hygiene and Public Health
Senator A. Spallicci	Vice-High Commissioner for Hygiene and Public Health

Professor A. Missiroli	Istituto Superiore di Sanità
Professor G. Bastianelli	Marchiafava Institute of Malariology, Rome
Professor G. Raffaele	Marchiafava Institute of Malariology, Rome
Professor G. Buonomini [2]	University of Pisa
Professor A. Giovannardi	University of Venice
Professor G. Brotzu	University of Cagliari
Professor S. Cramarossa	Chief Medical Officer, Rome Health Department
Professor G. Cotronei	University of Rome
Professor F. Silvestri [2]	University of Naples
Professor G. Grandi [2]	University of Bologna
Professor V. Puntoni	University of Rome
Dr. T. Patrissi	Italian High Commission for Hygiene and Public Health (ACIS)
Dr. P. Moreschini	ACIS
Dr. C. Bessler	ACIS
Professor G. A. Canaperia	ACIS

The committee recommended that the project be continued, and the High Commissioner agreed to forward the ERLAAS request for funds to ECA, where it was approved.

SUMMER 1949 — MOP-UP OPERATIONS

On the conclusion of the 1948 campaign it was apparent that the eradication of *labranchiae* under Sardinian conditions imposed problems of a different nature than those met in Brazil and Egypt in the eradication of *gambiae*. It was necessary not only to adopt new methods but also to unlearn procedures that had originally been taken for granted. The principal fact established was the need for flexibility in planning, time limits and budget. The plan developed for the 1949 campaign provided for this flexibility and also made use of new techniques already tested and proved in Sardinia.

The regional type of administration (figure 6) was maintained because it had functioned well during the previous year.

[2] Unable to be present.

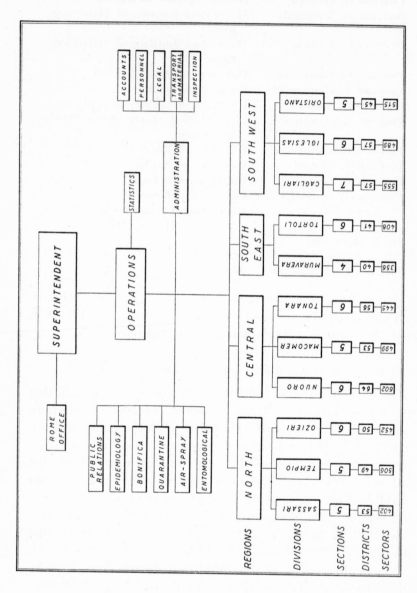

FIGURE 6. Organization chart, 1949.

Scouting was the major type of field work scheduled for 1949, and a special operations section was established to take charge of the technical aspects of this work together with any eradication activities which might be necessary. These latter activities became increasingly important as the year progressed.

It was agreed that the sector system used in the 1948 campaign was not realistic, in that the average size was too large to be adequately scouted or treated by a single workman in one week. The entire island was therefore remapped, with the following changes:

COMPARISON OF 1948 AND 1949 SUBDIVISIONS

	1948	1949
Regions	3	4
Divisions	11	11
Sections	57	61
Districts	340	534
Sectors	3,400	5,229
Average Sector Area	7.0 sq.km.	4.55 sq. km.

These revisions were subsequently made in the field, and all sector and district boundaries were re-marked to conform to the new plan.

The practice of numbering breeding places, started in 1948, was adopted and standardized for the entire island. The basic numbering was completed by the end of March. Although the task of numbering and recording over 1,250,000 breeding places was a difficult and costly undertaking, its value was unquestioned. The numbered breeding places formed the basis for all scouting operations.

During January training schools for divisional and sectional chiefs were held in Cagliari to review the fundamentals of scouting, residual spraying, larviciding and administration. Special courses were held for microscopists, of whom nearly four times as many were needed; they were assigned one per division instead of one per region. During February the regional directors and the divisional and sectional chiefs selected the scouts and gave them field instruction. Most of the forms used during 1948 were revised and simplified on the basis of the year's experience.

The original plans called for a third island-wide residual spray treatment during the winter months; however, this did not seem justified because of the high cost and the small reduction in *labranchiae* that could be expected. Instead, it was decided to spray all areas where *labranchiae* had been found after August 1, 1948. As this gave a spotty and not entirely rational pattern, the areas were joined and extended to give a more uniform coverage. Both DDT and chlordane were used. Approximately one-third of the island was treated, involving a population of about 215,000. The treatment within this area was not consistent, for village centers were sometimes omitted and in certain localities only animal shelters were treated.

In order to increase the efficiency of the mop-up operations several new items of equipment were purchased. They included two helicopters and two light crawler tractors equipped with Martin ditchers. The helicopters were obtained from the ECA mission on behalf of the Italian Department of Agriculture, with the understanding that they would eventually be used for experimental work in connection with the spraying of crops. Two pilots and an engineer from the Italian Air Force were specially trained to operate the helicopters, which were routinely flown and maintained by the Air Force. These machines proved to be much more versatile than fixed-wing aircraft and gave better coverage on the areas treated. During the winter, the fixed-wing machines were equipped with spray booms so that both aerosol and spray treatment could be carried out, either separately or at the same time.

A valuable addition to the equipment was the Rich fire tool, or mower-toothed rake, which was originally developed for clearing underbrush in front of forest fires. It was useful for opening up ditches and swamps in preparation for larviciding.

Misled by the great reduction in anophelism in 1948, the extent of the remaining mosquito positivity was underestimated in planning 1949 operations. It was believed that anophelines could be kept under control by the sectional scouts if larviciding was combined with their basic duty of checking on the positivity found by district scouts. *Labranchiae* eradication was to be achieved by permanent squads of men assigned to the sections found positive after August 1, 1948. These squads were to be responsible for the preparation and treatment of all *labranchiae* foci.

It was soon evident that the combination of larviciding and scouting was not satisfactory. The standard of scouting dropped considerably, and the casual treatment carried out by the sectional scouts during their checking operations was not sufficient to control anophelines, particularly *claviger*. This, together with a rapid increase in the number of *claviger* collections, led to a reconsideration of the objectives. It was decided to abandon the attempt to eradicate all anophelines and to concentrate on *labranchiae*.

As the permanent sectional eradication squads proved too inflexible to cope with the *labranchiae* positivity, a special eradication technique was developed. This consisted of the establishment of an eradication zone with a radius of three kilometers around each *labranchiae* focus. Six men were assigned to each zone to carry out a residual spray treatment of all man-built structures and grottoes, to do whatever drainage and water surface preparation were necessary and to complete four cycles of larviciding treatment.

This technique also proved inadequate because the period of treatment was too short and the allocation for clearing and drainage insufficient. A revised technique developed by midsummer lengthened the period of treatment, increased the time devoted to drainage and clearing and intensified the scouting in the eradication zones.

During 1949 weather conditions were much better than in 1948, and this tended to increase the efficiency of both larviciding and scouting operations. A fundamental error, however, was the decision to adopt a policy of a heavy scouting concentration in the early months of the year. It was originally believed that the sooner residual positivity could be detected the more time would be available for eradication, and that early scouting would be economical. Experience showed that scouting could not be efficient before there had been a considerable diminution in water area and an increase in larval densities. Much of the early scouting was, therefore, wasted.

As the 1949 scouting reports came in, it became clear that, besides the rapid development of *claviger* and culicine mosquitoes throughout the island, a number of pockets of *labranchiae* resistance remained, particularly in the northeast corner of the island. In order to confine this postivity, an emergency area was established toward the end of May. This area, which included six sections in the vicinity of Olbia and Arzachena, was given a complete residual spray treatment and was larvicided once a week for a period of six weeks. The treatment was not fully effective, for mosquitoes reappeared here later in the year. As considerable parts of this area received four residual spray treatments in all, it was obvious that this form of treatment was ineffective.

Toward the middle of the campaign the number of *labranchiae* eradication zones passed the maximum number that had been estimated, and, as the treatment of each zone was being carried out more intensively than originally planned, a budget revision was necessary. Since economies could be effected only in the scouting services, these were reduced as much as possible in areas where eradication appeared to be successful. Still, the savings were insufficient and a decision had to be made either to stay within the budget limitations and acknowledge failure, or to overspend and take a calculated risk in achieving the primary objective of eradication. It was decided to exceed the budget limitations, with the understanding that the 1950 program would be correspondingly reduced.

In spite of the large number of *labranchiae* collections the year's operations ended on an optimistic note. All efforts had been directed at *labranchiae*. The measures taken in positive areas appeared effective, and considerable areas of the island had remained negative for the entire year. More experienced and more carefully selected, the staff available for 1950 promised substantially greater efficiency than in previous years.

The first meeting of the WHO Expert Committee on Insecticides was held in Cagliari in 1949 to investigate the recommendations which had been put forth for the establishment of a Sardinian quarantine service. A report of the Committee's findings has been issued as an official WHO publication (1950a).

The problem of inaccurate malaria reporting, on the basis of clinical diagnosis alone, was dealt with by arrangements with the three provincial medical officers to have blood slides made on all suspected cases. A further reduction in the total number of cases of malaria was noted, 1,314 in 1949 as compared with 15,121 for 1948.

Summer 1950 — The Final Phase

At the close of the 1949 campaign, the winter months offered an opportunity to re-examine and re-analyze the previous year's work. Analyses during the period of operations had, of necessity, to be made quickly so that decisions could be immediately translated into action. More *labranchiae* were present than had been expected and it had been necessary to abandon, not only the attempt to eradicate all species of anophelines, but also the efforts to keep them under control. Because of the overexpenditure of the 1949 budget, the funds left for 1950 were inadequate to take care of any extensive recurrence of *labranchiae*. A new decision had to be taken, since this overexpenditure made it impossible to follow the previous plan. The choices were: (a) to close down the project completely; (b) to abandon further attempts at eradication and to utilize the remaining funds for malaria control; (c) to plan on extensive scouting only (the check for eradication) in the hope that no more *labranchiae* would be found; or (d) to obtain additional funds to complete the original plan.

Although the amounts already spent (about $11,000,000) greatly exceeded the original estimate, the goal of eradication seemed near. It was therefore decided to request supplementary funds to complete the project. Both the High Commissioner for Hygiene and Public Health and ECA gave their approval, and 500,000,000 lire from the Lire Fund were made available. The Rockefeller Foundation agreed to provide additional dollar funds for the completion of the work and for the preparation of the final report.

For 1950 operations, the elasticity of approach required during the trial and error period of 1948 and 1949 was no longer necessary, and control could be further centralized (figure 7). The number of divisions was increased from 11 to 12, each under the direction of a division chief who was directly responsible to the superintendent. Three principal services in Cagliari, entomology, eradication and administration, directed field operations. The epidemiological, statistical, quarantine, public relations and Rome offices functioned as formerly, but an important new addition was a budget control office. This office was established in recognition of the fact that many ERLAAS decisions had to be made, not on the basis of what was scientifically desirable but what was financially possible.

From the experience gained during the mop-up operations it was agreed that the eradication plan should be oriented toward greater emphasis on the treatment of prepared water surfaces. Instead of carrying on clearing and drainage operations and larviciding simultaneously, as in 1949, the entire eradication zone was first of all to be fully prepared for treatment. The period of treatment was extended to a minimum of eight weeks, the preparation of water surfaces to occupy the first week or ten days of this period. It was agreed that an eradication zone with a three-kilometer radius around the positive focus was adequate, except in the case of rivers. For rivers the zone was extended an additional two or three kilometers both up and downstream. More supervision of

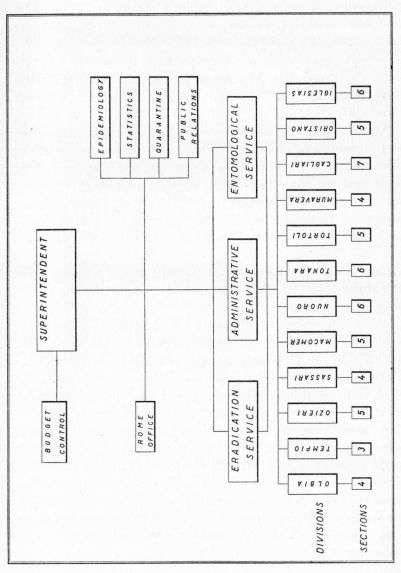

FIGURE 7. Organization chart, 1950.

operations within the eradication zone was considered necessary. All possible breeding places within a given zone were to be renumbered during the first week following the discovery of *labranchiae*. To avoid the difficulty of having larviciders who were unfamiliar with the zone working individually it was decided to use the squad system of treatment, with the work under the supervision of foremen who knew the area thoroughly.

Although the original plan established the treatment period at a minimum of eight weeks, this could be lengthened at the discretion of the eradication service. In practice, larviciding continued for more than eight weeks, except in those places where the delayed discovery of positivity caused work to commence late in the season. Residual spraying against adults was only carried out when it was felt that the circumstances warranted it.

One of the problems in field operations in previous years was absenteeism. During 1950 this was reduced by the use of a bonus system for key personnel paid on a monthly basis. A weekly bonus, increasing in size as the year advanced, was given to all satisfactory personnel, on the condition that they remained with the organization until the end of the season.

Scouting was considered the most important operation in 1950, and a great deal of thought was given to the development of a scouting plan, which, within the existing budget limitations, would give maximum returns. It was agreed that scouting operations carried out early in the year were inefficient due to the presence of large water areas, together with the fact that larvae did not usually appear in recognizable densities before April or May. Scouting operations in 1950 were postponed for the most part until June 1. It is significant that by the end of the second week of July, 70 per cent of the total *labranchiae* collections had been made. By comparison, only 46 per cent of the collections had been made by this date in 1949, even though scouting had been in progress much longer. This suggested that 1950 operations were more efficient than those of the previous year.

Although adult scouting had not given a satisfactory indication of the presence of *labranchiae* and larval scouting had been consistently more effective, it was recognized that in the extensive swamps of the island it would be difficult to obtain complete larval inspection. In these areas the relatively small number of natural and man-built resting places would tend to increase the efficiency of adult scouting. Although on occasion *labranchiae* were found in all types of aquatic habitats, experience indicated that they had a preference for certain types at different seasons of the year. Both of these factors were given consideration in the 1950 planning.

The plans for eradication had to be flexible because there was no accurate way of predicting either the extent or location of positivity. Financial allocations were made for as many as 100 positive zones. Eradication was directed by an eradication chief with four field assistants and two liaison officers who covered the island collecting report forms, checking on supplies and statistical returns and transmitting service orders. Responsibility for air-spray operations was in the hands of the eradication service. Field operations were the direct responsibility of the division chiefs, each of whom was given several eradication supervisors. The latter could be transferred from one division to another. A third crawler tractor with Martin ditcher was used in the early part of the year, together with the original equipment, to carry out a series of preventive drainage projects.

The first *labranchiae* collection in 1950 was made on May 15 at the mouth of the Liscia River in the northeastern part of the island, an area in which a number of foci had been found in 1949. As the routine inspections proceeded, the phenomena of repeat positive findings became the rule rather than the exception, and this proved one of the principal features of the year's operations. Of the total of 151 sectors positive for *labranchiae* in 1950, as compared with the 302 in 1949, 45 were positive in both years, and the remaining 106, with few exceptions, were in sectors immediately adjacent to 1949 positivity.

As *labranchiae* proved to be more widespread than anticipated and as it was decided to take more intensive action in
eradication than originally planned, it was necessary, in July,
to advance the schedule for making cuts in the scouting strength.
While the number of scouts was lower than that used in 1949,
this was partially offset by the fact that in 1950 the scouts were
more experienced than in preceding years and concentrated
their efforts later in the year. The service was both better
organized and better controlled.

The high percentage of *labranchiae* found in 1949 eradication zones called for a continual analysis of the eradication
technique. Prior to the initiation of the 1950 operations, the
staff had felt certain of their ability to eradicate once they knew
where *labranchiae* existed, and the major concerns were how
to detect positivity and to prevent the rapid development and
dissemination of *labranchiae* from undiscovered foci. This way
of thinking had to be radically changed as the 1950 campaign
progressed. More confidence was developed in larval scouting
as a tool to indicate the presence of *labranchiae* and it was
noted that the development of the species after it had been
reduced to a low level was relatively slow. Contrary to expectations, no explosive increase in *labranchiae* occurred. Even
in areas considered negative from early 1948, and untreated
for eighteen months, *labranchiae*, if still existing, were found
in fives or tens, not hundreds.

One logical explanation of the inability to eradicate in all
1949 positive areas seemed to be the failure of the larvicide.
Contributing factors may have been the shortness of the treatment period, ineffective larviciding due to delays in water
surface preparation and inadequate control of personnel.
Failure of the larvicide was indicated by reports from the
field that culicine mosquitoes did not succumb to repeated heavy
dosages of insecticide. Furthermore, in field tests run in the
Ozieri division with *claviger*, some larvae remained alive as
long as 13.5 hours after applications 25 times those normally
considered adequate. A series of investigations carried out

during the summer showed that although the larvicide possessed adequate spreading power and contained highly lethal concentrations of DDT, the chemical was apparently not getting into the tracheae of the larvae. While this penetrating power at first seemed to depend directly on the spreading agent, it was later found to fluctuate because of wide variations in the character of the oil. Even though oil complying with United States Public Health Service standards was used, no standard formula for the DDT-oil-spreading agent mixture could be determined. An attempt therefore was made to control the larvicide formulation by biological tests.

Eradication operations in 1950 were under better supervision than in previous years. The larviciders worked in squads under foremen, and their work was checked in turn by the zone eradication chief, by scouts, by special observers and by the divisional and central office staff. The treatment of water surfaces was greatly aided by the preventive work done prior to the initiation of eradication operations and also by the extremely dry year and the excellent work accomplished by the tractors, ditchers and mechanical brush-mowers.

Even though 151 sectors were positive for *labranchiae* in 1950 (as compared with 302 in 1949), it was believed that the goal of eradication was nearer than the figures indicated. Most of the 1950 positives were repeats, and *labranchiae* apparently had not dispersed widely from any given point since the start of eradication measures. This meant that in both 1949 and 1950 it was possible to isolate the positivity and, with a fair degree of accuracy, indicate where the species survived. In addition, 1950 eradication operations were, in every way, more efficient and more rigorous than those in 1949. The improvements in 1950 operations were:

(a) *Length of treatment*. In 1949 the initial treatment period was only four weeks; this was later increased to six, and in some cases seven weeks. In 1950 the treatment period averaged about 11 weeks, with a range of from four to twenty weeks.

(b) *Larvicide.* From the first week of August, a more efficient larvicide was used than that employed in 1949 and greater quantities were applied.

(c) *Controls.* The system of control of eradication operations was superior to that used in 1949:

    1. A mobile reserve of experienced eradication chiefs directed the work in the positive zones. The fact that these men were allocated according to the intensity of the positivity permitted a more rational distribution of supervision than in previous years.

    2. The eradication chiefs were given assistants (observers) whose sole duty was to check on the efficiency of eradication operations.

    3. Scouting operations carried out in the eradication zone afforded an independent check on the work of the eradicators.

    4. A bonus system gave assurance that all key salaried personnel stayed on the job.

    5. The centralized control of all eradication operations in Cagliari brought considerable advantages in matters of standardization and the allocation of transport, equipment and personnel.

(d) *Experience.* As in the case of the entomological service, 1950 eradication operations were staffed with men selected from the best trained in previous years.

(e) *Methods.* Emphasis was placed on the preparation of the eradication zone prior to the initiation of treatment. The larviciders worked in squads, rather than singly, and were more directly supervised than had previously been possible.

(f) *Administration.* The administrative service (transport, supplies, accounting and finance) reached a peak of efficiency.

In view of these factors it was believed that *labranchiae* had been eliminated from most of the known infested areas, and that any remaining positivity would be so isolated and scattered that it might take a number of years to discover and eliminate.

No malaria transmission was verified during 1950 (except for cases caused by blood transfusion) and the number of relapses reported was reduced to 40.

1951

According to the original plans, 1950 was to have been the year of final eradication operations, the initiation of a permanent quarantine service and the establishment of the ERLAAS successor agency. But, by the end of the campaign, while *labranchiae* had been reduced to very low densities, eradication had not been achieved. Nevertheless, the staff agreed, early in 1951, that eradication appeared feasible with routine scouting patrols and constant attrition applied over a period of years and that, under the circumstances, this would be the preferred method of control. A recommendation and plan to this effect were presented to the Italian High Commissioner for Hygiene and Public Health. After due consideration the proposal was rejected and it was decided that malaria control for the future would be carried out by residual spraying. The Regional Government decided, however, to continue the eradication program as a basic part of its insect control plan and this work is now continuing.

During 1951 both scouting and larviciding were carried out and, up to October 1, *labranchiae* was found in 72 sectors. Scouting was most intensive in the areas believed to be infested, on the basis of 1950 experience. However, the entire island was covered to some extent. Owing to the small number of scouts used (380), it is probable that other positive sectors remained undiscovered. It is surprising that of the 72 positive sectors, 67 or 93 per cent were either positive or under treatment in 1950.

The downward trend in malaria continued during 1951. The total number of cases reported (to September 15), including relapses, was reduced to nine. Of these nine cases three were reported as primary infections, but two of these were later found to be relapses.

This rapid decrease in malaria, together with the extent of the island's unexploited resources, led to a great deal of interest in rehabilitation. The Regional and Central Governments have accordingly established a commission to carry out a social-economic survey of Sardinia with a view to proposing a long-range development plan. This study is being carried out along lines suggested by ERLAAS in consultation with Lord John Boyd-Orr and will cover the fields of agriculture, mineral resources, social sciences, industry, public works, commerce and finance.

CHAPTER III

RESIDUAL SPRAYING OPERATIONS

The killing of adult mosquitoes by house spraying with pyrethrum played an important part in the successful *Anopheles gambiae* eradication campaign in Brazil (Soper and Wilson, 1943, p. 162), but the house spray method was not used routinely in the Egyptian campaign because both pyrethrum and DDT were in short supply (Shousha, 1948). The decision to use house spraying in Brazil was based on the success of this technique in previous operations for the control of the adult vectors of both yellow fever and malaria. While Gorgas in Havana and Oswaldo Cruz in Rio de Janeiro had used fumigation to control yellow fever almost 50 years ago, the first large-scale application of spray insecticide for the destruction of adult mosquitoes was the 1928-29 anti-*aegypti* campaign for the control of yellow fever in Rio de Janeiro (Fraga, as quoted in Soper and Wilson, 1943, p. 125).

As early as 1922 fumigation was tried for the control of malaria in Italy by Missiroli, who made an unsuccessful attempt to use cyanide gas as a fumigant against overwintering *maculipennis* mosquitoes near Nettuno, in the Pontine marshes (Missiroli, 1947). Later, pyrethrum spray applied once a week in rural villages during the transmission season proved an effective malaria control measure in various parts of the world. Soper and Wilson (1943) reported as examples of this technique the work done by Park Ross in Natal and Zululand, and by Covell, Mulligan and Afridi, and Russell and Knipe in India. In Brazil, Natal and Zululand, the weekly spraying resulted in a great reduction in the number of *gambiae* mosquitoes in the sprayed buildings. In India, however, although spraying brought a marked reduction in malaria transmission, it had no visible effect on the population of the vector species, *Anopheles culicifacies*, ". . . which was not essentially a domestic species."

Planning the Campaigns

As *Anopheles labranchiae* was originally considered predominantly a domestic or house-haunting mosquito, it was believed that residual spraying in Sardinia would not only control malaria but would also drastically reduce the mosquito population. Both of these premises were apparently confirmed by the experimental DDT residual spraying campaigns in the Castel Volturno (Aitken, 1946) and Tiber Delta (Soper *et al.*, 1947b) areas in 1944 and 1945. The reduction in the *labranchiae* population in both of these areas was so great as to suggest that *labranchiae* eradication might be achieved in Sardinia by DDT residual spraying alone. However, the first approved ERLAAS plan (UNRRA, 1945), which specified the completion of the project within a one-year period, while based on a DDT residual spraying campaign carried out during the winter months against the overwintering *labranchiae*, also provided for a summer larviciding campaign to destroy any surviving members of the species.

The 1946 entomological survey of the island produced enough evidence of the sylvatic nature of *labranchiae* to confirm the opinion that eradication could not be attained by residual spraying alone. It was concluded that, regardless of the help that residual spraying might give in the reduction of *labranchiae*, final eradication would depend on larviciding.

Because of the delay in starting the program and the decision to confine the first year of larviciding to an experimental operation in the southwest corner of the island, the residual spray campaign of 1946-47 was carried out primarily as a malaria control measure and not as a part of the eradication plan itself. The intensive spraying in 1947-48, however, was organized and conducted as an integral part of the eradication plan with the aim of killing the greatest possible number of overwintering *labranchiae*. This latter operation confirmed the earlier doubts about the effectiveness of residual spraying against *labranchiae*. Also, since anophelines were seldom found

6. A view of Nuoro, the capital of Nuoro Province.

7. Winnowing grain in Cagliari Province.

8. Plowing with oxen in Nuoro Province.

9. Cultivating with the *zappa* in Nuoro Province.

10. Harvesting olives in Nuoro Province.

resting in sprayed structures, the extensive treatment seriously interfered with adult scouting which was originally considered the most precise criterion for testing eradication (Soper and Wilson, 1943, p. 116). As a result, the second intensive spraying campaign planned for 1948-49 was replaced by a limited treatment of areas known to be particularly dangerous. Unfortunately, even in the absence of continued residual spraying, adult scouting proved inefficient under Sardinian conditions. Less and less reliance was placed on residual spraying as a part of the eradication technique during 1949 and 1950, and in the end this measure was practically abandoned except for fly and domestic insect control.

The residual spray programs, as finally carried out, may be summarized as follows:

Winter 1946-47 (November 1946—June 1947)
>   Island-wide partial DDT treatment to control malaria. Only part of the interior surfaces of selected buildings were treated. As the season advanced only the sleeping rooms were treated and certain mountain villages were omitted entirely.

Winter 1947-48 (October 1947—February 1948)
>   Island-wide complete DDT treatment of the interiors of all man-built structures to destroy the maximum number of overwintering *labranchiae*. Eradication type of residual spraying.

Summer 1948
>   DDT spraying of structures in the centers of large cities and in isolated buildings missed during the winter operations. Limited fly control with chlordane.

Winter 1948-49 (November 1948—February 1949)
>   Partial treatment with DDT or chlordane restricted to zones in which *labranchiae* were found after August 1, 1948.

Summer 1949
>   Residual spraying of eradication zones with either DDT or chlordane. Limited fly-control spraying with chlordane.

Summer 1950
>   Limited use of residual spraying in eradication zones considered especially vulnerable to this form of treatment, using either DDT or chlordane. Limited domestic insect control program by the Regional Government using chlordane.

The extent of the various treatments is indicated in table IV.

TABLE IV

SUMMARY OF RESIDUAL SPRAYING OPERATIONS IN SARDINIA

Campaign	Number of rooms treated	Population protected	Per cent of total population	Island area covered (square kilometers)	Per cent of total area
Winter 1946–47	1,504,547	1,082,395	86.6	23,166	96.1
Winter 1947–48	2,129,532	1,097,629	87.8	24,070	99.5
Summer 1948	573,694	619,250	49.5	*	*
Winter 1948–49	428,167	214,732	17.2	4,532	18.8
Summer 1949	175,756	84,029	6.7	2,079	8.6
Summer 1950	49,964	26,377	2.1	519	2.1

* Treatment of towns and villages only.

ORGANIZATION AND PERSONNEL

The 1946-47 and 1947-48 winter spraying operations were directed by central residual spray departments, but from the summer of 1948 until the summer of 1950, this work was supervised by the regional administrations. The limited 1950 program was under the control of the eradication service. During 1946-47 the field organization varied considerably, and the size and location of the divisions, sections and districts changed as the work progressed. Beginning with the 1947-48 operations, an island-wide organization came into existence with established areas and headquarters.

Spraying was normally done by squads made up of five operators and a foreman. The number of squads in a given area varied depending on the amount of work to be done, two or more squads being under the direction of a supervisor. Each group of squads worked from a central warehouse which was in the charge of a storekeeper responsible for checking the supplies of insecticides and equipment. Weekly insecticide inventories were made through the squad supervisors who were responsible for making an independent check on consumption. It was also the supervisors' duty to record the day-by-day progress of the squads under their supervision, including the number of buildings and rooms treated and the quantity of insecticide used. The supervisors also checked with each squad foreman on progress and workmanship, observed and corrected faulty spray techniques and informed property owners of the approach of the spray squads. After a structure was treated, a sign was painted on the outside wall and a control card fastened on the inside of the structure. Weekly work summaries were compiled for statistical purposes. Supervisors were permanent ERLAAS staff members, but foremen and operators were temporary workers.

Training was originally given by the apprentice system, Cagliari serving as the instruction center. Men selected from the Cagliari training squads acted as supervisors in other parts of the island. These supervisors, in turn, selected foremen and operators in the field and before work was started instructed them briefly in the operation and maintenance of the pumps and in spraying technique. After the first campaign, training was decentralized and made the responsibility of the field directors. A nucleus of trained personnel from the 1946-47 campaign greatly facilitated the 1947-48 and subsequent residual spraying operations.

Some difficulty was encountered because the local authorities insisted that daily labor used in their communes be drawn from their unemployed. This meant that ERLAAS constantly had to dismiss workers once they had become efficient and fill their places with inexperienced men. The problem became less intense after the first campaign, not only because it was possible in the village to employ men who had had previous experience but also because selected semipermanent squads were used for rural areas. It was seldom possible, however, to use " foreign " workers within the villages themselves.

During the 1946-47 campaign, several spray squads were organized by the Italian army, the navy and the national railways. These squads used ERLAAS equipment and techniques, and although they operated independently they were under ERLAAS supervision. They treated such buildings as barracks, stations and maintenance establishments.

EQUIPMENT

Spraying operations were carried out with shoulder pumps equipped with special nozzles to produce a flat, fan-shaped spray. Before use, all pumps were thoroughly overhauled, all seams on the pump body were soldered or welded, air pump valves were reconditioned and gaskets were replaced where necessary. At the same time certain modifications were made in the pumps to increase their efficiency. The original discharge tube, which was not sturdy and tended to cut through the discharge hose, was removed and replaced by a bottom outlet equipped with a brass wing-nut connection to facilitate rapid removal of the hose. The standard 65-centimeter discharge hose was too short and was replaced by one two meters long. The 60-centimeter spray lance furnished with the pump was satisfactory for low walls, but to increase the spraying range, adapters were provided so that longer lances could be substituted. Originally two-meter auxiliary lances were supplied, but later three and four-meter lengths were also used. These auxiliary lances were made by fitting a six-millimeter copper pipe inside a rigid bamboo pole. At the discharge end of the lance the copper pipe was extended about ten centimeters and curved at an angle of 65 degrees to facilitate manipulation in the field and produce a more even distribution of insecticide on the walls.

Each squad of operators was provided with a tool kit for changing lances, cleaning nozzles and making minor repairs in the field. These kits also contained spare nozzles, spare lances, gaskets and equipment for mixing the insecticide and charging the pumps, including funnels with fine mesh sieves for straining the insecticide.

For large buildings which could not be conveniently sprayed with shoulder pumps, disinsectization was carried out with smoke generators (either Todd Insecticidal Fog Applicators (TIFA) or DDT or benzene hexachloride smoke canisters). Both methods produced a dense fog which, in the case of DDT, left a small residual on the treated surfaces. It was difficult to evaluate the mosquito destruction achieved by these means, but in view of the number of dead flies and other insects collected after treatment it was assumed that the fogging effectively destroyed all *labranchiae* present. The residual effect was too slight to be of practical value. The TIFA machines were later tried in the field, both for larviciding and for control of free-flying insects, but the results were unsatisfactory. Fog generators were also manufactured locally by fitting a shoulder pump so as to discharge a liquid spray through an atomizing nozzle attached to the exhaust of either a jeep or weapons carrier, but as this equipment was not satisfactory for larviciding purposes, its use was abandoned.

INSECTICIDES

The insecticide used in the first residual spray program was a 5 per cent DDT water emulsion prepared from a 26 per cent DDT concentrate. It had been calculated, on the basis of work done in continental Italy, that an application of 100 grams of DDT per inhabitant would be sufficient to control malaria and that this average could be attained by spraying at a rate of 1 gram DDT per square meter. In practice, because of the tendency of the workmen to spray wall surfaces until they were wet, the 5 per cent emulsion was in the beginning actually applied at a rate of from 1.6 to 2.0 grams per square meter. This overapplication was corrected by reducing the DDT content of the insecticide, and from April 1947 until the end of the season a 2.5 per cent DDT emulsion was used.

As the second residual spray campaign in the winter of 1947-48 had as its objective the destruction of the greatest possible number of *labranchiae*, it was decided to spray at a rate of 2 grams DDT per square meter and to treat all man-built structures. Again the bulk of the insecticide applied was a 5 per cent DDT water emulsion prepared in the field from a 26-32 per cent DDT concentrate, but 5 per cent DDT in kerosene and 2.5 per cent DDT water suspension were also used. The suspension was prepared from a 50 per cent DDT wettable powder, giving a residual of 2 grams of powder but only 1 gram of DDT per square meter. As the suspension was not absorbed by the surfaces to the same extent as the emulsion or the kerosene solution, the 1 gram DDT deposit was considered satisfactory. The DDT-kerosene solution was prepared in a mechanically powered mixing plant (see appendix 6) utilizing railway tank cars, while the suspension was prepared by the individual operator in the field.

During the campaign the 32 per cent DDT concentrate caused a considerable amount of trouble. This material, which in some instances was two or three years old, had been stored in steel drums, and deterioration was accompanied by the formation of what appeared to be hydrochloric acid and free chlorine. The acid, in some instances, ate through the steel, causing leaks; in other cases, sufficient gas pressure was built up to deform the drums. The deteriorated concentrate was discolored and difficult to emulsify; however, in chemical and biological tests carried out on samples of the altered concentrate no apparent reduction in potency was noted. The discolored material was therefore used in outbuildings.

The DDT in concentrations of over 26 per cent had a tendency to settle out, and as a factor of safety, all such concentrates were considered to be only 26 per cent in strength.

Only a limited amount of the DDT wettable powder suspension was employed. Its use was confined to rural areas where the white deposit left on the walls was not a problem. Some variation in the stability of the suspension was caused by differences in the local waters. In all instances, however, suspensions could be satisfactorily maintained by shaking the pump occasionally during use. The main difficulty with the powder was that it frequently clogged the spray nozzles.

For the remaining campaigns, DDT emulsions were normally used, the concentrate varying in strength from 20 to 34 per cent. However, chlordane, which was introduced for fly control in 1948, was also employed, mainly because of its effectiveness (until the development of fly resistance) against flies as well as against *labranchiae*. Both refined and agricultural grades of chlordane were made up into a 34 per cent emulsion concentrate by adding five parts by weight of chlordane to nine parts of kerosene and 0.75 parts of Triton X-100. The chlordane concentrate was produced in the central warehouse in Cagliari, while the chlordane emulsion was prepared in the field immediately before use. The rate of application of chlordane was 0.8 gram per square meter. While its residual effect was not as enduring as that of DDT, the 0.8 gram rate was considered adequate.

A summary of the consumption of insecticides in the various campaigns is given in tables V, VI and VII.

TABLE V

CONSUMPTION OF INSECTICIDES IN RESIDUAL SPRAYING OPERATIONS

Insecticide	Quantity used		Quantity of pure insecticide in Kg.		Finished spray produced	
	Liters	Kg.	DDT	Chlor-dane	Liters	Per cent of total
DDT emulsion						
32.7–34.4 per cent	62,801		17,706		354,116	5.4
30 per cent	4,309		1,284		25,689	0.4
25–26 per cent	674,749		168,693		3,442,918	52.5
20 per cent	15,688		3,137		62,752	1.0
Chlordane emulsion						
34 per cent	54,383			18,433	915,624	13.9
DDT suspension						
50 per cent wettable powder		23,543	11,771		474,051	7.2
DDT kerosene solution						
DDT (technical)		64,308	64,308		1,286,158	19.6
Total			266,900	18,433	6,561,308	100.0

TABLE VI

CONSUMPTION OF TECHNICAL DDT IN RESIDUAL SPRAYING OPERATIONS

Campaign	Kg. DDT used	Population protected	Grams per person protected	Number of premises treated	Grams used per premise treated	Number of rooms or shelters treated	Grams per room or shelter treated
Winter 1946–47	81,910	1,082,395	76	257,671	318	1,504,547	54
Winter 1947–48	145,355	1,097,629	132	336,661	432	2,129,532	68
Summer 1948	11,600	111,895	104	15,760	736	142,863	81
Winter 1948–49	13,873	132,194	105	49,785	279	257,400	54
Summer 1949	10,299	39,749	259	23,692	435	84,226	122
Summer 1950	3,863	26,217	147	10,124	382	49,470	78
Total or Average	266,900	2,490,079	107	693,693	385	4,168,038	64

TABLE VII

CONSUMPTION OF CHLORDANE IN RESIDUAL SPRAYING OPERATIONS

Campaign	Kg. chlordane used	Population protected	Grams per person protected	Number of premises treated	Grams used per premise treated	Number of rooms or shelters treated	Grams per room or shelter treated
Summer 1948	11,815	507,355	23	88,289	134	430,831	27
Winter 1948–49	3,618	82,538	44	31,614	114	170,767	21
Summer 1949	2,918	44,280	65	22,835	127	91,530	32
Summer 1950	82	160	513*	68	1,206	494	166*
Total or Average	18,433	634,333	29	142,806	129	693,622	26

* This figure is abnormally high due to the limited use of chlordane in eradication zones having a low population but a high number of mosquito resting places.

Supply Methods

The logistics involved in keeping the large number of spray squads supplied with pumps and insecticide so that spraying could be completed within the specified deadlines with a minimum of lost time was a special problem. Fortunately ERLAAS had excellent warehouse and garage facilities in Cagliari, sufficient transport and adequate regional, divisional, sectional and district warehouses strategically placed throughout the island.

To supplement the normal supply and transport services, a special equipment repair section was established in Cagliari. Here, besides testing and repairing pumps and scouting equipment of various kinds, thousands of small items such as funnels, measuring cans and pails were made. A large mechanically operated DDT mixing plant, utilizing railway tank cars, was a very important facility. First set up in 1947 to mix DDT and kerosene, it was later used for making both residual insecticide and larvicide preparations (see appendix 6).

Spray Techniques

During the 1946-47 campaign, residual spraying was limited to private houses and their outbuildings. Public buildings, such as schools, churches, stores and warehouses, were omitted. The upper limit of treatment was determined by the length of the longest auxiliary spray lances available, two meters. Walls and ceilings over four meters high were never treated. The lower one and one-half meters of wall space were omitted (except in very small rooms such as pigsties), and treatment was not carried out under beds, under cupboards or under low stairwells. Particular attention, however, was given to dark corners and ceilings. The quantity of DDT was limited to a maximum of 100 grams per capita, applied as a 5 per cent DDT water emulsion.

During the 1947-48 campaign, complete treatment was given

to all man-built structures in the island. Many natural shelters such as caves and grottoes were also treated. The 1946-47 practice of marking treated buildings with crayon was replaced by a system of stenciling reference numbers (designating the squad and the structure and the date of treatment) in black paint on the main wall of the sprayed structure, thereby providing a permanent record of the treatment. On the ERLAAS treatment cards posted inside the main entrance of each building treated during the 1946-47 campaign were entered all subsequent treatments and adult inspections. Objections to the system of stenciling were that it was time-consuming and unnecessarily complicated. In later campaigns standardized simplified signs, such as triangles, were adopted with the number of the month of treatment placed inside them.

From 1947 onwards, operators were trained to spray at a speed calculated to leave a deposit of two grams DDT per square meter when 5 per cent formulations were used. No change in the speed of spraying or the quantity of liquid applied was necessary when chlordane or DDT wettable powder preparations were used. A residue of 0.8 gram of chlordane was considered sufficient, and since DDT in wettable powder form was absorbed far less by wall surfaces than DDT solution or emulsion, a deposit of one gram DDT per square meter was adequate.

Squads were supplied with both short and long lances. Normally the men worked in pairs, those with short lances spraying the lower two meters of walls and those with long lances treating the higher portions. The nozzle of the lance was usually held 50 centimeters from the surface sprayed. A uniform speed of spraying was required to obtain a standard surface coverage. Undue overlapping of treated surfaces was avoided. Special attention was paid to the upper corners of rooms and to overhead beams.

The average output per man varied considerably from campaign to campaign (table VIII). The average rate of output depended upon many factors. Zones in which there were few

TABLE VIII

LABOR USED IN RESIDUAL SPRAYING CAMPAIGNS

Campaign	Direct labor* in man-days	Number of premises treated	Premises treated per man-day	Number of rooms treated	Rooms treated per man-day	Population protected	Persons protected per man-day
Winter 1946–47	47,399	257,671	5.4	1,504,547	32	1,082,395	23
Winter 1947–48	59,367	336,661	5.7	2,129,532†	36	1,097,629	19
Summer 1948	13,538	104,049	7.7	573,694	42	619,250	46
Winter 1948–49	11,675	81,399	7.0	428,167	37	214,732	18
Summer 1949	7,600	46,527	6.1	175,756	23	84,029	11
Summer 1950	2,869	10,192	3.6	49,964	17	26,377	9
Total or Average	142,448	836,499	5.9	4,861,660	34	3,124,412	22

* Does not include foremen, supervisors, storekeepers or labor engaged in transport.
† Includes 548,814 natural shelters.

buildings consumed more labor than built-up areas, and partial treatment of rooms took slightly less time than complete treatment. Better organization of the work, for example in making more satisfactory advance arrangements, helped to raise the labor output. Bad weather often delayed the work, particularly in rural areas in the winter. An important consideration was that the thoroughness and care with which the work was done was often in inverse relation to the speed, so that high output was not necessarily advantageous. The low output in 1949 and 1950 is indicative, in part, of a very thorough approach, and in part, of a large proportion of work done outside of villages. The exceptionally high output in the summer of 1948 was mainly due to a concentration of the work within villages.

CONTROLS

The personal inspection of spraying operations at frequent intervals by squad chiefs, supervisors, section chiefs, division chiefs and regional or central office inspectors was considered the most effective method of control. In addition to the actual observation of the spraying, the dampness of the walls, the presence of DDT crystals on glass or paint, sprayed cobwebs and specially placed test papers all served as indicators of proper treatment.

The stenciled sign placed on the outer wall and the treatment card posted inside were always fairly certain evidence that the premises had received treatment, but, of course, did not indicate the quality of the treatment. Scouting reports of the presence of living insects in buildings were usually a sign of inadequate treatment or of failure to treat. Biological testing with caged mosquitoes was superior to chemical testing (because of surface absorption of the insecticide), but did not lend itself to routine use.

Wall scrapings were tested for DDT content by the colorimetric test (Alessandrini, 1948). Chemical tests of DDT supplies and of the solutions produced in Cagliari were also made, but field analyses of the finished spray were insufficient in number to check the correctness and honesty of mixing. The fact that adequate chemical laboratory facilities were not established in Sardinia was undoubtedly a serious oversight. Although the Istituto Superiore di Sanità in Rome was most cooperative and its laboratory facilities were used to a considerable extent, the distance from Sardinia made rapid checking and control of work in progress impossible.

The statistical records of treatments and insecticide consumption served mainly as a psychological control. The great variations in local conditions and the time lag before the records could be checked at headquarters made such records of slight value as an immediate control of the efficiency of the work. Although the forms were as simple and as few in number as possible, delays in their receipt and tabulation in Cagliari could not be avoided. These delays were inherent in widespread operations.

EVALUATION

As the ERLAAS program was based on a combination of residual spraying and larviciding, it has been almost impossible to evaluate the results of residual spraying alone, either in terms of the reduction in *labranchiae* densities or in malaria transmission. The most relevant evidence is the reduction in malaria in 1947 following the 1946-47 spraying. This must be attributed essentially to the effect of the DDT spraying because the only larviciding carried out during 1947 was the experimental work done in the southwestern corner of the island.

The effect of the 1946-47 treatment on the incidence of adult *labranchiae* is illustrated in table IX which shows comparative results in both treated and untreated shelters during 1947. The 1947 collections were made in areas unaffected by larviciding operations.

Under Sardinian conditions, residual spraying was much easier to organize and administer than larviciding. It was possible to make a fairly accurate estimate of the population,

TABLE IX

INCIDENCE AND DENSITY OF ADULT *Anopheles labranchiae* IN TREATED AND UNTREATED SARDINIAN SHELTERS DURING 1947

Month	Treated shelters				Untreated shelters			
	Number of shelters inspected	Shelters positive Number	Per cent	Number of mosquitoes collected	Number of shelters inspected	Shelters positive Number	Per cent	Number of mosquitoes collected
January	0	0	0	0	1,155	81	7	266
February	0	0	0	0	1,522	189	12	1,274
March	32	0	0	0	1,170	41	4	141
April	193	2	1	2	527	49	9	261
May	225	14	6	71	421	44	10	291
June	662	71	11	314	315	67	21	839
July	1,995	134	7	841	79	30	38	808
August	1,597	69	4	242	111	33	30	112
September	1,829	103	6	906	149	39	26	433
October	4,992	100	2	547	280	68	24	397
November	1,143	32	3	366	235	41	17	161
December	611	3	1	11	113	12	11	62
Total or Average	13,279	528	4	3,300	6,077	694	11	5,045

the number of man-built structures and their size and location. From these, the man power, equipment and insecticide needs for each area were readily calculated and an adequate organization was planned. The technique of residual spraying was also much easier than larviciding. Only one treatment per campaign was needed, as compared to the weekly or semiweekly treatments required for larviciding. There was no particular technical problem involved, as compared to the problem of larviciding swamps, running water and overgrown streams. When the residual spraying campaign included all man-built structures in the island, this introduced the arduous task of finding and treating isolated shepherds' shelters (*capanne*) and grottoes and caves used by animals, but this was much less complex than finding and treating the tens of thousands of breeding places scattered through the wildest and most uninhabited parts of the island.

Because residual spraying was relatively easy to carry out, there was a tendency to forget that it was a technical operation for which men had to be carefully trained and which had to be done correctly. When the objective was malaria control, a considerable variation from perfection did not seriously jeopardize the results. When, on the other hand, the objective of the treatment was eradication (as in 1947-48) and perfection was desired, it was difficult to attain. The logistical problem was complicated by the necessity for transporting large quantities of insecticide into sparsely settled areas without roads. Eradication spraying was also expensive because costs rose sharply for all treatment outside of village centers. High costs, however, are implicit in the eradication concept.

If *labranchiae* had turned out to be as domestic as first believed, a high marginal expenditure on residual spraying would probably have been justified. As it was, the problem of deciding how far residual spraying should be developed towards perfection was a difficult one. The belief in island-wide spraying was finally abandoned in favor of confining the campaigns to areas considered particularly hazardous, and where the advantage for purposes of total eradication was commensurate with the effort and money involved.

Some other practical problems have already been briefly noted. The difficulty of having to employ local labor instead of permanent squads, although eventually overcome in part, was always a problem. Locked premises, particularly those far from villages, caused a waste of both effort and time. In the early campaigns there was no trouble in getting public cooperation for the program, especially after the effects of DDT on flies were evident. Later, the development of DDT-resistant flies aroused opposition to spraying, but this was overcome by introducing chlordane spraying. Had it not been for chlordane, there might have been considerable difficulty in securing the cooperation of householders, particularly in the urban areas.

There was some difficulty with insecticide supplies because either DDT settled out from certain of the emulsion concentrates in winter or some of the concentrates deteriorated in iron containers. Dissolving 5 per cent DDT in kerosene was a problem in the cold winter months, but this was solved by fitting a heating system to one of the mixing tanks.

One of the principal problems was the high degree of absorption of the insecticide by wall surfaces. This absorption could be reduced to a minimum through the use of water suspensions, but, unfortunately, this was not evident in time to revise insecticide orders.

The degree of absorption depended on the nature of the surface sprayed, being greater in such porous materials as adobe and coarse plaster, which are extensively used as building materials in rural areas. The degree of absorption was first noticed in comparing DDT analyses of wall scrapings. It was found that the amount of DDT recovered depended directly on the weight of the wall scraping, and, as the area scraped was constant (five centimeters square), the weight variations indicated differences in the depth of the scrapings. An analysis of

724 wall scrapings made in 1949 and 1950 (table X) showed that a high percentage of the DDT had penetrated a considerable distance into the wall.

TABLE X

MEASUREMENTS OF THE QUANTITY OF DDT PER SQUARE METER BY VARIATIONS IN THE WEIGHT OF THE SAMPLE SCRAPED FROM A SURFACE OF 5 x 5 CENTIMETERS

Weight of sample wall scraping (gm.)	Number of sample wall scrapings	Average quantity of DDT (gm. per sq. m.)
Less than 0.21	244	0.23
0.21–0.41	217	0.47
0.41–2.00	208	0.59
Over 2.00	55	1.19
Total	724	

Although 2 grams DDT per square meter were applied, only about one-tenth of this amount remained at the surface. This residual, however, remained active up to nine months after treatment. Most of the samples were taken from plaster or adobe surfaces where absorption was high. Harder and smoother surfaces would have absorbed less DDT, but there would have undoubtedly been a greater loss from the action of air movement and mechanical friction. The variations in the results obtained by these chemical tests indicate certain advantages in the use of practical biological field toxicity tests.

Only one claim for damage to interior furnishing by spraying was made, and this was settled with the payment of a small indemnity.

It is the custom to whitewash houses in certain parts of Sardinia, particularly at Easter. As most of the residual spraying was done during the winter, this practice would have prevented any residual from remaining through the summer. Appeals were therefore made to postpone the whitewashing until the fall.

CHAPTER IV

ANTILARVAL OPERATIONS

The Egyptian *gambiae* eradication campaign (Shousha, 1948), the Wadi Halfa project in the Anglo-Egyptian Sudan (Lewis, 1949) and the *Anopheles* Eradication Service in Cyprus (Aziz, 1948 and 1949) relied almost exclusively on larviciding measures for their effectiveness. On the other hand, the *gambiae* eradication campaign in Brazil (Soper and Wilson, 1943) and the ERLAAS project employed both anti-adult and antilarval measures. The antilarval work in Sardinia comprised the major part of the operations, in terms of both cost and organization, and its nature differed from that of all of the previous projects in that successful larviciding could not be carried out without first preparing the larval habitats for treatment. This procedure accounted for a large part of the expense and much of the difficulty of the ERLAAS campaign.

The entomological investigations conducted in Sardinia during 1946-47 demonstrated that while *labranchiae* preferred sunlit water, it might be found in any collection of fresh water in the island. This meant that treatment could not be restricted to preferred habitats or preferred parts of habitats, as had been the case with *gambiae* in Brazil and Egypt, and which would have been sufficient in Sardinia in a control, rather than an eradication program. Treatment in Sardinia had to be universal, and the problem confronting ERLAAS was, therefore, to develop and maintain an organization capable of preparing and treating the more than one million breeding places distributed over the island.

The antilarval program as carried out from 1947 to 1950 may be summarized as follows:

84

Experimental campaign, April to October, 1947. Trial larviciding in a 5,400 square kilometer area in the southwestern corner of the island. The trial area at first comprised two divisions and ten sections, but during the first week of September work was suspended in all except the three most southern sections and a barrier zone. Larviciding continued in these areas until the third week of October.

Island-wide campaign, February to October, 1948. Island-wide antilarval operations against all anophelines.

Mop-up campaign, February to October, 1949. Antilarval operations originally directed against all residual anophelism. Due to the extensive positivity, the attempt to eradicate all anophelines was abandoned in March and the efforts against *labranchiae* were intensified.

The final phase, June to September, 1950. Intensified eradication measures directed against all residual *labranchiae* infestations. The extent of the coverage in the different campaigns is indicated in table XI.

TRAINING

In 1947 there were very few men available in Sardinia who had been trained in malaria control work and who could be used in ERLAAS activities. While this lack of trained personnel had a minor advantage in that techniques which would be unsuitable in eradication work did not have to be unlearned, it meant that a great deal of time was required to select, by trial and error, the thousands of employees needed and, subsequently, to train them in an absolutely new field.

The amount of training required by each worker varied greatly with his status in the organization. The supervisory personnel required instruction in a wide range of techniques, administrative details (including transport, supplies and accounting), statistical reports and sufficient malariology to understand what they were doing. District chiefs required a more elementary, yet still fairly broad knowledge of the various

TABLE XI

NUMBER OF STANDARD SECTORS (4.61 SQUARE KILOMETER AREA) AND PERCENTAGE OF ISLAND AREA UNDER LARVICIDAL TREATMENT EACH MONTH DURING THE PERIOD 1947 TO 1950

Month	1947		1948		1949		1950	
	Number of sectors	Per cent of island area	Number of sectors	Per cent of island area	Number of sectors	Per cent of island area	Number of sectors	Per cent of island area
January	0	0	0	0	0	0	0	0
February	0	0	1,718	0	0	0	0	0
March	0	0	4,518	50	12	0	0	0
April	0	0	5,139	88	149	1	0	0
May	701	0	5,207	99	338	3	0	0
June	1,188	10	5,229	100	714	6	360	9
July	1,529	18	5,229	100	1,128	14	809	18
August	1,559	22	5,220	100	1,458	22	1,266	30
September	1,559	22	5,220	100	1,277	20	1,598	9
October	728	11	5,149	99	345	7	481	0
November	0	0	1,961	36	0	0	0	0
December	0	0	76	1	0	0	0	0

antilarval techniques, and of storekeeping and the completion of forms. The larvicider required training in the use of his tools but above all needed a simple, clear explanation of what he was supposed to do. Once he was convinced by practical demonstration of the ubiquity of larvae and the effectiveness of proper larviciding most of the problem of his training was solved.

Originally, in 1947, an attempt was made to train supervisors by an apprentice system. Each man was required to work for a fortnight as a larvicider, another fortnight as a scout and then a final fortnight as a district chief before passing, after a simple examination, to the rank of temporary supervisor. Since there was an almost complete absence of trained personnel to whom trainees could be apprenticed, it was inevitable that the system was slow, cumbersome and largely unsuccessful. In August 1947 the apprentice system was therefore abandoned.

It was clear that the key to the situation lay in the rapid provision of a large number of well-trained supervisory personnel capable of instructing and controlling large numbers of men and of representing the organization with initiative and firmness. To this end a training school was opened in August in the village of Sarrok near Cagliari. The course placed special emphasis upon field work, but covered all branches of ERLAAS activities and concluded with a reasonably difficult examination. The success of this first school justified a second course at Sarrok and the opening of another school in the village of Sanluri. These schools provided the nucleus of the supervisory personnel, particularly in the southern region, but additional schools had to be set up in the central and northern regions in December 1947 and January 1948.

Once the supervisory personnel had been trained they were assigned to divisions and sections to train, in turn, the district chiefs and larviciders. A system of cross-checking was developed whereby section chiefs tested larviciders to insure that they had been properly trained by the district personnel, and division chiefs made spot checks to verify the work of the section personnel. Questionnaires were circulated to various members of the supervisory staff asking significant questions on the training program, and requiring them to verify that the training had been carried out effectively. The questionnaires were useful both as psychological and as practical checks.

In 1949 and 1950 refresher courses for key supervisory personnel were held in Cagliari before the start of the antilarval campaigns. Discussion group methods proved most valuable in stimulating interest in these courses and in arousing the necessary intelligent enthusiasm. Following these courses the personnel concerned passed on the new information to their assistants in the sections and districts.

Clearing and Drainage Equipment

Hand tools. Most of the drainage and clearing operations were done with hand tools. Overhanging vegetation, the most stubborn of which was the ubiquitous bramble, was almost always removed with brush hooks. The Sards showed great dexterity in using this tool, and in fact usually provided their own, which they preferred to the heavy-bladed, long-handled, imported model. Emergent vertical vegetation, such as reeds and rushes, was cut with brush hooks, sickles or scythes. The workers were most accustomed to brush hooks and hence preferred them to the other implements. Rakes were used to remove cut vegetation and to eliminate horizontal surface vegetation. The most successful types were made in the workshops by bending the prongs of ordinary pitchforks. Mower-tooth rakes (Rich tools) were the most efficient for removing shoreline vegetation.

Picks and crowbars were used to loosen rocks in stream beds. The *zappa*, or Sardinian hoe, also served for this purpose as well as for small canalization work. Varying in width and heaviness from village to village, the *zappa* was a favorite local tool and again, workers were usually able to provide their own.

Shovels were the key tools in drainage work. The Sardinian

models were almost always unsatisfactory because they were badly shaped, of inferior material and fitted with unsuitable handles. As much as possible their use was discouraged in favor of long-handled, round-pointed steel shovels imported from the United States. The output from workmen using this model was vastly superior to that from men using the local variety. Short-handled shovels, particularly those with square ends, were highly unsatisfactory.

In 1950, standard sets of tools were prepared, approximately sufficient for one eradication zone, made up as follows:

11 brush hooks	1 crowbar
1 ax	5 mower-tooth rakes (Rich tools)
6 shovels	6 sickles
5 picks	5 scythes
3 heavy hoes	9 long-pronged rakes
1 sledge hammer	30 pairs of rubber (or used leather) boots

Power tools. Two crawler-type tractors were purchased in 1948 and a third in 1950. The crawler plates were 25 centimeters wide and the crawlers were spaced 150 centimeters apart, assuring stability, good traction and the essential short turning radius. The distributed weight was low enough to allow the tractor to travel over soft, water-soaked terrain. The motor base was mounted about 50 centimeters above the ground, giving sufficient clearance to avoid drowning the motor under usual operating conditions. A power take-off was attached. Martin ditchers were used with the tractors. The combination of tractor and ditcher proved of great value and was widely used in draining swamps and training river beds. It could operate under as much as 60 centimeters of mud and water, and on frequent occasions the ditcher was completely submerged.

Two mowers were equipped to operate from the power take-off of the tractor. On suitable sites this outfit was a most economical and efficient means of cutting vegetation, but there were few places in Sardinia where it could be used.

The tractors, ditchers and mowers were normally transported

in a General Motors van, which made the outfits mobile. In areas where the tractors could not be transported, or where the amount of work to be done did not warrant their use, ox-drawn plows were used to good purpose. Deep ditches could not be dug, but often it was possible to drain large areas of land by very simple shallow herringbone furrows.

Dynamite. Ditching by dynamite was expensive in relation to hand or tractor ditching, and this method, in 1948, cost approximately 600,000 lire per kilometer. As this cost was the equivalent of more than 600 man days, dynamiting was of value only in zones where drainage by hand or tractor would have been practically impossible or where such methods would have taken too long. Two kinds of dynamite were employed. The mining type, available locally, was used for breaking up banks of rock which obstructed ditches, and for the main canalization work special ditching dynamite was imported.

The loading technique for ditching dynamite varied slightly according to the terrain and the depth of ditch required. In general, charges consisting of three or four half-pound sticks of explosive were placed in the ground 40 centimeters apart in a straight line. If the ground was soft, the charges were pushed into the ground with a tamping rod made of wood, always to the same depth. If the ground was hard, a preliminary hole was bored either with the tamping rod or with a pointed steel bar. The sticks of dynamite were usually placed one directly above the other, but sometimes two sticks were placed at one level with the remaining charge directly above. Stumps, gravel bars, boulders and other obstructions in the ditch line had to be treated as special problems. When the desired length of canal had been prepared, it was necessary to explode only one of the charges as the others detonated by propagation.

The operating crew normally consisted of five to seven men: a foreman, one or two laborers to punch holes, one or two laborers to place charges and one or two men to carry the dynamite to the location. Work progress depended upon the conditions encountered; in difficult terrain as little as 100 meters, but under ideal conditions as much as one kilometer could be completed in a day.

Attempts to speed up clearing by the use of such weed killers as 2-4-D and 2-4-5-D failed almost completely in the case of aquatic vegetation. Some plant life was destroyed, but usually it was immediately replaced by more resistant types.

Larviciding Equipment

Sprayers. Larviciding was usually carried out with either hand or shoulder pumps. In 1948 shoulder pumps were used in a ratio of about one to every four hand pumps, but this ratio steadily increased until in 1950 the former comprised over half of the pumps in service. The shoulder pumps were the same as those used in residual spray work. Normally one-meter lances were used. Both flat and conical spray nozzles were found satisfactory for larviciding. Mist-type nozzles were also used, but their low discharge rate was a serious disadvantage, as high dosages were necessary to produce the 100 per cent kill desired. The hand pump in use was a continuous spray unit, mist-type, of one U. S. quart (946 cc.) capacity.

A number of motor-driven, mist-type sprayers were used, some of commercial design and others produced in the ERLAAS workshop. The machines were mounted in boats and were particularly convenient for treating the shore lines of the larger rivers and lakes where vertical vegetation was abundant. A variation of these machines was one which, by using a vertical discharge, elevated the larvicide spray so that it could be carried by the wind for a considerable distance. It was used to advantage in dealing with tall vegetation which sometimes extended as much as 100 meters out from the shore; the vegetation was often too dense to allow a boat to penetrate, and the water was frequently too deep for a larvicider to work effectively. The eventual solution in such cases was to cut down the vegetation, but before that could be done this machine proved useful.

Bubblers. Several types of automatic larvicide "bubblers" were employed in the treatment of isolated pools, wells and water holes. They were particularly helpful where, because the surface of the water was being constantly disturbed, continuous treatment was highly desirable. The most successful bubbler was a cement-covered, seaweed-ball type consisting of an inner absorbent portion made up of two or three of the small, loosely packed seaweed balls (*Posidonia oceanica*) which are prevalent on Mediterranean beaches. The balls were firmly sewed together with a cord and suspended by a free end of the cord in a rich mixture of white, quick-setting cement. After being taken out they were left hanging until the cement had set, and then redipped repeatedly until a coating of cement about eight millimeters thick had formed. This coating was strong enough to be resistant to fuel oil and to withstand fairly heavy handling. In preparation for charging, four holes, two millimeters in diameter, were drilled in the coated balls, two in each end. Charging was done by putting the balls in a pail of standard DDT-fuel oil larvicide. When the bubbler was placed in water for treatment purposes, the larvicide, being lighter than water, was forced out. It was not necessary to keep the ball upright as it appeared to operate satisfactorily from any position. One bubbler was sufficient to keep the surface of a well covered with an oil film for as long as two weeks. The speed of larvicide emergence could be partially controlled by plugging one or two of the four holes. Over 70,000 dispensers of this sort were used.

Another type of bubbler used was a terra-cotta container which had larvicide escape holes stoppered with fibrous material such as seaweed or fiber from the ferula (*Ferula vulgare*) plant. Other bubblers were made of lengths of cane filled with larvicide-soaked sand from which the larvicide escaped through small perforations at the end of the cane. These bubblers, although satisfactory, were more complicated to use and, in the case of the terra-cotta containers, more expensive than the cement-covered seaweed balls. Balls made of cork dust impregnated with larvicide and cemented with plaster of Paris were employed to some extent in 1948, but were less effective than the seaweed bubblers.

Boats and rafts. Boats and rafts were essential not only for larviciding but also for scouting and for clearing vegetation. Heavy boats were usually hired for operations along the lower stretches of rivers and for the transport of men and supplies to the islands and inaccessible coastal areas. For normal use flat-bottomed aluminum boats proved to be the most valuable. These boats were steady; they could be used in very shallow water and could skim over most aquatic vegetation. Their extreme lightness facilitated transport. The only serious disadvantage was their high cost.

In 1948 the growing demand for boats was largely met by the construction of 73 " marsh boats," or *paludine,* from used oil drums. Outrigger pontoons devised from small metal barrels (previously used for DDT) gave stability. The boat was unsinkable even when capsized. It had a shallow draft and its narrow beam made it useful in small channels.

Various types of naval life rafts were also used. Although too heavy for most purposes, they could be left moored in difficult or extensive breeding places. Reed rafts were employed to some extent, but they were neither stable nor durable and accomodated only one man. Rafts made from drums were occasionally found to be useful.

Auxiliary equipment. Large supplies of accessory equipment were also needed. Many items (larvicide containers, for example) were manufactured at low cost in the ERLAAS workshop. The standard larviciding kit supplied to each eradication zone in 1950 will serve to illustrate this material:

30 hand pumps (with spare parts)	1 flat file
20 shoulder pumps (with spare parts)	1 hammer
15 larvicide containers (3-liter)	1 oil can
6 larvicide drums (20-liter)	1 lock

1 bucket for larvicide
2 fire buckets
2 brass taps for larvicide drums
2 keys for opening drums
1 old tire for unloading drums
1 funnel (with sieve)
1 screwdriver
1 adjustable wrench
1 triangular file

30 cardboard folders (for forms, maps, etc.)
20 knapsacks
2 kilograms of black paint
6 paintbrushes
maps of area
supply of larvicide for 2 weeks

The normal equipment for an individual larvicider was as follows:

hand or shoulder pump
larvicide container—3-liter for hand pump or 20-liter for shoulder pump
larvicide measure—0.25-liter for hand pump or 2-liter for shoulder pump
yellow arm band
pencil
lumber crayon
map of sector (1: 25,000)
knapsack
cardboard folder to hold forms
pair of leather boots
pair of trousers
daily work forms
printed instructions for larvicider

LARVICIDE

The larvicide normally used was a DDT solution in light distillate fuel or Diesel oil with the addition of a spreading agent. Unfortunately, because of Sardinia's island location and shipping limitations, it was impossible to specify the type of oil purchased and it was necessary to take whatever stocks were available. Except in unusual cases, however, it is believed that the oil conformed to U.S. Public Health Service Standards (U.S.P.H.S., 1946).

According to the information available late in 1946, when it was decided to use a DDT-oil larvicide instead of Paris green, excellent results could be obtained by the use of the following formulation, applied at the rate of 1 gallon per acre (U.S.P.H.S., 1946) : 1 gallon Diesel oil, 0.05 pound DDT and 0.5 per cent Triton B-1956. In Georgia, when no hazard to fish or wild life existed, DDT was applied at a rate of 0.1 pound per acre, using a solution of 1.25 per cent DDT in fuel oil containing 0.5 per cent of Triton X-155 or B-1956 (Barbieri, 1946). The 0.1 pound per acre dosage was equivalent to approximately 5 milligrams DDT per square meter. Dr. J. A. Kerr, in his diary in February 1947, notes that in the Egyptian Oasis Eradication Project a dosage of 10 milligrams was used; Triton X-100 was employed as the spreading agent (Madwar and Shawarby, 1950).

In order to economize on oil and transport it was decided to use a 5 per cent [1] DDT solution in Sardinia, using Triton X-100 as the spreading agent, at a rate of approximately 10 milligrams DDT per square meter. Triton was first used at 0.75 per cent and later at 0.50 per cent. It was soon found that it was impossible to limit the dosages applied in the field to 10 milligrams DDT per square meter, so that in part of the 1947 experimental area the DDT content was reduced to 2.5 per cent.

Field tests by the entomological service carried out during 1947 confirmed the efficacy against *labranchiae* of the 2.5 per cent DDT larvicide applied at dosages of as low as 4 milligrams of DDT per square meter. A pond near Donori, 80 meters by 20.5 meters, covered with heavy mixed vegetation was treated at this rate, using a hand pump. Before treatment a series of ten dips made in various parts of the pond produced an average of 22.6 *labranchiae* per dip. A reduction of 99.75 per cent was obtained 24 hours after treatment (based on more than 7,500 dips). Fourth instar larvae and pupae showed the greatest tolerance to the larvicide. Although a complete kill was not

---

[1] All percentages are given in terms of weight/volume.

obtained, it was believed that this was not necessary, as the use of a weekly larviciding cycle would rapidly reduce the population to zero. It was also believed, though incorrectly, that sufficient penetration of the vegetation was obtained to make clearing unnecessary.

While satisfactory results could also be obtained with DDT emulsion concentrates, such larvicides had no particular advantage over normal DDT solutions. In June 1947 three experiments showed that a 99 per cent reduction in immature stages of *labranchiae* could be effected by spraying through vegetation with a 5 per cent DDT solution prepared from 26 per cent DDT emulsion concentrate by dilution with fuel oil.

Further field experiments were carried out in October 1947 to judge whether a different solvent might produce better results. A solution containing 5 per cent DDT plus 0.5 per cent Triton X-100 in fuel oil was compared with 5 per cent DDT in kerosene. The breeding places chosen for the experiment were heavily overgrown; the majority of the larvae were culicines. No essential difference was detected in the killing power of the two larvicides.

It appeared from these field tests that the DDT solutions were too strong for comparative purposes, as both rates of kill approached 100 per cent and differences were obscured. A further experiment was therefore carried out using the following larvicides:

(1) 1 per cent DDT in kerosene
(2) 1 per cent DDT in fuel oil
(3) 1 per cent DDT + 1 per cent Triton X-100 + 20 per cent kerosene + 78 per cent water
(4) 1 per cent DDT + 1 per cent Triton X-100 + 20 per cent fuel oil + 78 per cent water
(5) kerosene
(6) fuel oil

The only significant variation in toxicity was between those larvicides which contained DDT and those which did not.

In 1948 it was decided that despite the apparent effectiveness of the 2.5 per cent DDT larvicide against *labranchiae*, the cost of the DDT itself was low enough to justify the use of a 5 per cent solution as a factor of safety. The Triton X-100 content was increased to 1 per cent. By June, however, the rate of application was so much in excess of that considered necessary, that the cost of the DDT became a more important factor, and the percentage of DDT was again reduced to 2.5 per cent.

The amount of larvicide applied, together with the extensive vegetation clearing, made it reasonable to suppose that the *labranchiae* mortality must have approached 100 per cent. Although the kill was not complete, reliance for eradication was placed on the long period of treatment. However, the increase in anopheline collections in July 1948 called for further investigation into the effectiveness of the larvicide. Attention was concentrated on two particular aspects; it was thought either that the spreading power of the larvicide was inadequate or, conversely, that the larvicide film was too delicate and too easily broken.

Laboratory experiments were run by Mr. H. Kraan, using the Adam method of measuring spreading power (Adam, 1945). These tests indicated that an 0.5 per cent content of Triton X-100 provided the best combination of spreading power (over 40 dynes per square centimeter) and durability of film. The amount of Triton X-100 in the larvicide was therefore reduced to that quantity. Biological tests on *algeriensis* failed to demonstrate any significant difference in the killing rate when the Triton X-100 content was varied. (This was contrary to results obtained in 1950 with experiments on *claviger* when variations in the Triton X-100 content produced considerable differences in the killing rate.) It was also found that 23 milligrams of DDT per square meter was the minimum required for a satisfactory larvae kill.

The fact that even with the above dosages a 100 per cent kill was not obtained after nine hours of continuous exposure was not considered significant at the time; it was blamed on the failure of the oil film to make complete contact with the edges of the pans in which the tests were being run. In view of later studies it is evident that more attention should have been paid to these results.

The apparent difference in the reaction of the various species to larvicide points to one of the major difficulties which arose in the investigational field, namely, that of procuring sufficient numbers of *labranchiae* for experiments. Doubtless it would have been prudent to have started a *labranchiae* colony in Cagliari while the species was still plentiful, but the project was originally envisaged as a much shorter and less extensive operation than it eventually became.

The 2.5 per cent solution of DDT plus 0.5 per cent Triton X-100 in fuel oil was used throughout 1949, except for one short period when there was a shortage of DDT and 1 per cent chlordane was substituted. Routine tests were run throughout the year on both the DDT content and the spreading power of the larvicide.

In 1950 the high percentage of positivity which was recurring in 1949 eradication zones stimulated a careful review of the eradication technique. This review suggested the possibility that the larvicide did not have as much killing power as had been anticipated. Unfortunately, while spreading power and DDT content were routinely determined, the larvicide was not tested biologically. This was due in part to the difficulty in procuring *labranchiae* and also to a lack of time and adequate investigational facilities. The belief that the larvicide was at fault was supported by reports that culicines were not being killed in eradication areas following repeated heavy dosages of insecticide. Furthermore, pan tests run on *claviger* in the Ozieri division, following larvicide applications equivalent to 2.5 pounds of DDT per acre, showed some larvae still alive after as long as 13.5 hours of continual exposure.

A possible explanation was DDT resistance, as this phenomenon had been reported with culicine larvae in the United States (Deonier and Gilbert, 1950). In a series of laboratory observations (using M.L.D. tests) made in Cagliari and in

11. Shepherd making sheep's milk cheese in the mountains, Nuoro Province.

12. A typical village oven.

13. Fishing in a lagoon near Elmas, Cagliari Province.

14. One of the three thousand Sardinian *nuraghi*.

15. ERLAAS headquarters in Cagliari.

IN QUESTO EDIFICIO
DAL 1946 AL 1950
L'ENTE REGIONALE LOTTA ANTIANOFELICA
IN SARDEGNA
ELABORO' I PIANI E DIRESSE I LAVORI
PER REDIMERE L'ISOLA
DAL MILLENARIO FLAGELLO DELLA MALARIA

QUESTO RICORDO
A CELEBRAZIONE DELL'ARDITA IMPRESA
A ESALTAZIONE DEGLI UMILI EROI
CHE VI SACRIFICARONO LA VITA

16. Plaque erected on Cagliari headquarters to commemorate the work
of ERLAAS.

Ninfa (Latina), Trapido (1951a) showed that although Sardinian *claviger* were less sensitive to DDT than Sardinian culicines, the same was true on the Italian mainland in an area where DDT larvicides had not been used. This was, in itself, an interesting result, as similar tests run in the United States showed culicines to be consistently more resistant to DDT than anophelines (Deonier *et al.*, 1949).

Further studies demonstrated that against certain anophelines (excluding *labranchiae*, which were not available) the standard ERLAAS larvicide was not as lethal as had been believed. Although it was adequate for control purposes, it could not be relied upon to give 100 per cent mortality in locations where the film had a short duration. Variations in the amount and type of spreading agent greatly affected the lethal properties of the larvicide with a given fuel oil, although all formulations used had spreading pressures which were well beyond the range ordinarily considered suitable for a satisfactory larvicide. For example, a two-hour exposure of *claviger* to 1 per cent DDT in fuel oil plus 0.5 per cent Triton B-1956 at a rate of 0.5 gallon per acre gave a 100 per cent kill (after 24 hours), as compared tu a 60 per cent kill when the spreading agent was 0.5 per cent Triton X-100 (table XII). Tests carried out at the Istituto Superiore di Sanità against a laboratory strain of *atroparvus* showed that with the oil samples available, an increase in the Triton X-100 content of the larvicide to 2.0 per cent improved the kill to a point almost but not quite that obtained with 0.5 per cent Triton B-1956.

Increasing the quantity of DDT in the larvicide did not noticeably affect the results: 2.5 per cent DDT in fuel oil applied at a rate of five gallons per acre (one pound of DDT per acre) gave only 85 per cent mortality in one hour, 90 per cent in three hours and 100 per cent in 24 hours. Using a standard volume of oil, the amounts of DDT in solution were varied from 0.5 to 2.5 per cent, but no corresponding variation in kill was observed, particularly with exposure times ranging from one-half to two hours. It appeared, therefore, that even

TABLE XII

COMPARISON OF THE EFFECTS OF DIFFERENT SPREADING AGENTS ON THE LETHAL
ACTION OF LARVICIDES AGAINST WILD-CAUGHT *Anopheles claviger* LARVAE

Formulation (in fuel oil)	Application rate (gallons per acre)	Per cent mortality after:			
		1 hour	2 hours	6 hours	24 hours
1 per cent DDT	1.0	1	35	45	50
1 per cent DDT plus 0.5 per cent Triton X-100	1.0	10	30	50	60
1 per cent DDT plus 0.5 per cent Triton X-100	0.5	0	15	45	60
1 per cent DDT plus 0.5 per cent Triton B-1956	1.0	25	70	100	100
1 per cent DDT plus 0.5 per cent Triton B-1956	0.5	10	45	100	100

Note: Larvae were exposed to the larvicide for two hours and then removed to clean water.

with accepted standards of DDT content and spreading power the larvicide was not effective.

As a result of these tests, the basic larvicide formula was changed from 2.5 per cent DDT and 0.5 per cent Triton X-100 to 1 per cent DDT and 0.5 per cent Triton B-1956. With small dosages, the Triton B-1956 formulation could be considered some 50 times more effective against *claviger* (100 per cent kills in test basins attained in 30 minutes as compared to 24 hours with the Triton X-100 larvicide).

It was unfortunate that *labranchiae* larvae could not be obtained for these tests, as their reaction might have been different from that of *claviger*. The latter, for example, have a much more acute alarm reaction: when disturbed by mechanical agitation of the water surface, they assume a rigid position on the bottom of their habitat for long periods. In 198 trials Trapido (1951b) found that *claviger*, on being disturbed, returned to the water surface within one minute only 50.5 per cent of the time, and within two minutes 77.2 per cent of the time. The comparable figures for 383 trials with *labran-*

chiae were 97.9 per cent and 99.5 per cent. *Claviger* appears to be much less bound to the surface by its habits than *labranchiae*. In the laboratory tests with oil films, *claviger* exhibited a partial avoidance of the water surface similar to, although somewhat less pronounced than, that noted when the surface was mechanically disturbed. Bates (1949, p. 141) has pointed out that certain mosquito larvae, by means of cuticular respiration, are able to survive for prolonged periods in cold water with a high dissolved oxygen content when they are denied access to the surface. He further remarks upon the ability of *claviger* to hibernate in the larval stage in water under ice. The fact that *claviger* larvae are physiologically different from *labranchiae* suggests that the two species may react differently to the same larvicide.

The accumulated evidence indicated, therefore, that it was not sufficient to control only the spreading power and the DDT content of the insecticide; biological observations were also necessary. Shortly after these were begun, a fresh shipment of oil was received and it was found that the new B-1956 formulation was no more effective than the old one using X-100. Analyses by the supplier indicated that the new oil had different physical properties from the previous shipment: its specific gravity (at 15° C.) was 0.8424 as compared to 0.964; flash point 79° C. as compared to 56° C.; viscosity at 100° F., 1.27° Engler as compared to 1.14° Engler; boiling point at 10 per cent, 453° F. as compared to 372° F. and at 50 per cent, 541° F. as compared to 424° F. These differences, while possibly not significant in themselves, may reflect the presence of trace impurities affecting larvicidal efficiency. Similar variations may have been occurring all along, since the fuel oils used in Italy were imported from a number of different Middle East fields. It was believed, however, that any deficiencies in the larvicide were compensated for by the high dosages which were used.

While it was at first thought possible to obtain eradication by repeated applications of as little as 5 or 10 milligrams of DDT per square meter, it was found necessary to increase the dosages greatly in excess of this amount (table XIII). These increases were partially due to the need to reduce the length of the treatment cycle in certain areas because of running water and wind action, but a more important factor was the need to

TABLE XIII

QUANTITY OF DDT APPLIED AS LARVICIDE PER SQUARE METER OF WATER SURFACE, 1947 TO 1950

Period	Larvicide applied per square kilometer of water surface per week (liters)	Percentage* of DDT in larvicide	DDT applied per square meter of water surface per week (milligrams)
1947			
Average for year	104	4.25	4.4
1948			
April	180	5.0	9.0
May	410	5.0	20.5
June	643	5.0	32.1
July	1,020	2.25	33.9
August	1,410	2.25	31.7
September	1,520	2.25	34.2
1949			
Average for year	6,635	2.25	149.3
1950			
June–July	7,600	2.25	171.0
August–October	11,040	0.85	93.8

* Average for the period given on a weight/volume basis.

step up the efficiency of the kill for the short duration of the treatment period in the eradication zones during 1949 and 1950. Although the action of DDT-oil larvicides is poorly understood (Stage, 1950) it was believed that the excessive dosages used in Sardinia would kill by contact or suffocation, where death was not produced by the penetration of DDT through the larval tracheae. It was certainly true that increased kills were obtained following heavier dosages of larvicide.

During 1950 an attempt was made to color the larvicide in order to check on whether treatment had been carried out. Several shades of reds and greens were tested, the most satisfactory being Sudan Red M.B. Good coloring of the bulk larvicide was obtained, but when the oil was spread in a thin film on the water surface, the color was almost invisible. However, coloring in the amount of 50 parts per million was added to the new larvicide developed in July to identify it, but it was of little help in the inspection of treated surfaces.

Preparation of larvicide. During 1947 the larvicide was mixed by hand. The ingredients were placed in standard 200-liter drums and mixed by rolling the drum or by tipping it end over end at frequent intervals. This was a satisfactory procedure with the small quantities which were used at that time. To meet the 1948 requirements, however, an accelerated method of residual spray and larvicide production was necessary, and a motor-driven mixing plant was erected (appendix 6).

During 1948 and early 1949 all batches of finished spray and larvicide were chemically tested after production; a sample from each mixing tank was analyzed for DDT content by the Alessandrini (1948) colorimetric method. Deviations from the theoretical DDT concentration were seldom found. Later in 1949 only spot checks were taken and in 1950 the testing was virtually abandoned.

Paris green. Paris green was utilized in some areas where an oil larvicide was considered objectionable. In 1948 it was used in two localities where bee keepers claimed that DDT was killing their hives. In 1950 it was used in one instance because the local authorities protested against the effect of oil on sand filters, and in another case in a lagoon where the owner objected strongly to normal larviciding because of alleged damage to fish.

In addition to these special cases, a more widespread application of Paris green in 1950 was for the treatment of wells, because of objections to the presence of oil in the drinking water. Small envelopes were issued containing sufficient Paris green (0.02 gram) mixed with talc to treat one square meter of water surface. The number of envelopes depended on the size of the well; in all, more than 26,000 were used.

Air treatment. The fixed-wing aircraft normally used 20 per cent DDT in Velsicol NR-70 as a larvicide, but in 1949 this was diluted with fuel oil to 10 per cent DDT. The 10 per cent larvicide was also used for helicopter treatment in 1949 until the supply was exhausted; the standard ERLAAS larvicide, 1 per cent DDT in fuel oil plus 0.5 per cent Triton B-1956, was then substituted. The quantities used were as follows: 20 per cent DDT in Velsicol NR-70, 36,192 liters; 10 per cent DDT in Velsicol NR-70, 18,196 liters; and 1 per cent DDT in fuel oil, 17,450 liters.

Quantities used. The total amount of larvicide used was 4,640,653 liters (excluding that utilized by the airplanes and helicopters). There was a considerable variation in the quantity applied from month to month and from year to year, particularly on a unit water surface basis. The increase in average consumption from 1948 to 1950 was gradual, as can be seen by an examination of the monthly consumption records (figure 8). The drying up of breeding places during the year made this increase even more evident.

Furthermore, during 1948, the average consumption in certain areas of the island was considerably higher than in others. By and large, heavier applications appear to have been used in areas in which eradication was accomplished. Thus a comparison of 100 zones apparently successfully eradicated with 100 non-eradicated zones showed that the consumption in the eradicated zones was almost double that in the non-eradicated zones, although the water surface areas treated were approximately the same. It does not necessarily follow, however, that a similar success would have been obtained in the other zones if the average consumption therein had been raised to the same level. All that can be said is that the possibility of success might have been improved.

In 1949 and 1950, the zones under treatment represented the hard core of positivity in which extra pressure was essential to success. Such extra pressure was reflected, as far as larviciding

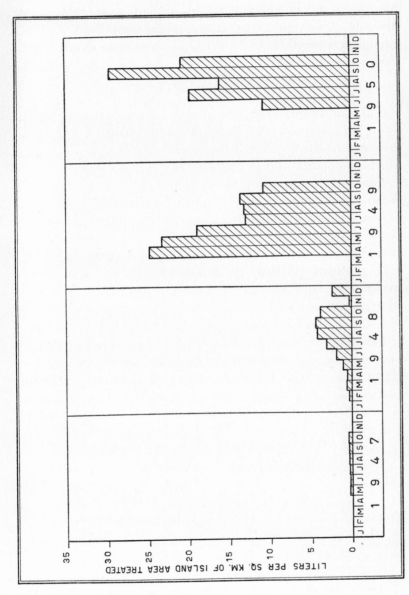

FIGURE 8. Consumption of larvicide per square kilometer of island area by months during 1947 to 1950.

was concerned, by more double treatment (twice weekly), in the greater use of shoulder pumps and in heavier dosages of larvicide. The failure to eradicate in some zones in 1949 brought a consequent increase in the pressure in these areas in 1950.

SECTORING

1947 Campaign. The planning of the experimental larviciding campaign of 1947 was based on a system of field reconnaissance which began with the formation of a single section; when the organization of that section was completed, adjoining sections were created, and so on. The ten sections which were eventually established were grouped into two divisions. Each section was divided into an average of nine districts, and each district into an average of six sectors; sectors were redivided into subsectors representing the area to be larvicided in a day. The subsector furthest from the district office was usually treated on Monday, and the one nearest was treated on Saturday. Districts and sectors were designated by numbers in accordance with the method used in Brazil. The 94 districts established had an average size of 57 square kilometers and the 579 sectors an average size of eight square kilometers (table XIV). Maps drawn to a scale of 1:50,000 were supplied to all section and district chiefs.

TABLE XIV

NUMBER AND SIZE OF ERLAAS ADMINISTRATIVE UNITS, 1947 TO 1950

Unit	Number of units				Average area (square kilometers)			
	1947	1948	1949	1950	1947	1948	1949	1950
Division	2	11	11	12	2,700	2,190	2,190	2,007
Section	10	57	61	60	540	423	395	401
District	94	448	565	565	57	53.8	42.6	42.6
Sector	579	3,400	5,229	5,229	8	7.1	4.6	4.6

In practice, districts and sectors proved too large. Since the sector boundaries were not marked by signs, larviciders had to rely on their memory; as a result some areas were not treated at all and others were treated more than once. Each larvicider was provided with a list of the breeding places in his sector, but these were not numbered. Since it was extremely difficult to describe these so that they could be readily identified, many breeding places, particularly the smaller ones, were overlooked. A trial numbering system was devised in one of the sections.

1948 Campaign. Beginning in October 1947, a more rational subdivision of the island was undertaken. It was divided into 57 sections. Whenever possible, sectional boundaries were determined by river watersheds, although this was often impracticable because of the necessity of forming sections approximately equal in size, and of taking into account the roads and labor supplies available. The sections were grouped into 11 divisions, and the divisions in their turn into three (and later four) regions.

Once this main planning had been completed in the central office, the further subdivision into districts and sectors was carried out by the regional directors, using 1:25,000 military maps. District and sector boundaries, ideally, were based on watersheds, particularly in the mountainous areas where the difficulty of passing from one valley to another made this especially important. For purposes of identification, roads or footpaths were chosen as boundaries wherever possible. Rivers and streams were not considered suitable boundaries because confusion might arise as to which sector would take responsibility for the watercourse; however, entire sections of rivers were frequently made into single sectors. Districts preferably were centered on villages. Circular pieces of celluloid, representing the average radius of the normal district, were useful in plotting districts in the drafting room.

After the boundaries had been traced on the master maps in the regional offices, section chiefs and supervisors were sent into the field to survey their sections. They checked to be sure the boundaries were satisfactory and located section and district offices and warehouses. Any necessary revisions were entered on the master maps. Blueprints of the map of each district were then made in large numbers and distributed to the divisions, sections and districts. A typical print is shown in figure 9; all the irrelevant detail of the original map was omitted, but prominent landmarks, boundary lines between sectors, sector identity letters and the various offices were indicated. The use of reference numbers for districts and sectors was confusing, and this system was replaced by the use of district names and sector letters. All sector and district boundaries were marked in the field by signs on walls, trees or rocks to prevent " no man's land " areas. Special certificates signed by the chiefs of adjacent districts guaranteed proper checking of district boundaries. A clerk from the central office visited each section as an additional check to see that the outlines of the sectional maps matched those of the adjoining sections.

The breeding places in each sector were listed and classified on special forms. The most satisfactory method of locating these was by covering each sector on foot and questioning farmhands and shepherds. The official government records of springs proved of little value because many of the smaller springs and seepages had not been recorded. While the breeding places were being listed, notes were made on those that required special treatment or presented particular difficulties.

While it had been hoped that the actual numbering of each breeding place would not be necessary, the difficulty of identifying these made a numbering system essential. The systems used in 1948 varied to some extent from division to division; they were not standarized until 1949.

As the campaign developed, and particularly as the clearing of vegetation progressed, new breeding places were continually discovered. The danger inherent in such unknown habitats was great, and various expedients were adopted to insure their detection. Special printed forms were made up, and " hunt the foci " weeks were held to encourage all field workers to look for unknown breeding places. Appeals were made to

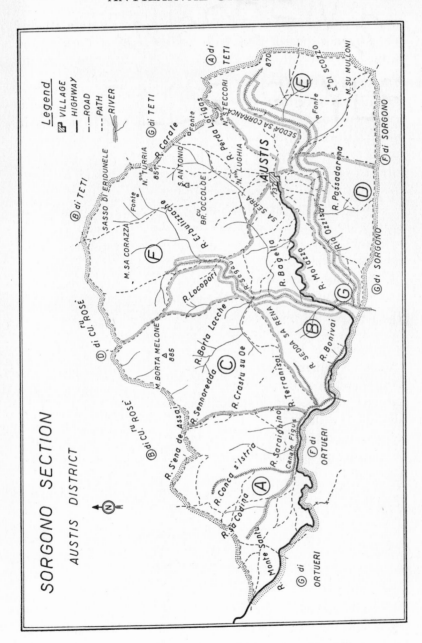

FIGURE 9. Typical district map used by scouts and larviciders.

local citizens to report any breeding places that were not being treated, and special ERLAAS water-searching squads were formed.

1949 Campaign. In 1948 it was found that the average sector was still too large for one worker to treat during a week, and it had been necessary to increase the number of larviciders in many sectors. Furthermore, some districts and sections were found to be too large or poorly located. It was decided, therefore, to revise the boundaries where necessary and to create extra district and sectional offices (table XIV and figure 10).

During 1948 a plentiful supply of maps, the painting of sector and district boundaries and the clear numbering of breeding places had all come to be considered essential to the eradication technique. These factors greatly increased the precision of the work. Rivers and localities ceased to be known by their normal dialect names and were commonly referred to by their number and sector letter. The illiterate worker, who previously had been unemployable owing to his inability to read the lists of breeding places, was often able to use the new system. Numbering was useful to both the larviciding and scouting services; there was far less chance of leaving numbered habitats uninspected, and positive breeding places could be identified with ease by their numbers. The absence of a number for a breeding place was normally prima-facie evidence of its being unknown, unless it could be shown that the number had been removed.

Signs were standardized. Sector boundaries were designated with a single horizontal line, with the letters of the adjacent sectors above and below it, thus:

A

———

B

District boundaries were denoted by double horizontal lines, again with the letters of the adjacent sectors above and below, thus:

FIGURE 10. Administrative subdivisions, 1949 and 1950.

A

B

Breeding-place signs consisted of a white triangle with the sector letter and breeding-place number superimposed:

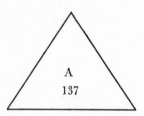

Boundary signs were usually painted with white cement or limewash. For durability, it was essential to mix the materials just before applying. White paint was used for the triangles and bitumen paint for the numbers. Triangles were chosen as the shape most economical to paint. Wire brushes were supplied to scrape off moss or other growths from rocks or trees before painting. Some difficulty arose in finding suitable objects to paint in treeless and rockless plains; in such instances the signs were painted on pieces of wood or tin attached to the top of canes or poles.

For uniformity, 50 to 100 meters of river or stream, or 20-meter strips of swamp or lake were considered one breeding place. In practice, however, size varied because signs could not always be placed at regular distances for lack of suitable rocks or trees upon which to write the numbers.

The number and the areas of breeding places varied from week to week, due to changes in weather. Table XV gives the number and approximate areas of the breeding places in a typical week in the spring (May 1949).

1950 Campaign. The delimitation of sectors, districts and sections, and the numbering of breeding places were sufficiently well done in 1949 to make preparatory field work unnecessary in advance of the 1950 campaign. A twelfth division was

TABLE XV

NUMBER AND APPROXIMATE AREA OF BREEDING PLACES, WITH AVERAGE NUMBER AND AREA OF BREEDING PLACES
PER SQUARE KILOMETER OF ISLAND AREA, AS OF MAY 1949

Class	Type of habitat	Number of breeding places	Per cent of total number	Average number of breeding places per square kilometer	Approximate area of breeding places (thousands of square meters)	Per cent of total area	Average surface area of breeding places (square meters per square kilometer of island area)
1	Lakes and swamps	37,385	3.0	1.55	9,346	12.9	388
2	Ground pools	123,890	10.0	5.14	12,389	17.1	514
3	Flowing rivers, canals, etc.	181,125	14.6	7.52	36,225	50.2	1,504
4	Interrupted rivers, canals, etc.	93,078	7.5	3.86	4,653	6.4	193
5	Rivulets	322,987	26.0	13.41	6,460	8.9	268
6	Springs and seepages	170,615	13.7	7.08	2,559	3.5	106
7	Wells and tanks	181,676	14.6	7.54	545	0.8	23
8	Water holes	131,032	10.6	5.44	131	0.2	5
	Total	1,241,788	100.0	51.54	72,308	100.0	3,001

formed in the northeastern part of the island, but this involved merely a redistribution of the sections already existing.

On the establishment of an eradication zone, however, a rapid revision of boundary signs and a complete check of numbering within the zone were made. Signs which had become illegible were renewed, and those which had disappeared were replaced. Both in 1949 and in 1950 all positive *labranchiae* foci were marked with a special sign. Where possible, a large white rectangle was painted on a nearby rock; superimposed in black was the date positivity had been detected.

The centralization of control in Cagliari in 1950 made it possible to maintain a complete visual record of eradication activities in a central map room. A wall map (scale 1:25,000) was prepared, showing the division of the island down to sector level. All 1949 *labranchiae* foci and eradication zones were indicated. *Labranchiae*-positive habitats discovered in 1950 were shown by means of black flags on which the pertinent details were written. The area placed under treatment was also shown. Hitherto, maps of this nature had been maintained in divisional and regional headquarters, but the value of an over-all picture in Cagliari was amply demonstrated during the year.

Clearing and Drainage Techniques

Extensive drainage and clearing operations were necessary to insure efficient treatment of all water surfaces. Until vegetation was removed there could be no certainty that larvicide would reach the entire water surface, and often considerable areas had to be cleared before the larviciders and scouts could approach the water, or before even the existence of water could be determined. The difficult task of establishing a standard for such work led to fluctuations in policy, from the one extreme of insisting that practically no clearance or drainage should be done, to the other extreme that all breeding places should be " as clean as a Swiss stream." The ideal standard lay somewhere in between and varied with each situation. Anything less prevented eradication, anything more was a waste of manpower and of money.

The timing of the work was also important and great care had to be exercised to avoid excessive drainage and clearance in the early months of the year. The value of draining breeding places which would dry up on their own account or of cutting vegetation in areas from which the water would eventually recede was always problematic. Such work had the merit of eliminating ground pools and other habitats which were highly dangerous in the spring months, but on the other hand the cost was generally high. The criterion adopted was to undertake such work if the cost was low and if the breeding places concerned were located in a particularly critical area.

The speed at which breeding places reduce in size or dry up after the conclusion of the winter rains is an important factor in the ease or difficulty—and even the success or failure—of eradication operations. The rate varies considerably from year to year depending on the intensity and distribution of rainfall, on the terrain and on the temperature. Typical of early spring in Sardinia are flooded rivers, swollen streams, countless small swamps and large stretches of shallow ground water. At that season efficient larviciding is out of the question; although selective treatment is possible, inevitably some mosquitoes escape. When the rains cease, the strong winds and the sun evaporate the water at a rapid rate. By early June the island is dry enough to absorb most of the infrequent summer rains, but these still cause ground pools in impermeable areas and increase the difficulty of treating water courses. The drying-up process continues throughout the summer until late September or October when the fall rains begin.

An indication of the rate of drying in 1949 is given in table XVI which lists the number of breeding places week by week for the period April 24 to September 18. In this table breeding places are listed as active until they have dried up completely; there is no indication of the progressive shrinkage in the size of individual habitats. The rate of drying was considerably lower in 1948 because the rains were later and heavier and also because the 1949 rate reflected an artificial speeding up of the drying process resulting from ERLAAS drainage works. In 1950, on the other hand, the rate was rather high owing to the exceptional dryness of the year.

TABLE XVI

EFFECT OF DRYING-UP PROCESS ON NUMBER OF ACTIVE BREEDING PLACES AND AVERAGE NUMBER OF BREEDING PLACES PER SQUARE KILOMETER FOR THE PERIOD APRIL 24 TO SEPTEMBER 18, 1949

Week ending		Number of breeding places	Average number of breeding places per square kilometer	Per cent of foci active as compared to week ending May 1
May	1	1,282,124	53.2	100.0
"	8	1,241,788	51.6	96.9
"	15	1,230,125	51.1	95.9
"	22	1,194,935	49.6	93.2
"	29	1,175,914	48.8	91.7
June	5	1,141,865	47.4	89.1
"	12	1,078,454	44.8	84.1
"	19	1,038,189	43.1	81.0
"	26	990,512	41.1	77.3
July	3	942,298	39.1	73.5
"	10	927,388	38.5	72.3
"	17	913,924	37.9	71.3
"	24	905,376	37.6	70.6
"	31	901,692	37.4	70.3
August	7	900,242	37.4	70.2
"	14	890,835	37.0	69.5
"	21	883,516	36.7	68.9
"	28	882,551	36.6	68.8
September	4	874,226	36.3	68.2
"	11	870,784	36.2	67.9
"	18	870,784	36.2	67.9

Drainage operations not only accelerated the natural drying process but also eliminated many breeding places which would not have dried by natural means; in other instances the area of water was reduced.

Clearing and drainage operations may be divided into three

principal types: (a) ditching and stream training, to reduce water areas; (b) clearing to expose breeding places so that they could be reached by scouts and larviciders; and (c) clearing of aquatic and shore-line vegetation to facilitate the spread of larvicide.

Ditching and stream training. A large number of swamps, marshes and seepages were drained either by digging new ditches or by opening up and improving those which already existed. New ditches varied in depth from a single plow furrow, which was often sufficient to eliminate shallow ground pools, to deep permanent or semipermanent canals which were capable of carrying a considerable flow of water. During 1948 the major part of the work was done by hand methods, but during 1949 and 1950 tractors and ditchers were used almost exclusively.

Ditching dynamite was employed in a number of special cases; blasting dynamite was extremely valuable in eliminating rock ledges. Some coastal swamps proved easy to drain by running short ditches into the sea. Such ditches were temporary and often closed up after the swamp had been drained, but this was of little importance because the summer rainfall was light. By opening up sand bars at the mouths of rivers, it was frequently possible to drop river levels substantially, and in some locations it proved economical to keep a semipermanent squad available to open up such channels whenever they were filled in by sea or wind action. Where there were no gradients to facilitate drainage, it was sometimes worthwhile to reduce the total surface area of swamps by concentrating the water in parallel canals.

Unlike ditching, stream training had only a seasonal effect, but it was one of the most valuable measures taken and resulted in an economy of larvicide and of the labor of both larviciders and scouts. Stream training began only after flood waters had subsided. Its purpose was to induce the fastest possible flow in the stream or river concerned. Gradients were established, or re-established, by removing such impediments as fish traps, boulders and brush from the water course, by rebuilding animal crossings, by straightening streams and by reshaping banks. In many streams these operations had to be done by hand and in those with rock beds there was often little that could be done. By using the tractor and ditcher in large rivers with sand or gravel bottoms it was often possible, in a very short time, to dredge a shallow channel down the center of the river bed; this either caused complete drying up of many kilometers of sluggish or stagnant pools, or restricted the water to a narrow central channel. It was sometimes possible to permanently drain large lateral swamps which had formed along rivers because of stream blocks or the meandering nature of the river itself.

Pumps were employed for the drainage of several swamps. This method was expensive as the pumps had to be hired and needed constant supervision, but it was worthwhile where ditching was either expensive or impossible. The biggest operation of this kind was the drainage of a 40-hectare swamp at Ollasta Simaxis, near Oristano.

Filling was usually too expensive, particularly with large water collections, due to the lack of such mechanized equipment as bulldozers or scrapers. Filling was of great value, however, in the elimination of small potholes in sand or gravel river beds.

Clearing. Clearing proved to be a long and labor-consuming job, as hand methods were the only satisfactory ones. Flame throwers were occasionally used but they were expensive and complicated; moreover, equally satisfactory results could usually be obtained with a lighted oil-soaked rag. The danger of fire precluded the use of either method in the dry summer months.

Once water surfaces had been reduced to a minimum by ditching and stream training, and when sufficient undergrowth had been cleared to expose the breeding place, the emergent and surface vegetation was attacked. The rules as to the completeness of removal varied from period to period, but the techniques remained the same. Foliage was always cut as low in the water as possible; in only a few instances was it possible or economical to uproot the plants by pulling or grubbing. Unfortunately, even short stubble rapidly grew again to a height which required further cutting, and the new growth was often thicker than that cut down the first time. In a short-term program, however, there was no alternative but to continue to cut the vegetation back as soon as it interfered with larviciding. For the larger rivers, continuous cutting was put on a routine basis by establishing permanent patrol squads. It was important to throw all cut vegetation well clear of the water's edge so that the surface would be free of floating vegetation.

The policy varied for handling horizontal vegetation such as *Ranunculus aquatilis* and algae. In the first half of the 1948 campaign it was not removed; in the second half it was. In 1949 the decision was normally left to the division chief responsible for the eradication zone concerned. In 1950 orders were issued prohibiting removal, as it was decided that heavy larviciding was more effective and less costly than clearing. Attempts to poison aquatic vegetation failed. Mechanical mowers were highly efficient and economical when used in extensive habitats, and their use was limited to these.

Job organization. The normal squad in clearing and drainage operations consisted of from five to seven, and sometimes as many as ten men. Each squad was directed by a foreman. Tractor work was done by specially trained crews. Each squad was supplied with a shoulder pump and the area cleared was larvicided at the close of the day's work.

In clearing streams the squads were divided into specialist groups and usually worked downstream, the first group going ahead of the others to clear out stream blocks such as fish traps, badly constructed stream crossings, brush jams and boulders. A second group followed to deepen the stream bed, dig ditches at critical points and connect oxbows and pools to the main channel. This work reduced the stream or river to its minimum level. A third crew then prepared the water surface for larviciding by clearing out the excess aquatic vegetation.

Intensity of work. The intensity with which clearing and drainage was carried out varied with the changing emphasis placed on this phase of eradication. During 1947 this type of work was virtually prohibited. For 1948 a limited program was planned and it had been hoped that, in addition, larviciders would be able to do a certain amount of clearing to facilitate treatment. Actually the combining of larviciding and clearing proved unsatisfactory and was abandoned early in the year. Instead, the larvicider was expected to advise his chief of any unusual difficulties in treatment so that, if confirmed, the necessary action could be taken.

The work scheduled for 1948 got under way in March and was completed by June. In the last half of June and early July, there was a considerable increase in anopheline positivity in areas which had not been cleared. Larviciding alone did not suppress this positivity, so there was no choice but to initiate a second clearing and drainage program and this became an integral part of eradication. The labor force rose rapidly so that by September an average of 17,128 men were engaged in clearing and drainage work. As the total man-days expended during the month amounted to 445,343, this put a severe strain on the island's manpower and on the organization. Because of the lateness of the season and budget limitations, clearing and drainage work was completely suspended early in October. The amount of labor expended averaged 44.2 man-days per square kilometer of island area. This appears to represent a very low output, even allowing for a large margin of error in the calculation of the water surface and the fact that the area cleared was generally larger than the water surface exposed. To a great extent, however, the low output was due to the amount of ditching and clearing which was done by hand, and by the necessity of having to recut aquatic vegetation.

Much of the work carried out in 1948 was still effective in

1949. Ditches needed only maintenance work; clearing, which was probably the most expensive individual operation, also gave semipermanent results. New clearing was necessary in areas which had been dry in the fall of 1948 but which contained water in the early part of the year. The control of aquatic vegetation was always a temporary expedient and the benefits of certain types of stream training were eliminated by winter floods.

In 1950 a certain amount of preventive drainage was undertaken in May and June in zones whose history indicated that they were likely to be positive. Apart from this work, much of which took place in areas later found positive, clearing and drainage were undertaken only in eradication zones. The amount of labor expended averaged about 12 man-days per square kilometer of area under treatment.

There were considerable variations both in the numbers and types of larval habitats per division and in the amount of clearing and drainage which was carried out. The amount of work done in each division depended not only on the number and types of the habitats but on their condition, the extent of positivity and the thoroughness of the work which was done.

A basic weakness in 1948 and 1949 was that the drainage and clearing were carried out simultaneously with larviciding. The radical change in the environment which was produced undoubtedly had an important effect on the destruction of *labranchiae*, but it became more and more obvious that, aside from the complete elimination of breeding places or the reduction of their areas, the primary purpose of clearing and drainage was the preparation of the habitat for larviciding. This simple truth was not fully appreciated until 1950, when it was adopted as a standard operating procedure. This meant that in 1950, larviciding did not begin until the eradication zone had first been scouted and fully prepared, the ditching and clearing finished, the water area reduced to a minimum and the water surfaces reasonably clean and in such condition that complete larvicide coverage was possible. It was believed that the timing, as well as the intensity, of the work was an important element in the results which might be expected.

LARVICIDING TECHNIQUES

The major part of the larviciding was done with either hand or shoulder pumps. Mechanical sprayers, airplanes and helicopters were also used in certain areas, but these methods were always considered as auxiliaries to, rather than as substitutes for, hand spraying. Labor is comparatively cheap in Sardinia, so when machine methods were used the reasons were usually technical rather than economic. In general, hand methods were not only cheaper but more efficient, for the eradication technique required a minute attention to detail which cannot as a rule be obtained by mechanical means.

The technique of hand spraying was simple and the only variation from year to year was a gradual increase in the quantity of larvicide applied and a growing preference for shoulder rather than hand pumps. The original treatment cycle of one week was retained throughout the project except under special circumstances which required double treatment. For example, at certain times of the year *labranchiae* showed a preference for rivers and the difficulty of treatment there led to a general double treatment of river habitats. Certain other habitats, including large expanses of open water exposed to winds, were also given semiweekly treatments. In 1950 these treatments were made on consecutive days.

During 1948 the dates for the initiation of larviciding operations in various parts of the island were established by the entomological service (figure 11). Treatment continued through the summer and fall months until the beginning of the *labranchiae* overwintering season early in October. During 1949 and 1950 the dates of treatment varied.

Hand spraying. Larviciding instructions were printed in booklet form, but written directions proved useless without adequate practical demonstration. Larviciders were required to

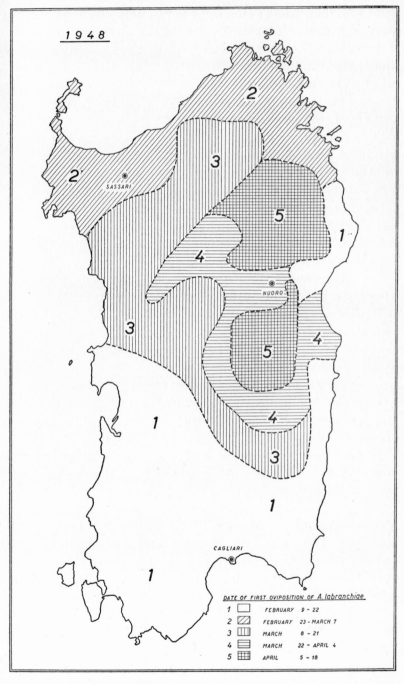

FIGURE 11. Deadlines established by the entomological service for the initiation of larviciding in 1948.

stand with their backs to the wind and in using the hand pump, spray with slow regular strokes low on the surface of the water if the wind was strong, or waist-high if there was little or no wind. An even, unbroken, reasonably substantial film of larvicide had to be left on the water surface. In treating any but the smallest breeding places, the larvicider had to go into the water to obtain proper coverage. In the larger breeding places, such as swamps, spraying was done by walking up and down imaginary parallel lines at right angles to the wind direction. In many cases canes were used as guide markers. Special attention was always paid to the treatment of the water margin.

In 1948 the average sector was too large to be properly larvicided by one worker, and assistant larviciders were often employed. In the reorganization prior to the 1949 campaign, the number of sectors was substantially increased, but even with this change some sectors needed more than one larvicider. There was, in fact, a continual increase in the average number of larviciders employed per square kilometer. From mid-1947 on, the wider rivers were always treated by two or more larviciders working together. In 1949 the treatment of all breeding places by pairs or squads of men was tried out in certain areas, and in 1950 the squad system became the general rule.

There are two principal arguments against larviciders working in squads: it is more expensive and it prevents fixing the responsibility for positive findings on any individual larvicider. Under Sardinian conditions, however, the advantages of the squad system outweighed the disadvantages. There was always a strong temptation, in the summer sun, to omit the last mile at the end of a day's work, and it often required real moral and physical stamina to carry on with a job which might not be inspected. The greater the distance from a road or a village, and the more difficult the terrain, the greater was this temptation. Larviciding was indicated by marking the breeding place numbers with colored crayons and checked by surprise visits and inspections for larvae. But in the last analysis, good work depended on the sense of responsibility of the larvicider. This was much higher when the men were allowed to work in groups —provided, of course, that these groups were well led. The use of flags and whistles to indicate the location of larviciders proved unnecessary and was abandoned.

After August 1948, special flying squads of picked workers (one squad per section) were useful in areas positive for *labranchiae*. The arrival of such squads, besides being of direct practical value, had a salutary psychological effect by creating a sense of emergency within the area.

Use of airplanes. The experimental campaign of 1947 demonstrated that air treatment of some of the larger breeding places would be advisable, especially for coastal swamps, river mouths and extensive ground pools. The main difficulty in the hand treatment of such places lay in actually getting to the water, particularly when it was both deep and heavily overgrown. It was also hard to distinguish between the areas which had been treated and those which had not been treated. The eventual solution to many of these difficulties was drainage, but in the belief that the problem might be temporarily met by the use of light, maneuverable airplanes, seven Stinson monoplanes were obtained from United States Army surplus early in 1948.

These planes were equipped locally with TVA-type smoke generators (Krusé and Metcalf, 1946). During 1948 aerosol treatment only was used, but in 1949 provision was made for both aerosol and spray treatment. The planes were completely serviced and operated by the Italian Air Force, whose pilots soon became highly skilled in the techniques involved.

Bases were established at the three principal airports—Cagliari, Alghero and Olbia. Flights were made early in the morning, just after sunrise, when the air was calm. The pilots were furnished with maps showing the areas to be treated and any special flying hazards, such as power lines. Guide towers made of lightweight cardboard DDT drums, painted with wide black and white stripes and erected on high poles, were often used to aid in obtaining accurate coverage. Where possible, ground crews lit smoke fires to assist the pilots in determining wind directions. Flight speed over the target was approximately 120 kilometers per hour and the ideal height for treatment was eight meters. The treatment swath was approximately 30 meters wide. The aircraft were equipped with tanks containing 120 liters of larvicide, which was discharged as either spray or fog at a rate of about 4.6 liters per minute. During 1949 the planes could carry out both operations at the same time, in which case the total discharge was increased by about 50 per cent.

The aircraft proved to be well adapted to this type of work, but despite the skill with which they were handled, the treatment was not considered successful from the point of view of eradication. The small number of bases necessitated long and expensive flights before the target was reached. The service was at the mercy of weather conditions and pilots were often forced to call off treatments even after they had reached their targets. The incessant "fishtail" winds of Sardinia restricted the treatment period to an hour or so in the morning. The minimum flying speed of 120 kilometers per hour was too great for accurate treatment, particularly along the margins of the target where trees and other obstacles forced the pilot to fly higher than the established eight meters. Because Sardinian rivers are tortuous and narrow, they were difficult to follow and treatment was usually restricted to swamps and lakes. During 1949 fixed-wing aircraft were replaced by helicopters.

Helicopter treatment. Arrangements were made with the Italian Ministry of Agriculture and the ECA Italian Mission for the purchase of two helicopters, with the understanding that ERLAAS would be allowed to use them for the duration of its campaign. An Italian Air Force crew was sent to the United States for training. The equipment arrived in Sardinia in May 1949, and after a brief shake-down period, the machines were put into service in June.

The helicopters were equipped with two aluminum booms,

one on each side of the fuselage, fitted with 16 spray nozzles, Type $\frac{1}{4}$ BAL-I. Each nozzle had a rated delivery of one liter per minute and the number used could be adjusted to the flight speed and the type of insecticide. The normal spray swath was 30 meters. The average pay load was limited to 90 liters, but two 100-liter capacity insecticide tanks were fitted and available.

The maneuverability of the helicopters eliminated most of the objections to air treatment by fixed-wing aircraft. The normal flying speed over the treatment area was 50 kilometers per hour where the course was straight and unobstructed, but in treating winding rivers or the edges of swamps the speed could be reduced, if necessary, to zero. The machines usually operated at a height of four to five meters, and the strong downdraft of the rotor forced the larvicide through protective surface cover.

Guide towers were not necessary, although they were occasionally used. It was a general rule that one of the local inspectors, who was familiar with the area under treatment, flew with the pilot as an observer to help direct the spraying operations. This provided the inspector with an excellent opportunity to check on the work and assured more accurate treatment. In cases of doubt, it was always possible to land and reconnoiter.

The helicopters were much more efficient than the fixed-wing aircraft since they could be refilled near the target and did not have to make frequent return trips to their base. The percentage of flying time spent in treatment by the fixed-wing aircraft was approximately 15 per cent, but for helicopters it was 28.7 per cent in 1949 and as much as 39.1 per cent in 1950. A summary of air larviciding operations for 1948 to 1950 is given in table XVII.

Length of treatment. The duration of treatment varied considerably from year to year as well as from zone to zone. It has been argued by Macdonald (1950a) that the treatment

TABLE XVII

SUMMARY OF AIR LARVICIDING OPERATIONS, 1948 TO 1950

	Fixed-wing aircraft		Helicopters	
	1948	1949	1949	1950
Number of treatments	545	363	97	100
Area treated (square kilometers)	406	229	48	32
Hours of flight*	535	323	108	69
Hours of treatment	82	51	31	27
Per cent of total flying time spent in actual treatment	15.3	15.8	28.7	39.1
Total larvicide consumption (liters)	22,605	1,606	17,872	8,435
Average larvicide consumption (liters per square kilometer)	56	70	372	264

* Excluding training, demonstration and test flights.

period is the most important factor in eradication, and that the best results could be obtained by maintaining a reasonable eradicating efficiency over a long period of time. While this was in general the system adopted in 1947 and 1948, during the last two years of the campaign it was believed that the eradication technique had reached a point of efficiency where shorter treatment periods would be effective.

Because of the experimental nature of the 1947 operations and the lack of adequate controls, the results during that year cannot be satisfactorily analyzed. In 1948 an attempt was made to start larviciding activities concurrently with the first *labranchiae* ovipositions. This early start allowed time, before the advent of heavy anopheline breeding, for the larviciders to develop skill in their work and for the administration to iron out the many logistical problems involved in an island-wide operation. Apart from these factors, and with due consideration of the prevailing weather conditions, it is doubtful whether general treatment so early in the year was advisable.

In 1948, because of heavy spring and early summer rains,

many breeding places were virtually untreatable. In one week, for example, there was so much rain that larviciding operations had to be completely suspended. It would appear more economical, during this early period, to concentrate only on such preferred habitats as ground pools—not so much for the purpose of immediate eradication as for reducing densities in preparation for more intensive treatment later.

At the end of the season, treatment in many parts of the island could have continued through October, but unfortunately, even though the month was both hot and dry, the budget did not permit treatment for more than the first fortnight. Nevertheless, the entire island was under treatment for a considerable period, 96.5 per cent averaging from 26 to 40 weeks. Only 3.5 per cent of the sectors, those in high mountain areas where snow and bad weather delayed operations until April, received less than 26 weeks treatment, the minimum being 18.

In 1949 the matter was more complex. During the early part of the year all anopheline foci were treated, but, owing to the extent of the residual positivity, this procedure was abandoned and treatment was initiated only following the discovery of *labranchiae*. The original period of treatment was established as four weeks, but this was later lengthened to from six to eight weeks.

In 1950 treatment was again limited to areas positive for *labranchiae*. Treatment started with the discovery of positivity and continued until the end of the campaign. One important difference between 1949 and 1950 was that in 1949 clearing and drainage went on simultaneously with larviciding, whereas in 1950 the eradication zone was fully prepared before larviciding began.

In 1949 over 88 per cent of the area treated received six weeks or more of treatment; in 1950 the average period of treatment was considerably longer, over 77 per cent of the area treated receiving eight weeks or more. While in 1949 the average period of treatment was from six to seven weeks, in 1950 this was increased to from eight to fifteen weeks.

Special Techniques

Inaccessible and emergency zones. In the original planning for 1948 two inaccessible areas were expected to give special trouble; one was centered at Lodè and the other comprised the upper Flumendosa Valley. The wild mountainous nature of these areas, their lack of roads and the almost complete absence of population made it appear that special methods and a special organization would be advisable. These zones originally were to be treated as separate divisions; in practice the problem was best met by including the areas in the regular logistical plan but making the size of the sections considerably smaller than normal.

In May 1949, following the unexpected widespread presence of *labranchiae* in the northeastern corner of the island, a special emergency zone was created with headquarters in Olbia.

Prophylactic and sterilization treatment. In the early months of 1949 certain swamps and large flooded areas were treated even though they had not been proved positive for *labranchiae*. This step was taken because such habitats were so extensive and difficult to scout that the possibility of detecting *labranchiae* within them was negligible. In addition to the difficulties inherent in scouting extensive water surfaces, the effect of the 1948 campaign in those areas where eradication was not achieved, was to reduce densities far below the low level customary in the spring. At that period of the year, habitats of this type were among those preferred by *labranchiae*, and it was believed that treatment, even if it did not eradicate, nevertheless helped to localize the infestations. Wherever possible, larviciding was done by airplane. These treatments were suspended at the end of May.

In September 1949 certain major rivers were given "sterilization" treatment because it was found that proper inspection consumed almost all the time of the scouting force. It was decided, therefore, to place the rivers under treatment and

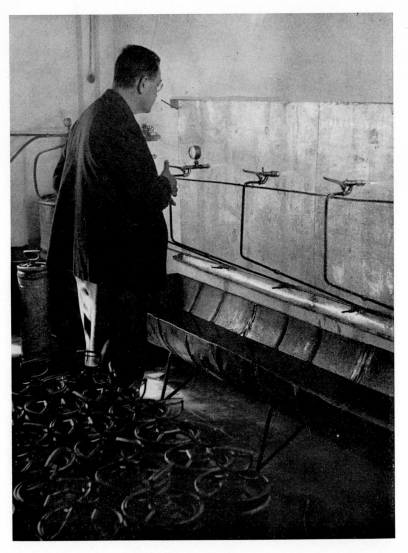

17. Shoulder pumps and nozzles being tested under pressure in Cagliari workshops.

18. Residual spraying with long lances; particular attention was paid
to the treatment of beams and corners.

19. Numbering a typical breeding place.

20. Signs on treated structures indicate the type of insecticide used, the squad and the time of treatment.

21. The drafting room in the Cagliari headquarters.

22. Residual-spray squad foreman checking on pump refill.

rely upon the scouting of the surrounding area to detect *labranchiae*.

The eradication technique. A special eradication technique was originated in the fall of 1948 in an attempt to eliminate the last anopheline foci which were found: mobile squads were used to clear and larvicide the infested areas. The method was improved in 1949 and standardized in 1950, as outlined below:

(a) As soon as *labranchiae* was identified in one of the divisional laboratories, a telegram was sent to Cagliari indicating the exact location.

(b) The division chief immediately inspected the infested area and decided upon the delimitation of the eradication zone. Where the zone fell partially within another division, he consulted the chief of that division. If the majority of the zone fell within the second division, or if the workload of that division was lighter than that of the first division, supervision of the work passed to the second division chief.

(c) A chief eradicator, directly responsible for the work in the area, was dispatched to the zone with a truck and a standard set of eradication equipment from the divisional reserve. Eradication headquarters were established, preferably in the nearest section office. Meanwhile a truck and reserve equipment were sent from Cagliari to replenish the divisional reserve, and, if necessary, a chief eradicator was transferred from the central pool. These measures were taken within 24 hours of the identification.

(d) Within seven days the division chief was required to send to the eradication service chief in Cagliari a map showing the location of the positive focus and the boundaries of the eradication zone. These boundaries were based on a circle having a radius of three kilometers from the focus, but were adjusted to coincide with sector boundaries where possible; special provisions were also made for topography. The information from the division chief was entered on the master map in the headquarters map room.

(e) Enough scouts were assigned to the zone to inspect it thoroughly in a period of one to two weeks. If further *labranchiae* infestations were found the zone boundaries were modified accordingly.

(f) Based on the estimate of the division chief, each eradication zone was assigned a labor budget sufficient for all daily-paid labor needs during the eradication period (except scouting which came under a separate service). This budget covered the renumbering of breeding places, clearing and drainage operations, residual spraying (if it was considered necessary) and larviciding.

(g) A minimum of three observers was assigned to the chief eradicator, usually from the sectional scouting force.

(h) In addition to scouting, the first week of field operations was devoted to preparing the zone for larviciding. This included renumbering and drainage and clearing operations. The only treatment during this week was the larviciding of the *labranchiae* focus, and, in a few rare instances, the residual spraying of all potential mosquito shelters in the zone. Although this work was supposed to be completed during the first week, it was not always possible and drainage and clearing operations sometimes extended into the second or even the third week. Treatment was started, however, at the beginning of the second week.

(i) It was the sole duty of the chief eradicator and his observers to make certain that all habitats were prepared and properly treated. When conditions warranted, double treatment was carried out.

(j) Weekly meetings of eradication chiefs were held in division headquarters. Summaries of the week's activities were presented on a special form designed for this purpose (ERLAAS Form 61, figure 12).

(k) After the first period of intensive scouting, the eradication zone was considered a normal part of the section for scouting purposes and given routine scouting coverage on a four-week cycle basis.

E.R.L.A.A.S.
FORM 61

SUMMARY OF THE PROGRESS OF ERADICATION ACTIVITIES

PART I

WEEK TO _____

a) Division _____

b) Eradication zone nº _____

c) Date of positivity _____

d) Number of sectors in zone _____

e) Transport assigned _____

f) Chief eradicator _____

g) Observers

	NAME	SECTORS INSPECTED DURING THE WEEK
1		
2		
3		
4		
5		

h) Man-days assigned _____

i) Man-days used:

	Numbering	Bonifica	Larviciding	Warehouse and guards	Total
To the end of the last week					
During this week					
Total					

NOTE: a) THIS FORM MUST BE COMPILED IN THREE COPIES, EVERY SATURDAY BY THE ERADICATION CHIEF

b) RED COPY TO BE HELD; GREEN COPY IS FOR THE DIVISION AND THE THIRD WHITE FORWARDED TO THE ERADICATION SERVICE - THE THIRD COPY MUST ARRIVE IN CAGLIARI BY THURSDAY

PART II

	DISTRICT	SECTOR	NUMBERING				BONIFICA				POSITIVITY FOR ANOPHELES OR CULEX			
			finished?	yes or no	If in progress		finished?	yes or no	If in progress		Positivity last week		Positivity this week	
					Nº OF MEN	ESTIMATED COMPLETION DATE			Nº OF MEN	ESTIMATED COMPLETION DATE	C. OR A. (1)	WHO TOOK ACTION?	C. OR A. (1)	WHO TOOK ACTION?
1														
2														
3														
4														
5														
6														
7														
8														
9														
10														
11														
12														
13														
14														
15														
16														
17														
18														
19														
20														

a) EQUIPMENT NEEDED _____

DATE _____

NOTE: (1) C = CULEX; A = ANOPHELES

SIGNED: ERADICATION CHIEF

FIGURE 12. ERLAAS Form 61 used in eradication zones in 1950.

(l) Eradication service inspectors checked on progress by means of personal visits and attendance at the weekly divisional meetings. The statistical office collected and posted all scouting and eradication data in the operational control room at Cagliari.

Aids to morale. Various methods were used to develop and maintain *esprit de corps* among the larviciders. The separation of the larviciding and scouting services did a great deal to foster a spirit of rivalry between the two groups, with the scouts trying to prove that an area was positive and the larviciders insisting that it could not be. Group larviciding aided in developing a team spirit, and flying squads of eradicators also helped.

Larviciders were graded into two classes and promotion came only when a larvicider had demonstrated superior efficiency. Honor awards, prizes and badges were given to exceptional men. Posters and periodic bulletins from the central and regional offices encouraged greater efficiency. Meetings were held by regional, divisional and sectional chiefs at regular intervals, and every effort was made to have the larvicider take individual responsibility for the success of the campaign. The men were also encouraged to make suggestions as to how techniques and methods could be improved.

In 1948 and 1949 district chiefs were required to post a large form on the outside of the district office announcing whether their districts were positive or negative. A blue form was used to indicate negativity, while a red form, used in cases of positivity, showed which sectors and larviciders were responsible.

Also in 1948 and 1949 the scouts used a special form to indicate *labranchiae* positivity or the presence of unknown larval habitats. This form was printed in red and the top half was detachable. Upon finding a positive or an unknown habitat, the scout filled out in duplicate the top half of the form with all the relevant details and left it in the district office. One copy was forwarded to the section office for information, while the other remained in the district office for inspection. After the district chief had taken the necessary remedial action he completed the bottom half in duplicate and again sent one copy to the section office and retained one in the district. By this means it was possible to insure that rapid action followed all notifications from the scouting service.

DIFFICULTIES IN ANTILARVAL WORK

The logistical and administrative problems involved in working in an area of over 24,000 square kilometers have already been described. The eradication concept required an unbroken continuity in the techniques practiced; work stoppages due to strikes, shortages of supplies, transport breakdowns or the failure to meet payrolls on time could produce considerable damage. The more important difficulties encountered in a special study of 200 representative zones are discussed in the following pages.

Natural factors. Natural difficulties (the extent of the breeding place, flowing water, wind action, difficulty of access, depth of water and vegetation) which had an adverse effect on the efficiency of larviciding are summarized in table XVIII, with indications of their relative importance at different times. These

TABLE XVIII

COMPARISON OF NATURAL DIFFICULTIES WHICH PREVENTED EFFICIENT
LARVICIDING IN 200 REPRESENTATIVE ERADICATION ZONES

Type of difficulty	Per cent of foci with difficulty				
	1948	September* 1948	1949	1950	September* 1950
Extent of habitat	43	37	29	23	21
Vegetation	73	41	65	30	15
Flowing water	32	10	9	5	5
Wind action	10	8	9	6	6
Difficulty of access	16	15	18	17	15
Depth of water	20	14	26	24	24

* Difficulties existing in September, near the conclusion of the larviciding campaign, were considered as particularly significant.

difficulties, if occurring in September 1948, near the conclusion of the campaign, were particularly significant. In 1949 the treatment period was limited to six or seven weeks, and the presence of difficulties at any time during that period was important.

The problem involved in " extent of the breeding place " was in making certain that large areas were completely treated; there was always a possibility that parts might be missed, so where practical, the water area was reduced by ditching. With extensive ground pools it was impossible to number each small portion and it was again difficult to ascertain whether the larvicider had treated each one. The presence of extensive vegetation in the large water areas complicated treatment, since larviciders tended to do spotty work if they did not have a satisfactory means of orientation. Guide markers were sometimes used, but the best solution, unless the water was too deep, was squad treatment with the larviciders working in line. It is interesting to note that the rice fields in the Arborea area did not cause any particular trouble. They were divided into small sectors by special arrangements made with the authorities as to the time of treatment. With a standard oil larvicide all anopheline species appeared to be eradicated within a few months.

Flowing water was always a problem, as it continually removed the larvicide film. This was not important during the early months of the year when flooded rivers and streams were not suitable larval habitats. The problem developed later when the current was reduced sufficiently to make rivers ideal habitats, particularly in the vegetation along the edges. An estimated 65 per cent of the districts of the island contained moving water, even in the driest months of the year. Doubts as to the efficacy of the larvicide intensified the problem. The most satisfactory method of overcoming the difficulty was stream training; by conducting the water into a narrow channel it was usually possible to induce a flow sufficiently fast to stop larval development. Treatments were also given semiweekly and in 1950 were undertaken on successive days in an attempt to maintain larvicide on the surface for a longer continuous period.

Wind action tended to blow the larvicide to one side, particularly in the larger, more exposed areas. The wind also made hand spraying much more difficult and air treatment impossible. In the worst instances the only answer was to postpone the work until the wind subsided; normally, however, the problem was solved by higher dosages and double treatment.

Problems of terrain, particularly steep gorges, were especially difficult to overcome in some areas. Resort to climbing ropes, larviciding from moored rafts and treatment by bubblers were among the methods used. Deep water was a handicap, particularly in areas situated at considerable distances from roads. Life jackets were necessary in some places.

Outside opposition. There was always a certain amount of resistance to larviciding on the part of the local people, and, although in most areas it was negligible, in others it was one of the most important difficulties which had to be faced. Except for an increased opposition to the treatment of drinking water, resistance rose only slightly from 1948 to 1950. Widespread or serious effects to animals or human beings in 1948 or 1949 would certainly have been followed by greatly increased antagonism.

Opposition took various forms; larviciders were sometimes threatened personally, and in a few instances were fired upon. Shepherds hid water holes with brushwood or swept off the larvicide immediately after treatment. Habitat signs were often damaged or removed. Occasionally larvicide drums were punctured or upset, and sometimes agreements were made with the larviciders to leave certain areas untreated.

Analysis showed that shepherds apparently protested more than farmers, and employers more than employees. Housewives were frequent objectors, perhaps because they were usually present at the time of treatment, or because they, especially, found the taste of larvicide in drinking water unpleasant.

The antagonism of fishery owners was a special problem, and complaints were received from about one-half of the fisheries treated. The fact that there were no complaints from the other half supports the evidence that very little actual damage took place. The objections to air treatment were strong, although actually the amount of larvicide applied was considerably less than in ground treatment.

Opposition to clearing and drainage was far less severe and was restricted to about 10 per cent of the zones; in these the protests were slight and came from only a few persons. Although it could not be defined as opposition, there was a widespread failure on the part of landowners to follow the laws regarding the maintenance of irrigation ditches. The provincial prefects tried to publicize these laws and threatened, at least, to enforce them. But the laws had fallen into disuse so long ago that such attempts had little effect. In the case of ERLAAS drainage being destroyed by livestock, the only remedy was by personal appeal to the owners.

Labor relations. Eradication depends on human nature and the willingness of workers of all grades to work conscientiously with a minimum of supervision. On the whole, ERLAAS was fortunate in its labor relations. Not only were serious disagreements between management and personnel extremely rare, but the majority of workers demonstrated a sincere desire to do a good job. However, the problems which did arise were important, as considerable damage could result from the poor work of one larvicider and even more from the laxity of a supervisor.

Probably the greatest single cause of difficulty was the unwillingness of many employees to work in water, especially during the cooler months of the year. Complaints about pay were rare, doubtless because of the great amount of unemployment on the island. Sporadic attempts made by the labor unions to call strikes never had the real support of the men themselves. Some difficulty occasionally arose over the choice of workers. The

compromise generally reached allowed ERLAAS to choose larviciders, while the local labor office selected the drainage and
clearing workers.

A more difficult problem was the shortage of suitable labor
at critical periods. Normally, unemployment was so high that
there was a supply of reasonably good workers in every village.
However, the demand was often so great that this category was
soon exhausted and men of inferior caliber had to be employed.
In some places during 1948, and in the northern area during
1950, workers were imported by truck from distant villages
because the entire local labor supply had been absorbed. The
problem was accentuated by the fluctuations in agricultural
employment during the year; harvest and threshing operations
often coincided with the peak periods of ERLAAS activity.

Lack of mechanized equipment. Although the low cost of
labor made the use of machinery less advantageous than it
would otherwise have been, there is no doubt that the work of
canalization and stream training would have been greatly expe-
dited, particularly in 1948, if more mechanical equipment had
been available. In addition to ditchers and mowers, bulldozers
or tractor-scrapers would have been most useful for large
filling operations; in their absence such projects were virtually
impossible.

Distance from village centers. The preference of the Sards
for living in village centers meant that in large areas of the
island ERLAAS employees had to work long distances from
their homes and frequently had to establish temporary accomo-
dations on the worksite. Over 100 district offices were constructed in uninhabited areas, and in many other localities the
workers made their own arrangements. Inspection in such
areas was arduous and time-consuming.

An examination of 100 zones which were not successfully
eradicated in 1948 showed that the centers of the zones were
situated as follows in relation to the nearest village: 9 per cent
less than two kilometers away; 22 per cent two to four kilo-

meters; 33 per cent four to six kilometers; 14 per cent six to eight kilometers; 8 per cent eight to ten kilometers; and 14 per cent over ten kilometers. The average distance was 5.1 kilometers.

Good roads naturally facilitated the movement of both supplies and labor. Classifying as a good road one which could be traversed by a Dodge weapons carrier, of the 200 zones examined 32 had no roads, 93 had few, 63 had enough and 12 had many. Jeeps, however, could travel where other vehicles could not, and some 50 per cent of the zones could be reached for inspection purposes by this means.

CHAPTER V

SCOUTING AND ENTOMOLOGICAL SERVICE

Checking on the presence or absence of mosquitoes is a normal part of any mosquito control operation. Where the abatement of a mosquito problem is the only objective, scouting activities are usually limited. On the other hand, eradication programs, by their very nature, require a large force of specially trained personnel to check on the progress of the operations. An approximate measure of the effectiveness of the antimosquito operations, which would be entirely sufficient in a control program, is unsatisfactory. Instead there must be concentrated searching of every potential mosquito habitat and precise recording of the results obtained. Eradication requires the maintenance of an efficient intelligence service to indicate weak points in the operations. Failure to detect promptly the presence of mosquitoes may seriously jeopardize the whole project.

The principle underlying eradication is rigid control. Control, however, cannot be entrusted to any single individual, and a system of checks and counterchecks must be used. Scouting is an essential part of the checking system and furnishes the measure of the success or failure achieved. It must be continued for a sufficient time after eradication measures have been lifted to insure that a true picture of the existing situation has been obtained.

PROGRAM

The methods used by the ERLAAS scouting service were based on those of the *gambiae* eradication campaigns in Brazil and Egypt. It was impossible, however, to adopt these previous organizational plans outright because of differences in terrain, mosquito biology and campaign techniques. The invading *gambiae* of Brazil and Egypt, for example, was a highly domestic insect and since there was no shelter spraying with residual insecticide during the campaigns in those countries, the search for adult mosquitoes was of much greater value than it was in Sardinia. In both of the former campaigns larval scouting served an important function and was carried out by the men in charge of the larviciders as well as by independent squads (Soper and Wilson, 1943; Shousha, 1948). In Sardinia, however, as it was believed that more accurate results could be obtained by larval, rather than adult, scouting, the program was primarily based on larval scouting.

Published reports of the Brazilian and Egyptian campaigns do not describe the scouting system in detail, but apparently spot checking rather than complete habitat coverage was emphasized. Checking was an integral part of the ERLAAS scouting procedure, but this alone was found inadequate in the case of a semisylvatic species. All breeding places had to be inspected thoroughly and regularly in order to determine the true *labranchiae* situation in a given area.

For logistical purposes, the island was divided into regions, divisions, sections, districts and sectors. The basic unit was the sector, which was the area assigned to one larvicider for weekly treatment. The sector also served as the basis for scouting operations.

The scouting program was based on the provision of basic coverage of all breeding places on a cycle basis by large numbers of scouts and successive checks by various categories of more highly trained personnel. The organization which provided the scouting varied somewhat from year to year, depending on the changing emphasis of the campaign and financial and other considerations.

ORGANIZATION

During 1947, scouting and larviciding were under the direction of the larviciding service, but on the conclusion of the trial larviciding in November, the director of the entomological service was made responsible for all entomological and scouting matters.

Throughout the project, division chiefs were in charge of all operations in their divisions, and section chiefs, in turn, were responsible for all operations, including scouting, in their sections. This made the entomological service essentially a technical, advisory and inspection, rather than an operating, agency. To assist in this advisory and inspection work, entomological delegates (one per division) were established in 1948 as direct representatives of the entomological service. A certain amount of difficulty was experienced as to authority and in 1949 the delegates were replaced by three senior inspectors who were experienced Italian malariologists. They were assigned specific areas and worked directly under the director of the entomological service. In 1950 the regions were eliminated and the three inspectors of 1949 became entomological field directors. They were assisted by seven inspectors.

The actual scouting was provided on a regional, divisional, section and district basis as follows:

(1) *Region squads (1948 and 1949)*. Independent mobile check squads (one per region) operating under the regional directors; small squads of selected men, usually about seven in number, equipped to undertake both larval and adult scouting activities anywhere in their region.

(2) *Division squads*. Mobile units operating throughout the division on fixed itineraries established by the division chief; normally two per division, one for larval and one for adult scouting. The number of scouts in each squad varied from eight to 25 men.

(3) *Section squads*. The basic scouting force, except during 1949. The squads varied in strength from eight men and a chief in 1947 to as many as 55 men with a chief in certain sections in 1950. They functioned on a fixed itinerary and a vehicle was available for transportation within the section. Their work consisted mostly of searching for larvae, but certain members of the squads also looked for adults. In 1950 a few squads

working in areas with large expanses of water (such as marshes) restricted their activities almost entirely to adult scouting, because it was believed that under such geographical conditions and with the limited personnel available, shelter inspections provided greater returns than larval searching.

(4) *District squads (1949 only)*. District scouts, selected from the best of the 1948 larviciders, provided the basic scouting coverage during 1949. They were originally assigned on the basis of one per four sectors, later one per three sectors and eventually, for a brief period, about one per two sectors.

(5) *Other elements*. During 1947 district chiefs and their assistants, in addition to supervising the activities of the larviciders, were expected to check the effectiveness of the work by making larval inspections. In actual practice, however, relatively few inspections were made, and as these men were poorly trained, their usefulness as scouts was questionable. District chiefs carried on limited larval inspections in 1948, and in 1949, when district scout squads were used, they spent their full time on scouting.

Certain field personnel, such as division and section chiefs and inspectors, were required to carry mosquito-capture equipment in order to make spot checks during their inspections. The amount of scouting done by this group varied greatly.

An alpine squad of six selected men was used in the Nuoro area in 1948. Their equipment included ropes for rock climbing and they covered the most difficult mountain zones which could not readily be included in normal scouting operations.

During 1950 a special category of scouts known as observers was used. These men were experienced scouts assigned to the eradication service to check the work of the larviciders.

TRAINING

The shortage of experienced personnel in Sardinia made the training of scouts an urgent necessity. Unfortunately, this matter did not receive the attention which it should have in 1947, although some formal instruction was given by the entomological service to the supervisory staff. The entomological service took an active part in the organization of, and the instruction in, the special training schools for field personnel which were established in the fall.

During the winter of 1947-48, after the entomological service had assumed the responsibility for scouting, special courses for chief scouts were set up. Based on examinations covering both practical and theoretical material, the most promising men were hired and sent to the newly selected section and division headquarters to train scout squads. Review courses were given before the 1949 and the 1950 campaigns and any changes in the program were explained and discussed at that time.

A close check was maintained on the efficiency of scouting personnel during the summer months. Entomological inspectors, regional directors, division and section chiefs and assistant chiefs observed scouting techniques, and checked mosquito identification, the observance of itineraries, the preparation of forms, the condition and completeness of equipment and the general attitude of the scout towards his work. Performance records were kept and incompetent personnel were gradually weeded out. Infringement of regulations was punished by fines, and if repeated, by dismissal.

Manuals were prepared describing the biology of culicine and anopheline mosquitoes and the duties of the scouting personnel. These handbooks also described scouting techniques, the use and preparation of work forms, the handling of mosquitoes, the observance of itineraries and the comportment of the individual while on the job. Equipment lists were included.

OPERATIONS

The primary objective of ERLAAS scouting was the examination of all larval habitats. It was obviously possible to examine any given habitat with varying degrees of thoroughness. The degree of anophelism reported in an area depended, therefore, on both the coverage and the thoroughness (intensity) of the scouting. During the first two years of the campaign the principal objective was to cover as much territory as possible; during 1949 and 1950, although widespread coverage was still essential, the intensity of scouting in individual breeding places was increased. During the last years of the campaign, the number of examinations per breeding place was not tabulated but was indicated by the number of scouts employed.

1947. In the original plan for 1947, basic scouting coverage was provided by the section scouts, but a sector was not checked as long as it was declared positive by the district chief. The theory was that if a sector was known to be " dirty," there was no point in wasting time looking for additional larvae, and it would be more profitable to check a " clean " sector. The scout was expected to remain in a sector either until anophelines were found or until, after a day of inspecting, the sector was declared negative.

The system was unsatisfactory as it placed too much reliance on the district chief. Furthermore, it was a blot on his record if larvae were found. The abandoning of a sector once anopheline larvae had been found was unsatisfactory, as there was no indication of the degree of infestation. Accordingly, at the end of July, orders were issued that all sectors were to be inspected weekly whether positive or not. In addition, section chiefs were urged to give more attention to scouting and to methods of increasing its efficiency. In theory, division scouts checked the effectiveness of the section scouts' work, but as the total force was so small, in practice the two groups supplemented each other. Aside from investigations carried on by the entomological laboratory, no adult scouting operations were undertaken in 1947 until October, when three squads of ten men each were organized and functioned for a period of three weeks.

1948. In 1948 basic coverage was again provided by the section scouts. Each scout worked by himself, spending each day of the week in a different sector. The following week he worked in a different group of sectors, so that the same man did not inspect the same sector two weeks consecutively. All sectors were supposed to be inspected each week. While the system had the advantage of permitting a given sector to be checked by several people, it was seldom possible for one man to inspect all the breeding places in a sector in one day.

Division and region squads checked the reliability of the section scouts' work. Being mobile and equipped for both adult and larval scouting, the squads were able to control areas where the division or region chief had doubts about reported negativity.

1949. The routine scouting in 1949 was done by the district scouts on a cycle basis. While the objective was to inspect all breeding places, this was impossible within the time limits of the cycle, which was originally three, but later reduced to two weeks. Generally each scout operated in a new sector each day, but in certain areas the men worked in groups, combing an entire sector before moving on to the next.

Work cards were prepared for each sector. These cards contained squares numbered from 1 to 500, each number representing a numbered breeding place, with extra squares in case more numbers were needed. Habitats were classified into eight types, and at the time of the inspection, the scout indicated the type of habitat in the appropriate square on the work card. Master lists and charts were prepared in each section, so that it was possible to check a scout's activities by his designation of habitat types and to record the breeding places which had not been inspected during the week.

The original plan for 1949 was based on the elimination of all anophelines, except *plumbeus,* and scouts were required to carry larvicide and to treat all positive anopheline foci at the time they were discovered. If the positivity proved to be due to *labranchiae,* an eradication zone was established. While the normal duty of the section scouts was to check the work of the district scouts they were, in addition, required to check a circular area with a radius of three kilometers around each positive in order to determine the extent of the infestation.

Because of the amount of residual anophelism which was found, it became evident that it could not be kept under control with the funds which were available, and it was decided to concentrate on the eradication of *labranchiae*. However, the scouts continued to apply a single larvicide treatment to all anopheline foci at the time of their discovery. This was a constant inconvenience because it diverted the scouts from their principal function and tended to mask the presence of *labranchiae*. The order was therefore rescinded.

In order to check on the extent or the possible spread of *labranchiae* positivity, a strip two kilometers wide around the periphery of all eradication zones was carefully checked by the section scouts at the time the zone was established and again following the conclusion of treatment. While the function of the division and region scouts was normally to check the work of the other squads, they were called in to help the section scouts if, following the discovery of several *labranchiae* foci and the establishment of the eradication zones, the work load became excessive.

1950. In 1950, for reasons of economy, the district scouts were eliminated and basic scouting was again provided by the section scouts. The allotment of section scouts was calculated by dividing the 565 districts into groups in three categories according to their estimated *labranchiae* breeding potential. The three categories were given inspection cycles of four, five and six weeks. Scouts were distributed among the district groups by applying mathematical factors based on: (a) the number and type of larval habitats; (b) the difficulty of the terrain; (c) the number of anopheline collections during August and September of 1949; and (d) the practicability of adult scouting. Working within budgetary limits and applying the above factors, personnel requirements were calculated for obtaining complete coverage of all breeding places during a basic cycle of six weeks. A fifth factor, determined by the *labranchiae* history of the area, was then applied to increase the scouting strength and reduce the cycle to four or five weeks in the areas most likely to be positive. On the basis of this system some sections had as many as 55 scouts and others as few as 20, but in general the squads averaged from 25 to 30 men. Areas having a four- or five-week cycle were allotted an additional week known as a *labranchiae,* or selective, week during which inspections of typical *labranchiae* foci were emphasized (figure 13).

The scouts operated as squads rather than as individuals. Each sector was completely inspected before the squad moved on to the next. Whenever an eradication zone was established, it was intensively scouted in order to determine the extent of the infestation. This was a departure from the 1949 practice which directed attention to the peripheral area. No larviciding was permitted until the scouting had been completed, and as a result, a number of additional positive foci were discovered which in some instances led to a change in the size of the eradication zone. After treatment had started, the zone automatically became a four-week cycle area and was given routine scouting on this basis. Division scouts in 1950 were used solely for checking purposes.

TECHNIQUE

Normally, larval and adult scouting were undertaken by different groups of personnel. This division of work permitted the scout to concentrate his full attention on either one activity or the other; in this way less time was lost and greater coverage could be obtained. In 1949, however, three scouts and the chief in each section squad assigned to larval scouting carried on limited adult scouting operations as well. Similarly in 1950, approximately one-third of the section scouts were equipped for the two types of work. In practice they spent more of their time searching for larvae, but an exception was made in two sections where the nature of the terrain justified emphasis on adult scouting.

Because of doubts regarding the accuracy of certain of the scouting techniques, a special study was made in 1950 to develop new methods. After careful consideration it was

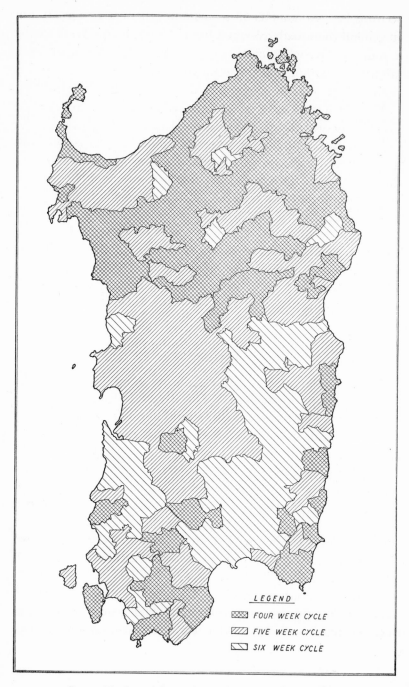

LEGEND
⬚ FOUR WEEK CYCLE
⬚ FIVE WEEK CYCLE
⬚ SIX WEEK CYCLE

FIGURE 13. Larval inspection cycles by districts in 1950.

decided that the general techniques already in use were those best adapted to the problem.

Larval scouting. The following methods were used:

(1) *Dipping with cloth nets.* The bulk of the larval scouting prior to 1950 was done with a small muslin net 15 centimeters in diameter and 20 centimeters deep. Whenever possible, the scout swept the water surface, each sweep being about a meter in length. If emergent vegetation created an obstruction, shorter sweeps were made, or else the man dipped directly with the plate. In general, a scout made about five sweeps before emptying the contents of the net into an aluminum plate which had been previously filled with water, but if flotage was abundant, the number of sweeps was reduced. Where vegetation was limited and the breeding place small, the scout could and usually did check all of it; otherwise his inspection was reduced to a sampling operation. Concentrated dipping by a large number of men was usually required for thorough inspection of the larger breeding places.

(2) *Dipping with metal dippers.* Metal dippers of about 400 cc. capacity were introduced late in 1949, and although not entirely satisfactory, they had the advantage of durability; nets had to be changed frequently because they tore or wore out around the binding of the wire loops. With dippers the scouts had to modify their technique of making long sweeps. The dipper had the disadvantage of limiting the amount of water surface that could be checked in any one operation. With practice, the amount could be increased, but it never did approach the surface area coverable by a net.

(3) *Use of well nets.* These were devised for checking wells too deep to be reached with the ordinary long-handled dipper or net. They were difficult to manipulate, and wherever possible the smoke method of adult scouting was substituted.

(4) *Observation at close quarters.* Where water collections were too small and shallow for dipping or where many rocks

were present, scouts were taught to muddy the water, then inspect the surface at close range. Any larvae coming to the surface were collected with a pipette.

(5) *Use of large nets.* During 1950 it became evident that extensive bodies of water densely overgrown with horizontal vegetation could not be adequately covered with small dippers. Large nets and more systematic dipping were substituted. The nets consisted of a heavy oval wire ring (diameters 65 and 30 centimeters), to which was attached a strong gauze bag 50 centimeters deep. A heavy wooden handle 1.5 meters long was attached. At frequent intervals, the contents of the net were emptied into a metal tub of water, which was then examined for larvae.

(6) *Saturation scouting.* Squads were often used to obtain complete coverage of an extensive breeding place. The men lined up approximately one and one-half meters apart and moved slowly forward, maintaining their ranks and skimming the entire water surface. Sometimes several squads operated together, the various lines of men approaching one another to avoid leaving any " no man's land." A similar system was used on land to comb an area for unknown breeding places. The practice was also used in 1949 and 1950 by scouts around known or potential *labranchiae* foci.

Adult scouting. Adult scouts usually worked in pairs; several methods were used for mosquito detection:

(1) *Flashlight and capture tube.* Shelter interiors were inspected with a flashlight and anophelines were collected with an aspirator tube. Each room was examined systematically, beginning at the door, working around the four walls and ending with the ceiling. Furniture was also included in the inspections.

(2) *Pyrethrum method.* Where mosquitoes could not easily be spotted, the pyrethrum method was useful. One man sprayed with pyrethrum while another held a catching sheet directly under the sprayed area. The catching sheet, usually

one meter square, was held in place by two canes which fitted into sleeves sewed in the margins. The spray used at first had a concentration of 0.12 per cent pyrethrins, but in 1950 this was increased to 0.25 per cent.

(3) *Smoke method.* This technique was used for wells, grottoes and mine galleries, high-ceilinged or poorly illuminated animal shelters and brush-covered shepherds' shelters. With the exception of one opening screened with mosquito netting, all exits were closed. Smoke from a grass fire was used to drive the mosquitoes to the net-covered opening, where they were collected with a sucking tube. In the case of wells, a smoking fire was lowered in a pail by means of a rope and wire extension.

(4) *Traps.* These had a limited use in ERLAAS activities. Small portable baffle traps, baited with rabbits, were tested along the margins of the Cagliari lagoon where *algeriensis* (and formerly *labranchiae*) existed, but they failed to attract adults. In 1950 a light trap was set up beside a newly discovered *labranchiae* focus; although a few culicines were attracted to the trap, not a single adult anopheline was caught.

(5) *Human bait.* When scouts spent the night in the field, they frequently attempted to make hand catches. At first, a few anopheline adults, including *labranchiae, claviger* and *hispaniola*, were collected in this way. When *labranchiae* densities became very low, however, this method proved unsatisfactory.

(6) *Sweeping nets.* Heavy canvas nets for sweeping vegetation were tried without success.

Inspections. Adult shelters were listed on report forms as houses, stables, pigsties or sheds. All other resting places were grouped under the general heading " various," but the scout specified the type of habitat in each case. Most man-made shelters had a number stenciled on the outside wall, which was used by the scout as a reference number on his work sheet. In addition, each sprayed structure had an inspection card indicating the date of treatment. If the card was missing, the scout posted a new one with a record of his inspection. Some shelters, because of their type of construction, did not lend themselves to the card system; in such cases, the scout recorded his visit (date and initials) with a lumber crayon.

Water collections were divided into eight types, and each was given a number in order to simplify reporting. The various types were as follows: (1) lakes and swamps; (2) ground pools, shallow collections of rain water usually present during the spring; (3) flowing rivers, streams and canals; (4) interrupted rivers, streams and canals; (5) rivulets, generally seepages from springs, but including any small collection of running water; (6) springs; (7) tanks and wells; and (8) water holes, borrow pits, etc. All breeding places were numbered. Whenever an inspection was made, the scout inscribed his initials and the date in the white triangle containing the sector letter and habitat number.

Work forms were based on those used in the Brazilian and Egyptian campaigns, changed and modified to meet local conditions. Master charts kept in section headquarters indicated every numbered breeding place by sector and district. All inspections were recorded in such a way as to give a visual portrayal of coverage. Other charts showed sector positivity and sector scouting coverage.

Each scout had an activity card on which his chief kept a weekly record of individual inspections and collections. Men with low activity records were investigated, and if they continued to show no sign of improvement, were released. The fact that an individual could not find larvae was not particularly significant unless it was evident that other members of the squad were more consistently successful.

Every weekend the squad chief compiled a detailed itinerary of each scout's work program for the coming week. Master lists were kept at the squad headquarters, so that it was theoretically possible for a visiting inspector to find any scout in the field at any time. In practice, this was not easy, particularly in mountainous or wooded country. Chief scouts were also required to keep a diary in which their activities and itineraries were briefly summarized.

At first the scouts carried their larval collection tubes one-third filled with 10 per cent formalin. To avoid falsification of collections (through the use of specimens from previous collections), it was later decided to add formalin at the end of the day when the scouts returned to their base. In 1950, when scouts worked in squads, each scout carried preservative with him, but he could not add it to a collection until the live larvae had been verified by a superior.

Scouting operations in the 1949 and 1950 eradication zones included the collecting of culicine larvae. It was believed that the presence of these was indicative of improper larviciding and should be called to the attention of the eradication service.

All collections were verified by the chief scout and then forwarded for laboratory identification. In 1947 the central laboratory in Cagliari served all of the experimental larviciding area. There were three regional laboratories in 1948, and in 1949 and 1950 the number was increased to one per division. The lapse of time between collection and identification was always a problem, particularly when districts were situated at long distances from roads. Nevertheless, the bulk of the material arrived in the laboratories within six days.

EQUIPMENT

All scouts were provided with the following items of equipment:

- (a) Leather boots (and occasionally rubber knee boots).
- (b) Trousers.
- (c) Knapsack.
- (d) Cardboard folder for work forms.
- (e) Red arm band.
- (f) District map (1: 25,000).

In addition, larval scouts received the following special equipment:

- (a)   Dip net (or, in 1950, metal dipper) with wooden handle.
- (b)   Reserve net.
- (c)   Well net.
- (d)   Aluminum pan.
- (e)   Two medicine droppers.
- (f)   Sixteen specimen vials.
- (g)   Two cardboard screw-cap mailing tubes for vials.
- (h)   Lumber crayon.
- (i)   Daily work forms.
- (j)   Mosquito collection tickets.
- (k)   Printed instructions for larval scout.

The following special equipment was issued to adult scouts:

- (a)   Seven celluloid (suction type) catching tubes.
- (b)   Flashlight and batteries.
- (c)   Ten pillboxes with absorbent tissue.
- (d)   Two mailing tubes for pillboxes.
- (e)   Hand pump (Flit-gun type).
- (f)   Pyrethrum (two liters).
- (g)   Catching sheet with canes.
- (h)   Mosquito netting (2 × 2 meters).
- (i)   Square of sheet metal (5 × 5 centimeters) for measuring the
        area of wall scrapings for the residual DDT test.
- (j)   Daily work forms, including extra inspection cards.
- (k)   Tacks for posting inspection cards.
- (l)   Mosquito collection tickets.
- (m)   Letter of identification.
- (n)   Printed instructions for adult scout.

Equipment based on fixed supply lists was distributed to the
field from the central warehouse in Cagliari. In the field, it
was drawn from divisional and sectional warehouses by the chief
scout, who passed it out to his men. A reserve of expendable
items was maintained by the chief. Each man was responsible
for the proper maintenance of his equipment.

LABORATORIES

As an outgrowth of the 1946 anopheline survey, an entomological laboratory was established in Cagliari. Its function was to continue biological studies of the Sardinian anophelines, investigate the action of insecticides and act as a consulting agency. In later years, the pressure of other work limited the activities of this laboratory to the identification of anophelines, the examination of blood smears and to training.

Training schools and refresher courses for entomological microscopists were held each spring. Not only were the men trained in the identification of mosquitoes (anophelines by species and culicines by genus), but they were instructed in the use of laboratory report forms, mosquito identification keys and the proper use and maintenance of microscopes. Detailed diagrams showing the distinctive morphological characteristics of the various species were prepared and distributed to the laboratories. Microscopists kept master charts of sector positivity according to species and of scouting coverage (also on a sector basis) by the various scouting categories. The Cagliari laboratory also served as the entomological training center for almost all monthly-paid field personnel.

In 1947 the Cagliari laboratory identified all of the mosquitoes collected in the experimental larviciding area. With the expanding program in 1948, branch laboratories were established in Nuoro and Sassari. In 1949 and 1950 the service was expanded still further, and division laboratories were set up (11 in 1949 and 12 in 1950). In 1949 the division laboratories forwarded their collections to the region laboratories for confirmation. This practice was abandoned in 1950, as by this time the microscopists had become more proficient. During 1950, however, all *labranchiae* collections were forwarded to Cagliari. A double purpose was served: not only were the identifications confirmed, but the collections were taken out of circulation, thereby reducing the possibility of false positives.

In 1947 two, and at times three, miscroscopists were occupied with identification work. The region laboratories in 1948 and 1949 were each staffed with two microscopists and the division laboratories during the latter year with one man each. The 1950 season also commenced with one microscopist per division laboratory, but it was recognized that these men would need help since the number of anopheline collections, other than *labranchiae*, was expected to increase rapidly; 23 assistants were eventually assigned to assist the 12 microscopists. A system of speeding up identifications was devised: one man prepared the larvae on slides, one man made the identifications and a third man washed the slides and filled out the laboratory work forms. When the work load was particularly heavy, there were two microscopists, two preparators, one clean-up man and one clerk.

During the height of the 1950 season some laboratories were receiving between 1,500 and 3,000 collections a week, containing from 7,000 to more than 13,000 larvae. Under such conditions, two microscopists had to examine 70 to 140 larvae per hour. During the season 701,450 anopheline larvae and pupae and 1,834 adults were identified, representing an increase over the 1949 figures of more than 700 per cent in the number of larvae and pupae examined and 333 per cent in the number of adults. This was in spite of the fact that there were approximately one-third fewer scouts and the season was one-third shorter.

DIFFICULTIES ENCOUNTERED

In addition to the basic entomological problems associated with the reduction of an indigenous species of mosquito to very low levels, a number of administrative and organizational problems were encountered. Some of these difficulties, such as morale, temporary shortages of transport and supplies, unexpected changes in program, the misinterpretation of instructions in the field, poorly trained and unsatisfactory personnel, were not peculiar to the scouting service but were inherent in the size of the project. The problems of particular importance to the scouting service may be summarized as follows:

(a) The desire to report negativity, particularly in 1947 and 1948, led to false reporting. Collusion between scouts and larviciders was not readily apparent, and although most of it was eventually uncovered by check squads it was both harmful and misleading.

(b) Insufficient numbers of scientific staff were available to carry on investigational work and to help in the direction of the scouting service. A number of outside scientists were available as consultants and for short assignments, and although they contributed a great deal to the project, they could not take the place of additional staff.

(c) As eradication activities were given priority, economy measures generally affected the scouting service first.

(d) Special training was necessary to develop judgment as to the most likely parts of a breeding place or adult habitat, to check the amount of time to be devoted to different areas, etc.

(e) The work of the scouts tended to become monotonous, particularly in areas which were negative, and it was exhausting, particularly in the hot months in difficult terrain.

EVALUATION OF SCOUTING

When mosquito populations are high, their presence is readily detected. Even with high numbers, however, care must be taken to assure adequate sampling in terms of both space and time if reliable information is required regarding seasonal variations, distribution and total population. When populations are low the problem is much more difficult. In order to establish the presence of mosquitoes, a certain minimum amount of searching is obviously necessary. From the extreme of no inspections being made and no mosquitoes found, all scouting results have to be interpreted, bearing in mind such factors as coverage and intensity, the training and efficiency of the scouts and the behavior of the mosquito. Eventually the laws of chance, or probability, become extremely important.

Theoretically, if mosquitoes exist in an area, it should be possible to find them with one inspection provided that all possible breeding or resting places were examined with sufficient thoroughness. This would involve both larval and adult scouting. In Sardinia it was found that larval scouting was more efficient than the search for adults; the scouting program was therefore based on larval scouting carried out during the *labranchiae* breeding season. Because of variations in the larval population, both from place to place and from time to time, it was believed to be more efficient to re-examine all breeding places at frequent intervals, or cycles, as thoroughly as possible within the practical limits imposed by finance and organization. To insure reliable returns it was, of course, necessary that complete coverage be obtained, or in other words, that every breeding place be examined.

Organization. In the final analysis, scouting was an individual operation and the results depended on the ability and the conscientiousness of the individual scout, plus, of course, the facilities which he had available and the planning and organization of his activities. A great deal of time and effort was therefore spent on training, on planning, on the choice of leaders and on equipment and transport. This provided, under the budgetary restrictions which were always existent, that the maximum number of trained personnel were able to inspect as efficiently as possible the largest number of habitats. But regardless of the facilities provided, the results obtained in a given area depended on the individual and his health, attitude and equipment on any given day. As the field leadership (chief scouts) was of such importance in the over-all efficiency of the scouting service, particular attention was paid to the selection, training and evaluation of this group.

The element of chance. With low population densities, the possibility of finding specimens in a given area depends to a considerable extent on chance. The part which chance plays in scouting under Sardinian conditions has been discussed by

Trapido (1951b). This element was reduced as far as possible by organization and planning, so that the chance element largely entered only in the final stages of the inspection of a given habitat. In other words, all training, organization and planning was directed at aiding the individual scout to reach and examine efficiently all potential foci; once, however, he reached a positive habitat the chance factor came into play as to whether or not he could find the few specimens which existed.

Coverage and intensity. During 1948 an attempt was made to measure the thoroughness or intensity of scouting by recording the number of plate examinations which were made. The idea was abandoned because of the practical difficulty of accurately defining an examination. The number of scouts, and to a lesser extent, the number of breeding places examined in a day, are therefore the only measure of intensity. The number of scouts, however, should be considered in relation to the water area existing at a given time. As there was a progressive drying up of breeding places during the summer, the intensity of scouting represented by five scouts in August would be considerably higher than by the same number in March or April.

While in 1947 and 1948 all areas were considered to be equally dangerous and were given uniform inspections, by 1949 it was believed that, based on the previous record of *labranchiae*, some differentiation could be made between one part of the island and another. In 1950 this differentiation was carried even further and the island was divided into four, five and six-week cycle areas (figure 13). A further complication was introduced by the fact that cuts in scouting strength had to be made on several occasions when unforeseen increases in positivity upset the budget calculations; this not only cut the amount available for scouting but made it necessary to transfer scouts to help out in eradication. These variables in turn directly affected the number of personnel employed in scouting (table XIX) and the number of inspections which were made.

The number of inspections made during the period 1947-

TABLE XIX

SCOUTING STRENGTH DURING THE PERIOD 1948 TO 1950

Month	Number of workdays in month			Average number of scouts, including supervisory personnel			Number of scouting man-days employed		
	1948	1949	1950	1948	1949	1950	1948	1949	1950
January	18	23		28	228	0	503	5,470	0
February	24	24		134	250	0	3,220	6,000	0
March	29	30	30	360	2,334	10	9,252	60,671	264
April	23	23	23	552	2,625	45	13,315	65,637	1,098
May	21	23	22	698	3,019	528	15,854	75,467	5,800
June	24	28	27	708	3,407	1,965	16,952	81,768	53,055
July	23	24	24	838	2,163	1,781	23,042	56,228	42,743
August	24	23	23	989	1,322	1,426	26,023	34,372	32,822
September	30	30	30	1,254	777	1,023	35,353	20,979	30,704
October	24			858	0*	0	20,603	0*	0
November	22			462	0*	0	6,000	0*	0
December	26			462	0	0	6,000	0	0
Total	288	228	179	7,343	16,125	6,778	176,117	406,592	166,486

* Limited amount of scouting by elements outside of the regular scouting service.

23. Clearing and burning debris after a swamp drainage ditch
has been excavated by dynamite.

24. Canalization by tractor and Martin ditcher near Olbia, Sassari Province.

25. Stream training.

26. Cutting reeds to prepare a swamp for larviciding.

50 varied considerably from month to month, the maximum being 2,300,000 made in June 1949 (figure 14). The average number of breeding places inspected per scout per day varied from less than five to about 26, with an over-all average of about 19. It will be recalled that the maximum number of breeding places was about 1,250,000 (Chapter IV), but that the number decreased during the summer because of the effect of drying. If the number of inspections made is compared with the number of breeding places existing in any given month, an estimate of the coverage can be obtained. It must be kept in mind however, that both in 1949 and in 1950 the coverage was not uniform over the island but that special attention was paid to areas which were considered dangerous for *labranchiae*.

Recognition at low densities. In certain parts of the island, in spite of the efforts made to discover the presence of *labranchiae*, there appeared to be a certain population level below which it was very difficult to detect the species, except by chance. A basic tenet in the original ERLAAS planning was that the biotic potential of *labranchiae* was so high that any residual population, if left for a short time, would soon increase to a point where it could easily be detected. The reduction of the species by eradication measures was expected to be followed by a corresponding increase in its multiplication rate. However, this did not happen, and there appeared to be no explosive outbreaks or rapid increases " up the exponential curve " which would have made detection rapid and relatively easy (Bates, 1950, p. 172). The low number of specimens in both the 1949 and 1950 collections would indicate that the re-establishment of the species was a relatively slow process; in a considerable number of the positive foci only one *labranchiae* was found. In 1950, 22 per cent of the 100 eradication zones which were established were based on a single specimen; of the 22 collections one was a first instar, three were second, eight were third, nine were fourth instars and one was a pupa. Of the 420 foci found positive during the year, in which 2,214,490 inspections

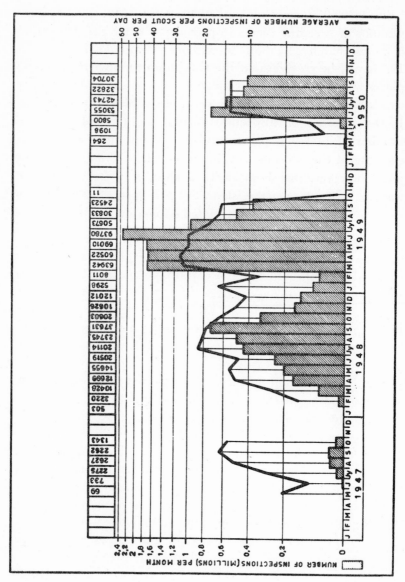

FIGURE 14. Monthly total and average daily number of larval inspections per scout, 1947 to 1950.

were made, the total number of larvae found was 1,379; an average of about three per positive focus. Eleven inspections were positive for adults and 16 specimens were collected. In 1949, 538 larval collections were made with an average of four per collection; 35 adult collections were made with an average of two adults per collection (table XX).

Adult scouting. Adult scouting was normally used as an auxiliary to larval scouting to check on the extent of the positivity after larvae had been found, or to increase the efficiency of scouting in extensive breeding places where it was hard to get adequate larval coverage. The adult scouting coverage was, therefore, additional to the basic coverage obtained by larval scouting.

During the three-year period 1948 to 1950, over 900,000 inspections were made for adults (over 400,000 in domestic shelters and over 500,000 in natural shelters). It is difficult to calculate the number of inspections per scout per day, as it varied depending on whether inspections were made in villages or in the country, on the ruggedness of the terrain and on the presence or absence of shelters. Scouts working in pairs could cover roughly four times as many rooms in villages as they could in rural areas; from 80 to 100 rooms in villages was probably a good average day's work, as compared with from 18 to 25 rooms or shelters in the country.

Larval scouting appeared to be about three times as efficient as adult scouting. As adult scouting was normally used as a check on the extent of an infestation after it had been discovered by larval scouting, the results obtained, in terms of the per cent of positivity established per inspection, cannot be compared directly with the efficiency of larval scouting. In 1950, however, when both types were used for checking purposes, only one shelter in 16,214 inspected was found positive; using larval scouting, positivity was established once in every 5,285 inspections.

General. The scouting program was based on a succession of

TABLE XX

NUMBER OF ANOPHELINE LARVAE AND ADULTS COLLECTED DURING THE PERIOD 1946 TO 1950

	1946	1947	1948	1949	1950
Number of breeding places inspected	891	112,445	2,930,724	9,405,395	2,214,490
Number of shelters inspected	510	13,795	214,382	521,957	178,359
Anopheles labranchiae					
Number of foci with larvae	551	†	†	516	352
Number of larval collections	551	4,332	2,127	538	420
Number of larvae collected	19,759	80,758	10,016	2,270*	1,379*
Average number per collection	36	19	5	4	3
Number of adult collections	90	2,996	116	35	11
Number of adults collected	1,191	9,488	354	52	28
Average number per collection	13	3	3	2	2
Anopheles—genus (including *labranchiae*)					
Number of larval collections	623	5,161	17,935	21,028	155,301
Number of larvae collected	20,730	88,669	84,738	99,338	701,450
Average number per collection	33	17	5	5	5
Number of adult collections	94	3,032	206	353	1,020
Number of adults collected	1,206	9,539	496	540	1,861
Average number per collection	13	3	2	2	2

* Note that in 1949 and 1950 this number represents *all* of the *labranchiae* larvae found in the foci inspected. In 1946 only one inspection of each focus was made.
† Data not available.

inspections of the same area, and the *labranchiae* situation was usually determined only after a number of inspections had been made. It was usually impossible to establish the presence or absence of the species after one inspection. This was illustrated both in 1949 and in 1950. In 1949, 14 cycles of inspection were completed during the period January 1 to October 26; in 1950 nine cycles were completed during the period May 15 to October 14. In 1949, while some positivity was discovered in each cycle, over 70 per cent of it was found during the fourth to eighth cycles; in 1950 positivity was also detected in each cycle, although almost 80 per cent of it was found in the first three cycles (figure 15).

In spite of the number of factors which made scouting difficult, a study of the *labranchiae* positivity for 1949 and 1950 indicated that the scouting service was able to establish the presence of the species with a surprising degree of accuracy. This is indicated by the high percentage of positivity that was found in the same zones and often in the same foci as in previous years and is particularly significant in view of the limited amount of emphasis placed on the re-examination of previously positive areas. If we consider as the positive zone the area within five kilometers of the positive focus, 72.74 per cent of the positivity found in 1949 had been positive in 1948, and 88.26 of this 1950 positivity was a repetition of the 1949 positivity (figures 16 and 17). There is reason to believe, therefore, that the returns for 1950 present a fair picture of the *labranchiae* positivity which actually existed.

RESULTS OBTAINED

The anopheline situation prior to ERLAAS. During the 1946 entomological survey, a total of 891 larval inspections were made, of which 66 per cent were positive for anophelines. Eighty-eight per cent of these positives were identified as *labranchiae*, indicating that 58 per cent of all breeding places examined were inhabited by this species. Of the 109 inspections

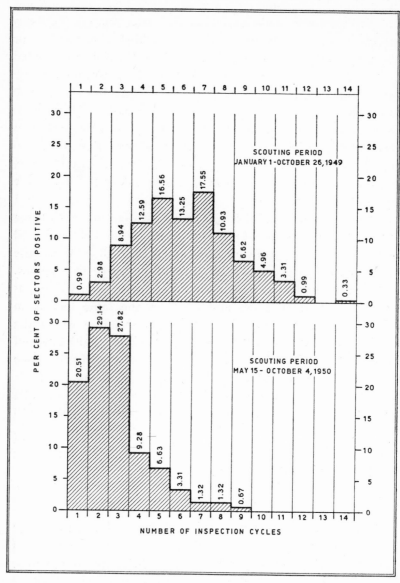

FIGURE 15. Number of inspection cycles necessary to establish the presence of *Anopheles labranchiae* during 1949 to 1950.

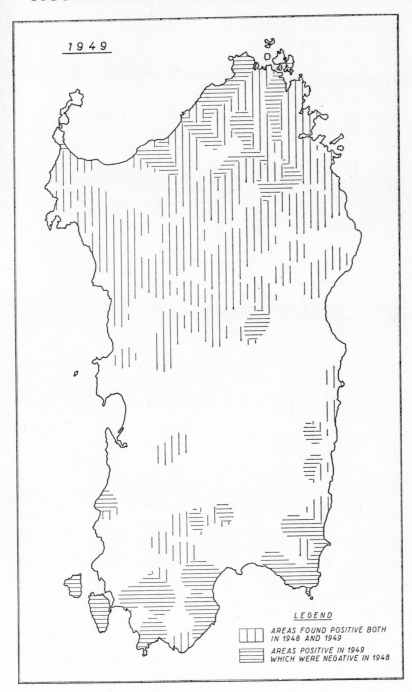

FIGURE 16. Areas within 5 kilometers of positive foci, showing new and repeat positivity for *Anopheles labranchiae* in 1949.

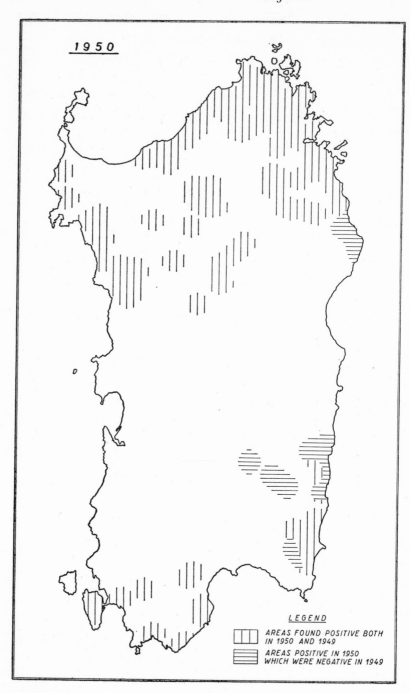

FIGURE 17. Areas within 5 kilometers of positive *Anopheles labranchiae* foci, showing new and repeat positivity in 1950.

for adults, 74 per cent were positive for anophelines and 94 per cent of these were *labranchiae*. On the basis of these findings, which showed that more than one-half of all the inspections made were positive, it may be assumed that of the approximately 1,250,000 breeding places in Sardinia, more than 625,000 could normally be expected to contain *Anopheles labranchiae*.

Of the 1946 larval positive inspections 88 per cent referred to *labranchiae*, 9 per cent to *claviger*, 1.5 per cent to *algeriensis*, 1 per cent to *melanoon* and 0.5 per cent to *marteri*.

During the 1947 trial larviciding campaign, which covered the southwestern fifth of the island, over 80 per cent of the 576 sectors examined contained anophelines most of which were *labranchiae*. This work was done after the 1946-47 residual spraying and was not intensive. Together with the subsequent scouting returns, it tends to confirm the widespread distribution of *labranchiae* prior to the campaign, and it seems safe to assume that at that time, the species might reasonably be expected in every sector in the island.

The anopheline situation after ERLAAS operations. The number of sectors found positive for the principal anopheline species, *labranchiae, claviger, algeriensis, hispaniola* and *marteri*, for the period 1948 to 1950 is shown in tables XXI and XXII. It must be kept in mind that the average size of sectors in 1948 was 7.1 square kilometers, while in 1949 and 1950 the size was reduced to 4.6 square kilometers. The number of scouts varied from month to month. For comparative purposes, the number of " standard," or 4.6 square kilometer, sectors positive for *labranchiae* per 100,000 man-days of scouting has been calculated and is shown in figure 18. The total number of specimens (adults and larvae) collected per 1,000 man-days of scouting, both for *labranchiae* and for anopheline species other than *labranchiae* is shown in table XXIII; it will be seen that there was a reduction in the case of *labranchiae* from 166,270 to 8. Considering *labranchiae* adults alone, in 1946, 170 shelters

TABLE XXI

NUMBER OF SECTORS POSITIVE FOR:

Month	Anopheles claviger			Anopheles labranchiae		
	1948	1949	1950	1948	1949	1950
January	0	3		0	0	
February	98	7		1	0	
March	772	176	1	190	9	0
April	680	333	7	139	19	0
May	768	536	177	108	27	6
June	836	1,255	3,128	276	61	56
July	824	1,192	2,498	217	91	62
August	300	895	1,500	42	61	29
September	166	779	1,044	11	33	6
October	72			5		
November	44			1		
December	51			0		

TABLE XXII

NUMBER OF SECTORS POSITIVE FOR:

Month	Anopheles algeriensis			Anopheles hispaniola			Anopheles marteri		
	1948	1949	1950	1948	1949	1950	1948	1949	1950
January	0	0		0	0		0	0	
February	24	0		0	0		0	0	
March	70	8	0	0	0	0	0	1	0
April	155	12	0	0	1	0	0	5	0
May	312	15	26	0	2	2	6	9	6
June	631	54	284	1	22	32	63	12	216
July	467	43	326	0	69	41	39	23	163
August	131	43	190	0	143	49	4	40	36
September	37	29	106	0	202	38	2	45	53
October	12			0			0		
November	7			0			0		
December	4			0			0		

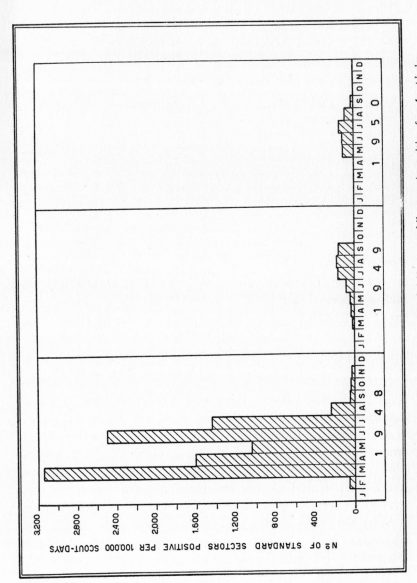

FIGURE 18. Number of standard sectors (area of 4.61 square kilometers) positive for *Anopheles labranchiae* per 100,000 scout-days during 1948 to 1950.

TABLE XXIII

NUMBER OF ANOPHELINE LARVAE AND ADULTS COLLECTED PER 1,000
SCOUT-DAYS DURING THE PERIOD 1946 TO 1950

Year	Man-days of scouting	Anopheles labranchiae		Anophelines other than labranchiae	
		Total number of specimens	Number of specimens per 1,000 man-days	Total number of specimens	Number of specimens per 1,000 man-days
1946	126	20,950	166,270	986	7,825
1947	9,309	90,246	9,694	7,962	826
1948	176,117	10,370	59	74,864	425
1949	406,592	2,322	6	97,556	240
1950	166,486	1,407	8	701,904	4,216

were inspected and 89 found positive, a ratio of 52,353 positives for every 100,000 shelters inspected. In 1947, based on 13,795 shelter inspections this ratio had dropped to 3,958; in 1948, based on 214,382 inspections the ratio was 54; in 1949, based on 521,957 shelter inspections the ratio was 7, while in 1950, based on 178,359 shelter inspections, the ratio was reduced to 6.

1951. On the conclusion of ERLAAS operations, the Italian High Commission for Hygiene and Public Health decided to abandon any further attempt at *labranchiae* eradication in Sardinia and to include the island in the national residual spraying program. The health department of the Regional Government later decided, however, to continue the attempt at eradication, and to this end reorganized the scouting and larviciding service, using former ERLAAS personnel. Operations in 1951 were carried on simultaneously with the residual spray work.

Information regarding the campaign is available to October 1, 1951, which covers the period of maximum *labranchiae* densities. Work was started in May. Scouts operated in all parts of the island, but gave special attention to those areas considered most likely to be positive for *labranchiae* on the basis of ERLAAS's previous experience. Treatment zones were established in an area of three to seven kilometers radius around *labranchiae* foci. All water surfaces in these zones were treated weekly from the time of discovery until October 1, using either Paris green or DDT in Diesel oil. A maximum of 380 scouts and 275 disinfectors were employed. Since ERLAAS, with a much larger organization, did not succeed in eradication in 1950, it is unlikely that it was achieved in 1951.

The regional scouts, working from May 14 through October 1, found *labranchiae* in 72 sectors, as compared with the total of 152 found in 1950. Most of the 1951 positivity was found near the coast. No *labranchiae* were found in the central four-fifths of the island, although the whole island was covered to some extent by the scouting program. Four *labranchiae* adults were found in three sectors, all in the southwestern coastal region. In two of these sectors no larvae were found.

In general *labranchiae* densities remained low, although two collections were made containing more than 100 larvae. A total of 268 collections were made, 3 adult and 265 larval. A total of 973 larvae of all stages were collected, giving an average of about 3.7 larvae per collection. Of the 70 sectors in which larvae were found, the presence of *labranchiae* was established in 11 on the basis of one larva in each, 27 on the basis of from 2 to 5, 10 from 6 to 10, 10 from 11 to 20, 7 from 21 to 50, 3 from 51 to 100 and 2 from 101 to 130. In more than half of the positive sectors the number of larvae was five or less.

Although only half (53 per cent) of the sectors found positive in 1951 had been positive in either 1949 or 1950, almost all of them were close to or directly adjoining sectors positive in one or both of the preceding years. Most of the sectors had been treated in these two years. Ninety per cent were treated in both 1949 and 1950; only three sectors (4 per cent) were untreated in both years; 6 per cent (four sectors) were untreated in either year. It is evident, therefore, that the majority of the 1951 positive sectors were included in both the 1949 and 1950 eradication zones.

THE EPIDEMIOLOGY OF MALARIA

The origins of malaria in Sardinia are shrouded in obscurity. According to one theory, the disease was introduced by the first North African immigrants (Protosards) and became endemic during the Phoenician and Carthaginian epochs, reaching epidemic levels at the time of the Roman conquest and remaining widely distributed throughout the island during the Middle Ages (Fermi, 1934).

In recent years, Sardinia has been the most malarious region of Italy. Annual malaria morbidity rates for all Italy ranged from about 50 to 70 per 10,000 inhabitants for the decade 1920 to 1929; they remained almost constant at approximately 50 per 10,000 from 1930 to 1934 and declined sharply from 1934 until 1939, when the rate of 12.61 per 10,000 inhabitants was the lowest since the reporting of malaria was started in 1902 (Istituto Superiore di Sanità, 1946, p. 157).

For the three-year period 1936 to 1938, and for the year 1939, morbidity rates were above the national rate in five of the 18 regions into which the country is divided (Puglie, Lucania, Calabria, Sicily and Sardinia). Table XXIV shows the mean annual number of cases and deaths for these two periods, with the corresponding annual morbidity and mortality rates per 10,000 inhabitants for these five regions and for the entire country (Ministero dell'Interno, 1941, p. 123). For the period 1936 to 1938 the five southern regions accounted for 86 per cent of the total number of malaria cases and 80 per cent of the total mortality from malaria reported in Italy; during 1939 they accounted for 83.5 per cent of the cases of malaria and 75 per cent of the malaria mortality. The morbidity and mortality rates in Sardinia were higher than those in any other region.

176

TABLE XXIV

ANNUAL MEAN MALARIA MORBIDITY AND MORTALITY RATES IN THE FIVE REGIONS
OF ITALY WHICH HAD RATES ABOVE THE NATIONAL AVERAGES, FOR THE
YEARS 1936 TO 1938 AND FOR 1939 (Ministero dell' Interno, 1941)

Region	Morbidity				Mortality			
	1936–1938 (annual mean)		1939		1936–1938 (annual mean)		1939	
	Number of cases	Rate per 10,000	Number of cases	Rate per 10,000	Number of deaths	Rate per 10,000	Number of deaths	Rate per 10,000
Puglie	16,864	63.12	5,532	20.33	149	0.56	84	0.31
Lucania	5,418	98.33	2,753	49.15	59	1.07	29	0.51
Calabria	15,459	86.32	10,614	58.46	164	0.92	91	0.50
Sicily	16,820	41.74	10,147	24.83	225	0.56	126	0.31
Sardinia	36,655	349.57	17,215	160.41	221	2.11	138	1.27
Five regions	91,216		46,261		818		468	
All Italy	106,032	24.43	55,453	12.61	1,021	0.24	627	0.14

Two of Sardinia's three provinces had the highest provincial morbidity rates in Italy for 1939. The highest malaria rates in the nation were reported in the provinces of Nuoro, Sardinia (383.12 per 10,000 inhabitants); Sassari, Sardinia (163.80); Matera, Lucania (142.99); Catanzaro, Calabria (101.05); Agrigento, Sicily (75.02); and Cagliari, Sardinia (62.31) (Ministero dell'Interno, 1941). The rate for Cagliari Province has generally been lower than for Sassari and for Nuoro because approximately one-fifth of the population lives in the capital city, which is nonmalarious, and because much of the populated part of the province consists of a low, cultivated plain where breeding places dry up more rapidly than in the more mountainous areas.

During the war years, malaria increased markedly throughout Italy because of the disruption of sanitary services and the destruction of pumping stations and drainage installations caused by military operations. This situation is reflected in the statistics for 1946. Four of the five regions reported most malarious from 1936 to 1938 and in 1939 again had rates higher than the national average, both for primary cases and for relapses (figure 19). The region of Lazio also had higher rates than the national averages. This, which includes the Pontine Marshes and the Agro Romano, once highly malarious districts, suffered severe outbreaks of malaria in 1944 and 1945 due to the wartime destruction of large drainage installations. By 1946 the situation had again been brought under control by the use of DDT and by repair of the installations, but a residue of relapses was left, along with a low incidence of primary cases. Again in 1946 Sardinia had by far the highest rates. While the island has only about 2.7 per cent of Italy's population, it reported over 20 per cent of the total number of malaria cases.

Malaria case rates per 10,000 inhabitants in the most malarious provinces of Italy during 1946 indicate that for primary case rates, Sassari ranked first, Nuoro second and Cagliari fifth; for relapse and total case rates, Sassari was second, Nuoro third and Cagliari twelfth. A comparison of the primary and relapse rates for the different provinces shows that the relatively good ranking of the Sardinian provinces in the total case rates for 1946 is due to the fact that, in many provinces outside Sardinia, malaria had risen to abnormal levels during the war. The disease was again being brought under control, but there was a large residue of cases due to relapsing malaria which gave total rates far in excess of the amount of malaria normally occurring in these provinces.

THE VECTOR

Since the early work of the Italian Malaria Experiment Station in northern Sardinia, *labranchiae* (*maculipennis*) has been considered the important vector of malaria in the island. Hackett (1929) noted that the vector anophelines were *maculipennis* and rarely *sacharovi* (*elutus*) while *algeriensis*, though also present, could be ignored. Missiroli (1938, map, p. 16)

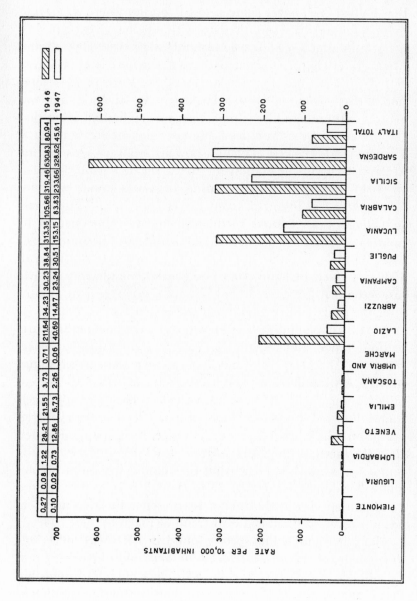

FIGURE 19. Malaria rates per 10,000 inhabitants in the regions of Italy, 1946 and 1947.

found *labranchiae* occurring in Sardinia and stated (p. 17) that he had ". . . never come across a locality where *A. maculipennis labranchiae* was present without the co-existence of malaria in a more or less severely endemic state." Hackett and Missiroli (1935, p. 49) stated that *labranchiae* is always associated with an intense malaria. Hackett (1949, p. 794) later noted that *sacharovi* occurred sparsely in Sardinia but was greatly outnumbered by *labranchiae*; he emphasized again that the presence of these species is always a sign of severe malaria. Putnam and Hackett (1946) showed, from records of the Malaria Experiment Station for the town of Portotorres, that in 1930 and 1931 the beginning of the summer wave of *labranchiae* was followed seven weeks later by the initial rise in malaria cases treated at the dispensary. The relation by months between the density of *labranchiae* and the number of cases of malaria reported in Sardinia during 1947 (Patrissi, 1949) is given in figure 20. The greatest number of malaria cases (both primary cases and relapses) occurred two months after the peak density of *labranchiae* in shelters.

Several anopheline species known to be vectors in other parts of their range, and previously reported from Sardinia (*sacharovi, messeae, atroparvus* and *superpictus*) were never found in ERLAAS collections. Of the species actually discovered, only *labranchiae* is an important vector. It has repeatedly been found infected in nature in Sardinia. *Claviger* is a proven vector only in a limited part of its range, for example in Palestine (Hackett, 1949, p. 797). In Sardinia, *claviger* was usually found in natural shelters, being uncommon in houses, stables and other domestic shelters. Even though it is, at present, the dominant species in the island, its presence in large numbers has not reversed the downward trend of malaria.

The other anopheline species found in ERLAAS collections (*melanoon, algeriensis, marteri, plumbeus* and *hispaniola*) presumably do not act as vectors in Sardinia, although it is possible that *claviger* and *algeriensis* were responsible for some secondary transmission in the presence of *labranchiae*.

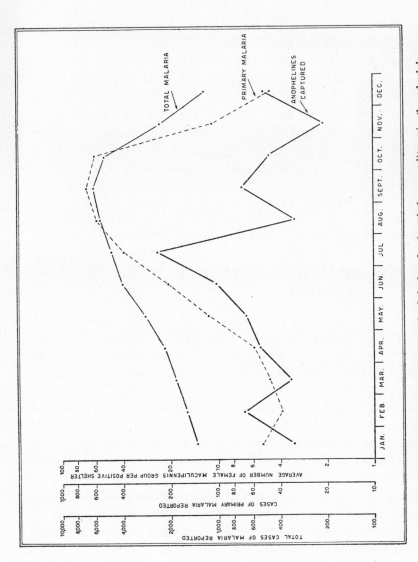

FIGURE 20. Relation between density of adult female *Anopheles maculipennis* (largely *labranchiae*) in inhabited, untreated, positive shelters, and number of cases of primary and total malaria reported in Sardinia, 1947.

A point of interest is the possibility of malaria transmission taking place outside the villages. About 92 per cent of the population normally live in villages and the remainder occupy scattered rural houses. However, many shepherds and their families from the villages spend the spring and summer months in the country, staying for weeks at a time in isolated brush huts known as *capanne*. During these months farmers and their families often work late into the evening in their fields, which are often far from their homes; during the harvest season they may spend several entire weeks in the fields, sleeping in the open. This practice is also common during rural festivals, which may last as long as ten days. These customs, together with the fact that *labranchiae* was frequently found in areas remote from inhabited centers, would give opportunity for a significant, but indeterminate, proportion of the malaria transmission to occur outside the villages; however, there is no information available to indicate whether or not this is important.

SEASONAL DISTRIBUTION

The incidence of malaria in Sardinia (as in Italy generally) is characterized by well-marked seasonal changes, due to the effect of temperature upon anopheline development and upon the extrinsic cycle of the malaria parasite. Although the first *labranchiae* ovipositions may occur as early as late January or early February, the first adults of the season emerge in late March or early April. This generation is not significant for the transmission of malaria because of low environmental temperatures. Jancso (quoted by Boyd, 1949a, p. 556) found that *Plasmodium vivax* did not develop in anophelines if the temperature was below 16° C. Knowles and Basu (quoted by Boyd, 1949b, p. 617) gave 15.5° C. as the minimum temperature necessary for the development of *vivax*, and 21.1° C. as that necessary for *Plasmodium falciparum*. Grassi (quoted by Boyd, 1949b, p. 615), working in Italy, found the required temperatures for these species to be 17.5° C. and 18° C. respectively. Mean temperatures for April for the years 1947 to 1950 in the three Sardinian provincial capitals varied between 7.4° C. and 16.5° C.; the latter reading, taken in Sassari in 1949, was the only monthly average above 15° C. For the same years and the same locations, average May temperatures ranged between 12.5° C. and 18.2° C., the lowest averages being in the city of Nuoro, at an altitude of 545 meters. Thus *vivax* would be able to complete its extrinsic cycle in May, in all except the highest parts of the island. Comparable temperatures for June ranged from 18.0° C. to 23.1° C., with the lowest averages again occurring in Nuoro. It seems probable that the extrinsic development of *falciparum* could not take place before June.

No data are available as to the time of year when naturally infected anophelines are first found in Sardinia. However, the situation is probably similar to that on the mainland. Bastianelli and Bignami (1899, quoted by Pampana, 1944, p. 170) found the first infected anophelines in June. Missiroli and Marino (1934) found *labranchiae* (*maculipennis*) infected (stomach and glands) in nature in Posada on June 3, 1931 and again on June 24, 1932, but they do not record examinations earlier in the year.

In general, it may be said that under ordinary circumstances the bulk of transmission does not begin until late May or June.

The curve of adult *labranchiae* density rises rapidly with increasing temperature, reaching its peak in July. The curve then falls off rapidly, associated with excessive heat and dryness and the drying up of many aquatic habitats. The last generation of adults develops in November. Putnam and Hackett (1946), analyzing a study carried out in Portotorres in 1930-31, made a comparison of the seasonal wave of *labranchiae* density (as measured by adult captures) with the number of malaria cases diagnosed in the local dispensary. In both years the initial rise in anopheline captures began early in May and was followed seven weeks later by the corresponding initial rise in malaria dispensary attendance. Anopheline adult catches rose to high levels which lasted during June and July and then fell abruptly.

The number of malaria cases treated in the dispensary rose rapidly in July of both years, reaching a peak in September of 1930 and in late July of 1931.

In general, the peak incidence of malaria has been reported in July, August or September, varying from year to year. In 1927, Putnam and Hackett (1946) found that the number of dispensary cases in the town of Siniscola was highest in July, decreasing only slightly in August and September but falling off sharply in October. In Portotorres in the same year, the number of cases reached a high level in July, decreased slightly in August and increased to the high point for the year in September. For Sassari city, the mean number of cases diagnosed at the San Giuseppe malaria dispensary by months from 1927 to 1942 showed that the incidence was highest from July through October, with the peak in September.

The distribution by months of primary and total cases for the whole of Sardinia during 1946 is shown in table XXV (Istituto Superiore di Sanità, 1950). Again the highest levels

TABLE XXV

MONTHLY DISTRIBUTION OF CASES OF PRIMARY MALARIA AND TOTAL MALARIA
IN SARDINIA, 1946 (Istituto Superiore di Sanità, 1950)

Month	Number of malaria cases	
	Primary	Primary and relapses
January	4	972
February	6	1,143
March	13	1,131
April	71	1,665
May	94	1,972
June	353	4,055
July	1,701	11,839
August	2,892	17,698
September	3,307	18,704
October	1,281	9,914
November	298	3,980
December	129	2,374
Total	10,149	75,447

for both primary and total cases occurred in July, August and September, with the peak in September. The fact that the distinction between primary malaria and relapses was of necessity based on the patient's history probably accounts for the fact that primary cases were diagnosed in the winter months.

GEOGRAPHICAL DISTRIBUTION

There is very little information in the literature on the incidence of malaria in various parts of Sardinia. The results of spleen and parasite surveys have been reported for only a few villages, or else these indices have been published for entire provinces without a breakdown by villages.

Fermi (1934) gives the following as the most malarious sections of the three provinces, according to the reported malaria rates:

> *Cagliari*—the southeastern coastal region, at the mouths of the Flumendosa and Picocca rivers; the Palmas River basin in the Sulcis, along the Cixerri and Mannu rivers in the Campidano and the region around Oristano.
>
> *Sassari*—the northern part of the Regione Vulcanica and the southwestern edge of the Logudoro, followed by the Anglona and the upper Tirso Valley.
>
> *Nuoro*—the Baronia (coastal zone of the northeastern part of the province). This area, including the towns of Posada, Torpè, Siniscola and Lodè, is the most malarious part of Sardinia.

Brotzu (1935) gives the distribution of malaria in Cagliari Province as follows:

> *Region of low endemicity* (less than 10 per cent malarious; total population 200,000)—the cities of Cagliari, Iglesias, Oristano and a few smaller cities.
>
> *Region of moderate endemicity* (10-25 per cent malarious; total population 150,000)—most of the communes of the Campidano and the surrounding hills.
>
> *Region of high endemicity* (25-80 per cent malarious; total population 120,000)—the Sulcis and Sarrabus regions, some communes of the Campidano and the Trexenta, and the region around Oristano.

Data from the province of Sassari prove that malaria is not confined to the lowlands, although it is more prevalent at lower than at higher altitudes. Canalis *et al.* (1950) reported case rates (year not given) at various altitudes, finding that they varied from 999.7 per 10,000 at 0-300 meters above sea level to 309.2 per 10,000 at 601-800 meters above sea level. There are no inhabited centers at altitudes above 800 meters in Sassari Province.

Almost all the published spleen and parasite indices are from the Portotorres Malaria Experiment Station which was operating in the northern part of the island from 1925 through 1935. Demonstration control projects were carried out in highly malarious villages, using such measures as larviciding, drug prophylaxis and mass treatment. Malariometric indices were determined periodically in children from one to 12 years of age. The spleen and parasite rates reported are given in tables XXVI and XXVII, respectively (Missiroli, 1927, 1928 and 1930; Hackett, 1929). The data presented are from protected villages, prior to the initiation of experimental control, and from three comparison villages.

The comparison villages were Posada and Torpè, where the only antimalarial measure was intensive drug treatment of the sick in an attempt to reduce transmission, and Lodè, where only routine quinine treatment of the sick was carried out. For these towns, Putnam and Hackett (1946) give the over-all parasite rate for the six-year period 1929 to 1934 as 24.5 per cent; during this period 8.5 per cent of the children were positive for *falciparum*, 15.2 per cent for *vivax* and 0.8 per cent for *Plasmodium malariae*.

The intensive treatment carried out in Torpè, with prompt and adequate medication of every discoverable case, did not prevent an actual increase in malaria (Hackett and Missiroli, 1930). In a population of slightly more than 1,000, 376 acute cases of malaria were diagnosed during 1927, with a parasite rate of 25 per cent in school children the following February. In 1929, after two years of intensive treatment, there were 744

TABLE XXVI

SPLEEN RATES AND SPLEEN SIZES IN NORTHERN SARDINIAN CHILDREN ONE TO
12 YEARS OF AGE (From Missiroli, 1927, 1928 and 1930; and Hackett, 1929)

| Town | Year | Number examined | Number negative | Number with spleens palpable | | | Total number enlarged | Spleen rate (per cent) |
				at costal margin	from costal margin to umbilicus	below umbilicus		
Porto-torres	1924	312	166	40	99	7	146	46.8
Oschiri	1925	317	149	46	118	4	168	53.0
Suburb of Olbia	1926	88	25	23	36	4	63	71.6
	1927	82	23	28	24	7	59	72.0
Siniscola	1926	309	135	84	88	2	174	56.3
	1927	344	161	115	67	1	183	53.2
Lodè	1927	99	13	31	53	2	86	86.9
	1928	94	9	17	63	5	85	90.5
	1929	169	12	58	91	8	157	93.0
Orosei	1926	158	30	29	91	8	128	81.0
	1927	223	51	72	91	9	172	77.1
	1928	180	31	45	102	2	149	82.8
Posada	1926	86	0	7	28	51	86	100.0
	1927	100	0	19	46	35	100	100.0
	1928	37	1	9	20	7	36	97.5
	1929	217	6	12	142	57	211	97.2
Torpè	1926	136	34	13	76	13	102	75.0
	1927	117	18	33	57	9	99	84.6
	1928	95	6	11	73	5	89	93.6
	1929	157	13	41	97	6	144	91.8

TABLE XXVII

PARASITE RATES AND PARASITE RATIOS IN NORTHERN SARDINIAN CHILDREN ONE TO 12 YEARS OF AGE

(FROM MISSIROLI, 1927, 1928, AND 1930; AND HACKETT, 1929)

Town	Year	Number examined	Number positive for parasites	Parasite rate (per cent)	Plasmodium species					
					vivax		*falciparum*		*malariae*	
					Number	Per cent of total	Number	Per cent of total	Number	Per cent of total
Portotorres	1924	802	274	34.2	140	51.1	118	43.1	16	5.8
Oschiri	1926	225	28	12.4	9	32.2	15	53.6	4	14.3
Suburb of Olbia	1926	210	17	8.1	3	17.6	9	52.9	5	29.4
Siniscola	1927	233	24	10.3	13	54.2	11	45.8	0	0
Lodè	1927	100	30	30.0	4	13.3	25	83.4	1	3.3
	1928	94	27	28.7	11	40.7	16	59.3	0	0
Orosei	1926	158	56	35.4	6	10.7	37	66.1	13	23.2
Posada	1926	89	38	42.7	7	18.4	23	60.5	8	21.1
	1927	100	24	24.0	10	41.7	14	58.3	0	0
	1928	37	12	32.5	4	33.3	8	66.7	0	0
	1929	221	100	45.3	70	70.0	27	27.0	3	3.0
Torpè	1926	136	26	19.1	4	15.4	17	65.4	5	19.2
	1927	145	36	24.8	17	47.3	16	44.4	3	8.3
	1928	95	12	12.6	6	50.0	6	50.0	0	0
	1929	157	57	36.3	47	82.5	7	12.3	3	5.3

acute cases of malaria in the same population, with a parasite rate the following February of 36 per cent.

Mosna and Canalis (1937) found that the spleen rate in school children in Posada was above 90 per cent each year between 1928 and 1934, while the parasite rate fluctuated from 23 to 48 per cent. Parasite rates in infants under one year of age were between 24 and 48 per cent.

Canalis *et al.* (1950) reported the results of a spleen survey made in 1946 among school children in various centers of Sassari Province. Over one-fifth of these children had enlarged spleens, the rate for individual villages varying from 12.1 to 75.5 per cent.

AGE DISTRIBUTION AND PARASITE SPECIES DISTRIBUTION

Available information on the incidence of malaria by age groups in Sardinia is as scant as that on its distribution by geographical areas. From January to October of 1930 Missiroli (1932) made monthly blood examinations of the inhabitants of Posada and classified the results for the age groups 0 to 12 years (241 persons), 13 to 19 years (88 persons) and over 19 years (327 persons). The percentage of individuals positive for *vivax* and *falciparum* in these age groups, by months, is shown in table XXVIII.

Vivax was predominantly an infection of childhood, with very few persons over 13 years of age positive for this species. The incidence of *vivax* infections reached a high point in March due to relapses of infections acquired in the previous transmission season, and a peak in July due to new infections. *Falciparum* malaria, while more common in the age group under 12 years, was relatively frequent in the older age groups. For all ages the peak incidence of *falciparum* positives occurred in July, which corresponds with the maximum *labranchiae* density observed in June and July.

The fact that some persons over 13 years of age showed *vivax* parasites and that considerable numbers of adults were positive

TABLE XXVIII

Distribution of parasite species, by age groups, in Posada,
January to October, 1930 (Missiroli, 1932)

Month	0–12 years (241 persons)		13–19 years (88 persons)		Over 19 years (327 persons)	
	Per cent positive for P. vivax	Per cent positive for P. falciparum	Per cent positive for P. vivax	Per cent positive for P. falciparum	Per cent positive for P. vivax	Per cent positive for P. falciparum
January	4.1	4.6	0.0	1.1	0.0	0.3
February	7.1	1.7	0.0	0.0	0.3	0.3
March	17.0	3.3	2.3	1.1	0.3	0.9
April	8.3	3.7	0.0	1.1	0.0	0.6
May	13.7	4.1	0.0	1.1	0.0	1.5
June	16.2	1.7	0.0	0.0	0.6	0.6
July	22.0	35.2	4.5	17.0	3.7	15.0
August	3.3	12.9	2.3	9.1	0.6	7.0
September	2.5	5.4	0.0	2.3	0.0	3.7
October	0.8	1.3	0.0	1.1	0.0	0.9

for *falciparum* indicates that malaria in Sardinia does not reach the highly endemic levels found in certain tropical areas. In such regions intense and continuous infection during childhood results in the formation of a solid immunity, so that adolescents and adults with circulating parasites are rarely found.

During July, August and September, when parasite rates were at their highest for the year, the age group under 12 years was further subdivided. Blood examinations were made of all the children who had fever during the three-month period. The data demonstrated that in the first year of life, *vivax* was five times as frequent as *falciparum*. After five years of age immunity to *vivax* appeared to be established, and thereafter the percentage of infections with this species decreased abruptly, resulting in a predominance of *falciparum*. The total percentage positive in each age group decreased progressively with increasing age.

Other data on the relative frequency of parasite species are given by Canalis *et al.* (1950). Over the years 1924 to 1946, 15,668 positive blood examinations were made at the anti-malaria dispensary in Sassari. Of these 50.7 per cent were positive for *falciparum*, 42.5 per cent for *vivax*, 3.7 per cent for *malariae* and 3.1 per cent were mixed infections (species not given). Floris (1948) reported that of 5,077 blood examinations made during 1947 at 12 malaria centers in Cagliari Province: 823 (16.2 per cent) were positive for *vivax* and 611 (12.0 per cent) were positive for *falciparum*; the parasite ratio was thus 57.5 per cent for *vivax* to 42.5 per cent for *falciparum*. Putnam and Hackett (1946) give the parasite ratios combined for Lodè, Posada and Torpè, over the years 1929 to 1934. In these towns, *falciparum* predominated only in 1929. The ratio for the six-year period was approximately two-thirds *vivax* to one-third *falciparum*. The decrease in the prevalence of *falciparum* from 1929 on correlates with the decline in malaria in these comparison towns over the years of the study. This decrease was probably due to natural factors, since spleen and parasite rates declined in Lodè, where only routine quinine treatment was carried out, as well as in Posada and Torpè, where the intensive treatment program was in effect.

Infant infection rates, of value in indicating the extent of recent transmission, have likewise been reported only on very few occasions. In addition to the data presented previously, Brotzu (1935) has reported these rates for three villages of Cagliari Province. In Domus de Maria in 1933, 100 per cent of the infants under one year of age were stated to be malarious; in 1934 this was reduced to 30 per cent (species of parasite and number of infants examined not given). In Piscinas in 1933, 80 per cent of the infants were malarious; in 1934, 33 per cent. In Elmas in 1933, 16 of 29 infants were malarious (55 per cent); in 1934, 10 of 29 infants had malaria (34 per cent). Missiroli (1927) made blood examinations of infants under one year of age in Portotorres, finding 2.7 per cent of 294 infants positive in 1925, and 3.1 per cent of 223 positive in 1926. At Siniscola during 1927, blood examinations showed 5.7 per cent of 175 infants to be positive (Missiroli, 1928).

MALARIA CONTROL BEFORE 1946

An early experiment in the control of malaria in Sardinia was that of Fermi and Tonsini (1902), carried out in 1898-99 in the island of Asinara, off the northwest coast of Sardinia. Fermi used smoke to kill anopheline adults in houses and also employed traps to diminish adult densities. In addition, all aquatic habitats where anopheline larvae had been found were oiled every 15 days from June to November. The number of anophelines in the island was greatly reduced by these procedures, as was the number of malaria relapses. It was stated that no primary cases of malaria occurred during the experiment.

The first Italian law relating to malaria control was passed in 1900, when the sale and distribution of quinine were removed from private channels. A government monopoly was established to make quinine available in all communes at low cost. This was followed by the law of November 2, 1901, requiring the delineation of malarious zones in all provinces; all communes situated in these zones were required to furnish free curative quinine to laborers, the cost to be met by a special tax on landowners and employers. A law of February 25, 1904, established the principle of free curative quinine for all the poor at the expense of the commune. On May 19, 1904, prophylactic quinine in addition to curative quinine was made available without charge to all workers in malarious areas.

The present-day system of malaria control was established in 1929, when provincial malaria committees were organized under the Italian Directorate General of Public Health and the prefects of the provinces. The committees were put in charge of all necessary procedures for the measurement and control of malaria in their respective provinces.

In Sardinia, there was theoretical provision in each commune for a malaria dispensary to diagnose and treat all malaria cases free of charge. The dispensary was the responsibility of the communal sanitary officer, who also directed the anti-anopheline campaign. A map was to be kept showing all known anopheline breeding places; these were to be treated during the breeding season, usually with Paris green larvicide. Treatment of the sick at the dispensary was the duty of the communal physician. Due to limited financial resources, however, many communes in Sardinia were without dispensaries; for the same reason, the provincial malaria committees were often able to provide only larvicide and were forced to leave to the commune the costs of labor and supervision for the antilarval work. Many of the communes were unable to provide funds for anti-anopheline work, or gave only inadequate support. The work was virtually unsupervised by the provincial authorities.

Another weakness of this system was that the poorer communes (which often were the most malarious) had only one public health official, who functioned as both communal physician and sanitary officer. Since this individual was occupied with the treatment of malaria cases during the summer months, he had no time to supervise the larviciding work also going on at that time. All these factors tended to make the anti-anopheline work, if any, inefficient.

INCIDENCE OF MALARIA SINCE 1946

The annual number of malaria cases reported from 1936 to 1950 by the provincial medical officers for the three provinces of Sardinia is shown in table XXIX. The reports are divided into new cases (including primary cases and reinfections) and total malaria cases. The distinction between primary cases, reinfections and relapses was made on the basis of the individual patient's history and is therefore subject to error.

Malaria case reporting, in Sardinia as elsewhere, is inaccurate. Under-reporting is caused by the fact that a number of private physicians do not report malaria cases, while many patients

TABLE XXIX

CASES OF MALARIA REPORTED BY PROVINCIAL MEDICAL OFFICERS IN SARDINIA, 1936 TO 1950

Year	Cagliari		Sassari		Nuoro		Island Total	
	New cases	Total cases	New cases	Total cases	New cases	Total cases	New cases	Total cases
1936	1,512	20,456	1,983	26,904	5,000	21,000	8,495	68,360
1937	1,112	12,798	2,017	22,103	10,387	25,116	13,516	60,017
1938	708	10,272	2,126	18,898	3,288	18,249	6,122	47,419
1939	1,148	9,573	2,416	19,669	3,150	19,747	6,714	48,989
1940	1,061	8,759	2,167	11,206	1,187	8,466	4,415	28,431
1941	2,986	20,369	3,544	13,402	2,214	15,689	8,744	49,460
1942	8,149	27,730	4,478	19,825	756	17,100	13,383	64,655
1943	8,125	18,857	4,436	22,836	2,734	21,785	15,295	63,478
1944	4,275	18,423	2,424	29,814	4,478	29,936	11,177	78,173
1945	3,109	15,669	2,559	34,564	2,851	24,408	8,519	74,641
1946	3,206	17,186	4,180	38,655	2,763	19,606	10,149	75,447
1947	861	6,470	1,862	25,181	245	7,652	2,968	39,303
1948	125	1,631	207	10,967	9	2,523	341	15,121
1949	3	173	2	922	1	219	6	1,314
1950	2	34	1	9	1	1	4	44

The term "new cases" includes both primary cases and reinfections; the differentiation between these and relapses was based on the case history.

27. Use of the mower-toothed rake in stream training operation.

28. The use of the long-toothed rakes in stream clearing.

29. Larviciding a well, using DDT bubbler.

30. *Posidonia oceania*—the sea iris, used for making DDT larvicide bubblers.

31. Larviciding operations using shoulder pumps, illustrating the type of boat
made in the ERLAAS workshops.

are never seen by a physician because of self-treatment or isolation. Additional error arises from the fact that the majority of diagnoses are based on clinical grounds; the usual tendency is to call all febrile diseases malaria, particularly when they occur in the summer months and when they are associated with splenomegaly. The net effect of this is probably over-reporting. It should be noted that the number of cases officially reported by the provincial medical officers often differed widely from the previously quoted reports published by the Central Government. The reason for this discrepancy is not apparent.

In spite of these deficiencies, the general course of malaria over the 15-year period can be traced. From 1936 to 1940, the total number of cases decreased by about 59 per cent. This coincided with the general decline throughout Italy during this period, except for the slight rise in the national rate during 1940. During the war years cases reported in Sardinia increased greatly, as in all Italy. The peak was reached in 1944, when there were almost three times as many cases as in 1940; the totals for 1945 and 1946 were only slightly lower. New cases reached their highest point in 1943, when they were about 3.5 times the level of 1940; the number of new cases decreased in 1944 and again in 1945, with another increase in 1946.

From this time on, there was a progressive and marked decline in the number of malaria cases. In 1947 the total cases for the three provinces decreased almost 50 per cent and the new cases approximately 70 per cent, in comparison with the 1946 levels. This decrease followed the first ERLAAS residual spraying campaign, carried out from November 1946 to June 1947. This was the only control measure in effect at the time, except for the experimental larviciding program in a small part of Cagliari Province and some treatment of the sick at the dispensaries. It seems probable, therefore, that the residual spraying program was largely responsible for the decrease in malaria.

The decline in malaria cases continued during the succeeding three years of ERLAAS activities. In 1949 only six new cases were reported from the entire island. These were investigated by the ERLAAS epidemiological service, and only one was considered a possible primary case. In 1950 four new cases were reported, with a total of only 44 cases for the island. Investigation of the new cases showed that two in Sassari and Cagliari provinces were children who had received paternal blood (a transfusion in one case, and eight daily injections in the other) and developed *vivax* malaria shortly afterwards. The transfusion donor was found positive for *vivax*; the blood of the other donor was not examined, but he had had malaria repeatedly in the past, the last attack being about a year previously. Both cases were considered to be transfusion malaria.

The third case, in Cagliari Province, was that of a man aged 39 years, who was seen by a physician because of fever and cough. A diagnosis of malaria was made because the spleen was palpable on deep inspiration. No blood examination was made. After treatment with an unstated amount of quinine, the spleen was still palpable on deep inspiration, and no parasites were found in a thick film. This patient's history was not suggestive of malaria, and the diagnosis was considered improbable.

The fourth case, in Nuoro Province, was that of a prisoner at the Sarcidano penal colony near Isili. This man became ill in June with chills and fever on alternate days. *Vivax* parasites were found by the provincial laboratory. The patient denied previous malaria. He was a native of northern Italy and had been in Sardinia about six months, working on the farm at the penal colony. When examined again about three months after treatment with quinine and quinacrine, no parasites were found and the spleen was not palpable. No other cases occurred at the colony during the summer.

No *labranchiae* had been found in the region of the penal colony since the end of June 1948, when larvae were discovered in three habitats 5.0, 6.5 and 7.0 kilometers from the colony. In 1950 the ERLAAS district and the sector in which the colony was located were examined intensively for *labranchiae*. From June 12-25, 1,233 possible breeding places were inspected in the district, of which 214 were in the sector surrounding the colony. From July 10-16, the most favorable habitats in the district were again inspected; 157 were examined, of which none was in the sector of the colony. From July 24 to August 6, inspections totaling 1,333 were made in the district; 229 of these were in the sector. All inspections were negative for *labranchiae*.

In summary, of the four cases reported during 1950 as new cases of malaria, two were probably transfusion malaria, one was probably not malaria and one was *vivax* malaria, perhaps primary.

Canalis *et al.* (1950) give confirmatory evidence for the decline of malaria, possibly in a more accurate way than by case reporting. They summarized the positive examinations made at the San Giuseppe dispensary in Sassari city for the years 1946 to 1949 (table XXX). The rapid decrease in the number of individuals positive for parasites of all species is apparent; in 1949 no persons were found with circulating parasites.

TABLE XXX

POSITIVE MALARIA EXAMINATIONS AT THE SAN GIUSEPPE MALARIA DISPENSARY, SASSARI CITY, 1946 TO 1949* (FROM CANALIS *et al.*, 1950)

Year	Total number of cases positive	Number considered primary cases	Positive for:			
			P. falciparum	*P. vivax*	*P. malariae*	Spleen†
1946	1,996	651	602	573	26	795
1947	1,144	172	293	480	14	357
1948	343	4‡	22	228	3	90
1949	166	0	0	0	0	166

* Total number examined and number of negative examinations not given.
† While it is not so stated, the data indicate that these were persons with splenomegaly but with negative blood examinations or in whom blood examinations were not made.
‡ All *vivax*.

Spleen and Parasite Surveys

No spleen and parasite surveys were made by ERLAAS before the initiation of eradication activities. The pressure of organizing and carrying out the first residual spraying campaign and the experimental larviciding program did not allow time for this work; furthermore, the requisite staff was not available. Malaria control was deemed secondary to the objective of anopheline eradication, and all possible efforts were devoted to the latter. Eventually, however, it was decided to undertake surveys to obtain an index of the trend of malaria during the campaign as well as to complement the anopheline scouting service by seeking evidence of any malaria transmission.

The first survey, carried out from November 1947 to March 1948 on school children 6 to 13 years of age, covered 66 villages (classified as Group I) which were a representative geographical cross section of the island. The total population of the 66 villages was approximately 190,000, or about 22 per cent of the population of Sardinia, excluding the 13 cities with more than 10,000 inhabitants. All children present at school were examined; thus the surveys represented, as is usual under such circumstances, the amount of malaria in healthy children. Subjects were examined in the recumbent position, with the abdomen bared and the knees flexed. Thick blood films were made for all children examined [1] and the slides stained in blocks by Giemsa. Subsequent surveys were made in the same way during May and September in 13 of these villages (known as Group II), with a total population of approximately 35,000. The villages were selected from the group of 66 so that all sections of the island were represented; within this limitation, an effort was made to include the more malarious villages.

This cycle of surveys was repeated each year. The same 13 villages were used, and the winter, spring and fall surveys were

---

[1] Differences in the numbers of spleen examinations and blood examinations in the tables which follow are due to loss or breakage of slides.

made in the same months every year. The same staff physician regularly made the spleen examinations. For the first three surveys, the slides were sent to be stained and examined in the laboratory of the Department of Parasitology of the Istituto Superiore di Sanità. Beginning with the fourth survey (the winter survey of 1948-49), all slides were examined in the ERLAAS laboratory. Greater attention was paid to negative slides; thick films were examined for ten minutes before being so classified. All positives were checked by a staff member.

The data for the spleen surveys, with the spleen rates, standard errors of the rates and spleen sizes (classified according to Hackett, 1944) are given in table XXXI. It is seen that the spleen rate declined progressively in both groups of villages. In general, the rate was higher in the small group of villages (Group II), due to the selection of villages known to have been especially malarious.

The chi square test was used to assess the significance of the changes observed. In the Group II villages, when the numbers of enlarged and normal spleens for the winter survey of 1947-48 were compared with those for the spring survey of 1950, the difference was highly significant (P = 0.0000). The difference between the winter survey of 1947-48 and the spring survey of 1948 is obviously not significant, but the difference between the first survey and the third survey (fall 1948) almost reaches the significant level (P = 0.06). The considerably greater differences in succeeding surveys are thus significant. The downward trend of the spleen rate was interrupted in the fall of 1949, when the rate rose to 26.7 per cent from its previous level of 24.5 per cent. This difference is not significant (P for the basic data = 0.07).

For the Group I villages, the difference between the numbers of enlarged and normal spleens in the first survey (winter 1947-48) and the second survey (winter 1948-49) was again highly significant (P = 0.0000).

Table XXXI records for each survey the size of the average spleen and of the average enlarged spleen, calculated on the

TABLE XXXI

Summary of spleen surveys in Sardinian villages, 1947 to 1950

Survey period	Number examined	Spleen class (Hackett)						Total number enlarged	Spleen rate (per cent ± S. E.*)	Average spleen size	Average enlarged spleen size
		0	1	2	3	4	5				
Group I : 66 villages (total population 190,000)											
Winter 1947–48	12,915	10,000	1,745	809	292	67	2	2,915	22.6 ± 0.37	0.35	1.55
Winter 1948–49	15,625	13,047	2,118	369	83	8	0	2,578	16.5 ± 0.30	0.20	1.22
Winter 1949–50	15,509	13,466	1,741	264	34	3	1	2,043	13.2 ± 0.27	0.15	1.17
Group II : 13 villages (total population 35,000)											
Winter 1947–48	2,376	1,564	409	242	125	35	1	812	34.2 ± 0.97	0.60	1.74
Spring 1948	1,999	1,312	351	188	143	5	0	687	34.4 ± 1.06	0.59	1.71
Fall 1948	2,400	1,641	557	152	46	4	0	759	31.6 ± 0.95	0.42	1.34
Winter 1948–49	2,924	2,184	564	126	46	4	0	740	25.3 ± 0.80	0.33	1.31
Spring 1949	3,041	2,296	496	191	53	5	0	745	24.5 ± 0.78	0.35	1.42
Fall 1949	2,294	1,682	461	112	36	3	0	612	26.7 ± 0.92	0.35	1.32
Winter 1949–50	3,092	2,487	490	102	11	2	0	605	19.6 ± 0.71	0.24	1.21
Spring 1950	2,863	2,354	399	75	30	5	0	509	17.8 ± 0.71	0.23	1.29
Fall 1950	2,282	1,954	272	45	8	2	1	328	14.4 ± 0.73	0.17	1.22

* S. E. = Standard Error.

basis of a weighting factor of one for a size one spleen, two for a size two spleen, etc. Non-palpable spleens were given a factor of zero. Both centering values decreased over the period of the surveys. As is usual, the average spleen size decreased more rapidly than the average enlarged spleen size.

The corresponding parasite data are given in table XXXII. In the case of the Group II villages, the parasite rate showed a general over-all decrease, from 4.28 per cent in the first survey to 0.66 per cent in the last survey. A chi square test applied to the data from which these rates were derived shows that the difference is highly significant (P = 0.0000). The decline in the parasite rate was interrupted in the winter of 1948-49 when the rate was 1.64, as compared with a rate of 0.54 per cent for the preceding survey (fall 1948). The difference in the data from which these rates were derived is also significant (P = 0.0002).

However, the increase in the rate is probably not a real one. As previously mentioned, the winter survey of 1948-49 was the first in which the slides were examined in the ERLAAS laboratory, with more attention being paid to negative slides and with closer control of the examinations. Favoring this interpretation of the apparent increase in the parasite rate is the fact that it was not accompanied by a higher spleen rate or by an increase in positivity for *falciparum*. An alternative possibility is that the rise, which was largely accounted for by an increase from 10 to 34 in the number of positives for *vivax*, represented the late winter and spring relapses of *vivax*, since the survey continued as late as the end of March.

A second interruption in the decline of the parasite rate was observed in the spring of 1950, when the rate reached 0.84 per cent, as compared with 0.49 per cent for the previous survey. This difference is not significant and can be accounted for by sampling variation (P value for the basic data = 0.11).

The Group I villages showed a progressive and uninterrupted decline in the parasite rate, from 3.02 per cent in the first survey to 0.32 per cent in the last. A chi square test applied to the data from which these rates were derived shows that the differ-

TABLE XXXII

SUMMARY OF PARASITE SURVEYS IN SARDINIAN VILLAGES, 1947 TO 1950

Survey period	Number examined	Number positive, by *Plasmodium* species						Total number positive	Parasite rate (per cent ± S. E.†)
		vivax	*falciparum*	*malariae*	VF*	VFM*	VM*		
Group I : 66 villages (total population 190,000)									
Winter 1947–48	12,665	232	147	3	0	0	0	382	3.02 ± 0.15
Winter 1948–49	15,634	76	12	19	3	1	1	112	0.72 ± 0.068
Winter 1949–50	15,517	32	6	8	4	0	0	50	0.32 ± 0.045
Group II : 13 villages (total population 35,000)									
Winter 1947–48	2,290	51	46	1	0	0	0	98	4.28 ± 0.42
Spring 1948	1,999	19	11	0	0	0	0	30	1.50 ± 0.27
Fall 1948	2,400	10	3	0	0	0	0	13	0.54 ± 0.15
Winter 1948–49	2,924	34	6	5	2	0	1	48	1.64 ± 0.23
Spring 1949	3,041	19	4	3	0	0	0	26	0.85 ± 0.17
Fall 1949	2,294	9	0	2	0	0	0	11	0.48 ± 0.14
Winter 1949–50	3,092	10	1	3	1	0	0	15	0.49 ± 0.13
Spring 1950	2,863	14	7	3	0	0	0	24	0.84 ± 0.17
Fall 1950	2,282	6	7	2	0	0	0	15	0.66 ± 0.17

* VF = *Vivax—falciparum.* VFM = *Vivax—falciparum—malariae.* VM = *Vivax—malariae.*
† S. E. = Standard Error.

ence is highly significant $(P = 0.0000)$. The incidence of both *vivax* and *falciparum* infections decreased markedly; there was a slight increase in positives for *malariae*.

It should be remembered that the earliest survey began five months after the completion of the first ERLAAS residual spraying campaign, which, as has been demonstrated, effected a 70 per cent reduction in the number of new malaria cases reported for 1947 as compared with 1946.

As no record was made of the density of parasites in blood films, it is impossible to state whether or not the intensity of infection decreased with the spleen and parasite rates. It was observed, however, that the number of parasites was very low in the positive slides in the fall survey of 1950. With approximately 50 per cent of the positive slides, only two or three parasites could be located in the entire thick film. When it was desired to find another parasite to confirm a species diagnosis, an additional search for as long as 30 minutes was frequently necessary.

Beginning with the fall survey of 1948, blood examinations were made of infants between two months and two years of age. Mothers were encouraged to bring infants in this age group to the schools where the survey was being carried out, and thick films were made for all those who appeared. The results of these examinations are shown in table XXXIII. Five infants (0.6 per cent) in the Group II villages were positive for parasites in this survey (made after one year of residual spraying and one year of eradication activities); thereafter, no positives were found in infants. Nor were any positives discovered during two winter surveys in the Group I villages. The parasite rates in infants thus demonstrate that transmission must have been at a very low level from 1948 on.

In table XXXIV the data from the spleen and parasite survey for the winter of 1947-48 are grouped according to the altitudes of the Group I villages. (One thousand meters above sea level represents the altitude of Fonni, the highest village in Sardinia.)

TABLE XXXIII

SUMMARY OF PARASITE SURVEYS OF INFANTS AGED TWO MONTHS TO TWO YEARS IN SARDINIAN VILLAGES, 1948 TO 1950

Survey period	Number examined	Number positive	Parasite rate (per cent)
Group I : 66 villages			
Winter 1948–49	1,574	0	0.0
Winter 1949–50	1,999	0	0.0
Group II : 13 villages			
Fall 1948	871	5*	0.6
Winter 1948–49	133	0	0.0
Spring 1949	309	0	0.0
Fall 1949	325	0	0.0
Winter 1949–50	350	0	0.0
Spring 1950	292	0	0.0
Fall 1950	296	0	0.0

* 4 *vivax*, 1 *falciparum*.

It is evident that both parasite rates and spleen rates generally decreased with increasing altitude. However, the important point is that both splenomegaly and parasitemia were found at all altitudes, although more frequently in children living at low altitudes. *Labranchiae* was also found at all altitudes but was less prevalent at high than at low elevations.

In table XXXV the spleen rates determined in this same survey have been grouped into four classifications and correlated with the mean and median altitudes above sea level and the range of altitude, the number of villages being given for each classification. The highest spleen rates (those over 50 per cent) were confined to six low-lying villages, none over 92 meters above sea level. The mean and median altitudes of the villages and the upper limits of the range of altitude decreased progressively with increasing spleen rates. However, there were villages at altitudes near sea level in all spleen rate groups, as seen from the lower limits of the range of altitude.

When the Group II villages were classified on the basis of spleen rates (as measured in the first winter survey of 1948-49)

TABLE XXXIV

SPLEEN AND PARASITE SURVEYS OF SCHOOL CHILDREN IN 66 SARDINIAN VILLAGES (GROUP I) NOVEMBER 1947 TO MARCH 1948, BY ALTITUDE ABOVE SEA LEVEL

Altitude above sea level (meters)	Spleen examinations			Parasite examinations					
	Number examined	Number with palpable spleen	Spleen rate (per cent)	Number examined	Number positive, by *Plasmodium* species			Total number positive	Parasite rate (per cent)
					vivax	*falciparum*	*malariae*		
0– 50	2,858	996	34.8	2,779	59	56	1	116	4.2
51– 100	2,015	595	29.5	1,861	39	29	1	69	3.7
101– 200	1,282	288	22.5	1,289	58	29	1	88	6.8
201– 300	1,215	226	18.6	1,201	26	11	0	37	3.1
301– 400	1,094	212	19.4	1,144	12	2	0	14	1.2
401– 600	1,540	215	14.0	1,539	12	10	0	22	1.4
601– 800	1,481	277	18.7	1,481	18	9	0	27	1.8
801–1,000	1,430	106	7.4	1,371	8	1	0	9	0.7
All altitudes	12,915	2,915	22.6	12,665	232	147	3	382	3.0

TABLE XXXV

MEAN AND MEDIAN ALTITUDES ABOVE SEA LEVEL AND RANGE OF ALTITUDE OF 66 SARDINIAN VILLAGES CLASSIFIED BY SPLEEN RATES OF SCHOOL CHILDREN, NOVEMBER 1947 TO MARCH 1948

Spleen rate (per cent)	Number of villages	Altitude above sea level (meters)		
		Mean	Median	Range
0–10	12	540	530	6 to 1,000
10.01–25	29	353	297	6 to 800
25.01–50	19	213	137	9 to 660
Over 50	6	30	20	9 to 92

into those of low endemicity (spleen rates from 10 to 25 per cent), moderate endemicity (25 to 50 per cent) and high endemicity (over 50 per cent), the improvement in spleen rates shown in table XXXI was seen to occur in all categories. Table XXXVI compares the original rates, averaged for all villages in these groups, with the rates measured in the same villages in the final survey (September 1950); over this period there was a decline of approximately 45 per cent of the original rate in the low endemicity category, 61 per cent in the moderately endemic villages and 63 per cent in those of high endemicity. The average enlarged spleen size decreased approximately 20, 28 and 35 per cent, respectively, in the three groups. Thus the decrease in both spleen rate and average enlarged spleen size was relatively greater in the highly endemic villages.

Individually, 12 of the 13 villages showed a decline in spleen rate over this time interval; the exception was Romana, where the rate increased from 17.3 per cent in the first survey to 17.5 per cent in the last. This small increase in spleen rate is not significant (14 of 81 children with enlarged spleens in the first survey, and 14 of 80 in the last). In this village the average enlarged spleen size decreased during this period from 2.07 to 1.00, and the parasite rate from 9.88 per cent to zero. The average enlarged spleen size also decreased in each village.

Table XXXVII shows the comparable parasite data for the

TABLE XXXVI

CHANGE IN SPLEEN RATES AND AVERAGE ENLARGED SPLEEN SIZE, FROM THE WINTER OF 1947–48 TO SEPTEMBER 1950, IN SCHOOL CHILDREN OF 13 SARDINIAN VILLAGES (GROUP II)

Spleen rate,* winter 1947–48 (per cent)	Number examined, winter 1947–48	Number with enlarged spleen	Spleen rate (per cent)	Average enlarged spleen size	Number examined, September 1950	Number with enlarged spleen	Spleen rate (per cent)	Average enlarged spleen size
10.00–25	987	177	17.9	1.40	952	93	9.8	1.12
25.01–50	1,012	348	34.4	1.67	951	128	13.5	1.20
Over 50	377	287	76.1	2.04	379	107	28.2	1.33
Summary	2,376	812	34.2	1.74	2,282	328	14.4	1.22

* There were no villages with spleen rates under 10 per cent in this group.

TABLE XXXVII

CHANGE IN PARASITE RATES AND NUMBER OF POSITIVES BY PARASITE SPECIES, FROM THE WINTER OF 1947–48 TO SEPTEMBER 1950, IN SCHOOL CHILDREN OF 13 SARDINIAN VILLAGES (GROUP II)

Spleen rate, winter 1947–48 (per cent)	Number examined, winter 1947–48	Number positive, by Plasmodium species			Total positive	Parasite rate (per cent)	Number examined, Sept. 1950	Number positive, by Plasmodium species			Total positive	Parasite rate (per cent)
		vivax	falciparum	malariae				vivax	falciparum	malariae		
10.01–25	986	11	7	0	18	1.83	952	2	0	1	3	0.32
25.01–50	927	27	23	1	51	5.50	951	4	5	1	10	1.05
Over 50	377	13	16	0	29	7.69	379	0	2	0	2	0.53
Summary	2,290	51	46	1	98	4.28	2,282	6	7	2	15	0.66

same villages. The parasite rates, averaged by groups in the original survey, varied directly with the spleen rates; subsequently, as measured in September 1950, the parasite rate decreased in all categories. The extent of the decrease was approximately 83, 81 and 93 per cent, respectively, for villages of low, moderate and high endemicity. The over-all decrease for all 13 villages was 85 per cent. The relative decline in the parasite rate was thus greater than that in the spleen rate, as is usual. The absolute numbers positive for *vivax* and *falciparum* decreased in all groups. Each village individually also showed a decline in parasite rate over this period.

Table XXXVIII shows the comparable data for spleen rates and spleen sizes in the 66 Group I villages surveyed once a year. As no spleen rates between zero and 10 per cent were originally present in the 13 villages of Group II, a fourth spleen rate category of lowest endemicity was added for Group I. In this category the spleen rate measured at the last examination, in the survey made during the winter of 1949-50, was the same as at the first examination (7.1 per cent), although the average enlarged spleen size decreased by 15 per cent of its original value. The three other categories, in order of increasing endemicity, showed decreases in spleen rate of 36, 50 and 48 per cent of the original rates, respectively; the average enlarged spleen size decreased by 18, 26 and 28 per cent. Considering the 66 villages individually, the average enlarged spleen size decreased from the first to the last survey in each of them, and the spleen rate decreased in 55 villages. The 11 villages showing the increases were all in the two lowest spleen rate categories. Only two of the changes were significant (Ardara, 12.5 per cent in the first survey to 23.6 per cent in the last; Uri, 6.7 to 17.9 per cent); the other increases were not significant, involving from one to seven percentage points. The increase for Ardara represented the largest percentage change, as well as the highest rate recorded in the last survey.

The parasite data for these 66 villages for the first and last surveys are shown in table XXXIX. All four categories showed

TABLE XXXVIII

CHANGE IN SPLEEN RATES AND AVERAGE ENLARGED SPLEEN SIZE FROM THE WINTER OF 1947–48 TO THE WINTER OF 1949–50 IN SCHOOL CHILDREN OF 66 SARDINIAN VILLAGES (GROUP I)

Spleen rate, winter 1947–48 (per cent)	Number examined, winter 1947–48	Number with enlarged spleen	Spleen rate (per cent)	Average enlarged spleen size	Number examined, winter 1949–50	Number with enlarged spleen	Spleen rate (per cent)	Average enlarged spleen size
0–10	2,864	204	7.1	1.25	3,500	250	7.1	1.06
10.01–25	6,176	1,027	16.6	1.36	7,348	787	10.7	1.11
25.01–50	2,904	1,041	35.8	1.61	3,615	643	17.8	1.19
Over 50	971	643	66.2	1.85	1,046	363	34.7	1.34
Summary	12,915	2,915	22.6	1.55	15,509	2,043	13.2	1.17

TABLE XXXIX

CHANGE IN PARASITE RATES AND NUMBER OF POSITIVES BY PARASITE SPECIES, FROM THE WINTER OF 1947–48 TO THE WINTER OF 1949–50 IN SCHOOL CHILDREN OF 66 SARDINIAN VILLAGES

Spleen rate, winter 1947–48 (per cent)	Number examined, winter 1947–48	Number positive, by Plasmodium species			Total positive	Parasite rate (per cent)	Number examined, winter 1949–50	Number positive, by Plasmodium species				Total positive	Parasite rate (per cent)
		vivax	falciparum	malariae				vivax	falciparum	malariae	VF*		
0–10	2,864	34	9	0	43	1.50	3,500	0	0	1	0	1	0.03
10.01–25	6,012	92	36	2	130	2.16	7,355	13	0	1	1	15	0.20
25.01–50	2,818	70	58	1	129	4.58	3,616	10	5	2	3	20	0.55
Over 50	971	36	44	0	80	8.24	1,046	9	1	1	3	14	1.34
Summary	12,665	232	147	3	382	3.02	15,517	32	6	4	8	50	0.32

*VF = Vivax–falciparum.

a decrease in parasite rates, the decline being 98, 91, 88 and 84 per cent of the original rates, respectively, with an over-all decrease for all villages of 89 per cent of the original rate. Here again, the parasite rate decreased to a greater extent than did the spleen rate. The absolute numbers positive for *vivax* and *falciparum* decreased markedly; there was a slight increase in positives for *malariae*. Individually, a decrease in parasite rate from the first to the last survey occurred in all villages with the exception of Portotorres, where the rate increased from 0.26 to 0.60 per cent. This is not significant because of the small number of positives involved (1 in 380 to 3 in 500).

PERSISTENCE OF *Plasmodium falciparum* INFECTIONS

Tables XXXII, XXXIII and XXXIX show that there were still *falciparum* positives in the last surveys made in both Group I and Group II villages. In the villages surveyed annually, ten positives for this species (six for *falciparum*, and four mixed infections for *vivax* and *falciparum*) were found in the last survey carried out in the winter of 1949-50. More important was the finding of seven *falciparum* positives in the group of 13 villages in the spring survey of 1950, and of another seven in the fall survey of that year, at the close of ERLAAS operations. Table XXXII indicates that there was a considerable decrease in the absolute numbers positive for *falciparum* from the first survey until these last two surveys, as well as an over-all decrease in the parasite rate. However, the prevalence ratio for *falciparum* in the last survey (47 per cent of the total positives were accounted for by this species) was exactly the same as in the first survey.

As previously demonstrated, the difference between the total numbers of positives and negatives in the winter 1949-50 and spring 1950 surveys was not significant (P = 0.11); nor was the difference significant between the former survey and that of the fall of 1950 (P = 0.40). The slight increase in parasite rates for the last two surveys over that for the winter of 1949-50 can thus be accounted for on the basis of sampling variation. However, the increase in the number of positives for *falciparum* in the last two surveys is statistically significant. The absolute incidence of *falciparum* (the number positive for this species in relation to the negatives plus the positives for other species) gives a chi square value of 7.01 (P = 0.008) for the difference between the fall surveys of 1949 and 1950, and a chi square of 4.60 (P = 0.03) for the difference between the winter survey 1949-50 and the fall survey of 1950, or a chi square of 9.56 (P = 0.002) for the last two surveys combined against the preceding two surveys combined.

The presence of positives for *falciparum* is generally considered an indication of recent transmission, because infections with this species are presumably short-lived. Most of the studies on the duration of *falciparum* infections pertain to clinical activity and to the length of time during which clinical relapses may follow a primary attack. It should be emphasized that the positives found in these surveys were apparently not accompanied by any clinical manifestations. All the *falciparum* positives in the spring and fall surveys of 1950 were investigated, and in none was there a history of recent illness. These were essentially healthy children with circulating *falciparum* parasites.

The only work relevant to the duration of *falciparum* parasitemia is that of Earle *et al.* (1939), who made weekly blood examinations of a group of Puerto Ricans for 60 weeks from the date on which they first became infected with *falciparum*. Of the blood examinations made 56 to 60 weeks after infection, 17.8 per cent were positive. Macdonald (1950b) believes that the chance of superinfection in this group was negligible, and on the basis of Earle's data, he has formulated an equation describing the natural recovery rate for *falciparum* infections, recovery being defined, not as freedom from clinical symptoms, but as disappearance of parasites from the blood. The equation

$$x = e^{-0.0048\,(t-31)}$$

where x represents the proportion remaining affected, and t

is the time in days since first observation. The equation, which corresponds closely to Earle's data, predicts that when $t = 731$ days (two years), 3.5 per cent will remain positive.

W. McD. Hammon, in a letter to P. F. Russell, gives evidence from his own history that *falciparum* parasites may be found in the blood over long periods of time. He remained positive for *falciparum* for approximately four years after moving from a malarious to a nonmalarious area. He was infected in the Belgian Congo where he lived from 1926 to 1930. During this time he had repeated attacks of malaria, which were treated with quinine. *Falciparum* was the only parasite found in numerous examinations. In 1930 he returned to live in the northeastern part of the United States, where there was no naturally transmitted malaria. From this time until 1932, he had occasional clinical relapses, also treated with quinine; *falciparum* trophozoites were present in his blood smears. During the next two years, *falciparum* crescents were repeatedly found; the liver and spleen were enlarged. In 1934 he took a prolonged course of quinine, following which he has had no further clinical attacks and no demonstrable parasitemia.

This is definite evidence that *falciparum* infections can on occasion give rise to parasitemia of long duration. It is therefore not necessary to assume that the positives found in the last three ERLAAS surveys resulted from infections acquired within the year previous to the date of the surveys.

An analysis was made of the individual case records of all children positive for *falciparum* in any one of the last three surveys. This showed that:

(1) There was no history of illness near the time of the survey for any of the children positive for *falciparum* in the spring or fall of 1950. It thus seems unlikely that any of these positives were due to new infections or reinfections.

(2) All except two of the children positive for *falciparum* in the last three surveys, and examined in at least one preceding survey, had evidence of previous infection in the form of

parasitemia, splenomegaly or both. The two exceptions, with no evidence of malaria in previous surveys, also had no illness attributable to malaria at the time the survey was made or thereafter. Subsequent parasite examinations were negative in both. It is possible that these positives were due to the transfer of parasites from other positive slides during the mass staining procedure.

(3) It has been demonstrated that *falciparum* parasitemia can persist, on occasion, for longer than the one-year period usually considered the duration of this infection. It is therefore possible that these positives were the residual of infections acquired as much as two or three years previously.

(4) Other evidence of recent transmission in the villages was lacking. Spleen and parasite rates decreased; malaria morbidity reports continued to decrease and in 1950 fell to an extremely low level. Only four primary cases were reported for that year; of these, two were undoubtedly due to transfusions, one was probably not malaria and one was *vivax* malaria, although it could not be established as a primary case. No infants were found positive for parasites.

(5) Anophelism was at a very low level; in many districts where there were positives for *falciparum*, *labranchiae* larvae could not be found in spite of the large number of inspections of aquatic habitats made in 1949 and 1950. In those districts where larvae were discovered during either of these years, the numbers of *labranchiae* recovered were so small that the possibility of transmission must have been very remote. In the districts under examination only one *labranchiae* adult was found in 1949, and two in 1950.

Malaria in 1951

Information regarding malaria is available up to October 1. The peak of the malaria transmission season is during July, August and September; it falls off rapidly in October and is virtually absent in November. The data available represent, therefore, a fairly complete picture for the year.

Malaria continued to regress in 1951. The official reports of the Provincial Medical Officers to October 1 showed a total of nine cases, six of which were classified as relapses and three as primaries. The three primary cases were investigated; one appeared to be due to a blood transfusion, the second was doubtful, while the third, a case of *falciparum* in an 18-month-old child, may have been a primary infection.

The spleen and parasite surveys were continued in 27 villages; 25 of these were selected from the original 66 villages because they had had spleen rates of over 25 per cent in the first ERLAAS survey during the winter of 1947-48. Two additional villages were added from the original 66 villages because of their special interest in relation to the persistence of *falciparum*. Except in isolated cases, apparently due to the small size of the sample, the spleen and parasite rates continued to decrease, the 1951 spleen rate being 13.8 per cent compared to the previous rate of 20.5 per cent for the same villages in the winter of 1949-50. In four of the five villages in which the laboratory work had been completed, the parasite rate decreased to zero; no parasites were found in infants under 24 months in these villages.

It is of interest that the northeast part of the island, which included 60 per cent of the 1951 positive sectors, and which also accounted for much of the 1949-50 positivity, has not been one of the more highly malarious parts of the island, either historically or in the ERLAAS surveys. Six of the towns routinely surveyed were in this area, Arzachena, Luogosanto, Luras, Berchidda, Laerru and Loiri. With the exception of Loiri, the spleen rates in these towns have been low. The persistence of *labranchiae* over the 1949-51 period has not been reflected in the parasite rates, which have decreased in all cases and were zero on the last examination in four of the six towns.

CHAPTER VII

THE ADMINISTRATIVE SERVICES

For the sake of convenience this chapter is concerned with both finance and the administrative services, although in practice the two were entirely separate. ERLAAS finance was closely tied up with policy, which was consistently determined not only by what action was desirable but by what action was financially and legally possible. The administrative services, on the other hand, were concerned with the daily arrangements for supplies, transport and cash. Because of this difference a budget control office was attached to the superintendent's office in 1950, and the distinction between administration and the administrative services was more clearly defined.

The administrative services, coordinated under one director, comprised the following departments: accounting, personnel, transport, supplies and legal. In 1947 and 1948 the statistics department was also a part of the administrative services, but in 1949 it was transferred to operations. Also in 1949 the accounting department was combined with the personnel department, and the transport department with supplies. These measures were successful in promoting greater efficiency and economy of personnel. In the discussion below, however, each of the departments is considered separately.

ACCOUNTING

The accounting department disbursed a great deal of money during the life of ERLAAS. The system of accounting required by the state was, by commercial standards, highly complicated. It followed that the proportion of administrative personnel engaged in accounting was extremely high.

The department had its main office in Cagliari. In 1947,

215

1948 and 1949 branch offices were located in each division, with suboffices in the sections. In 1950 it became possible to centralize all sectional accounts in the divisions.

Like all the ERLAAS administrative services, the accounting department did not foresee, in the early stages, how large the organization was to become and how long it was to last. The accounting system as it was originally set up was probably adequate for the smaller operations envisaged in the first months, but by the middle of 1948 its serious deficiencies were apparent. Although the department was eventually reorganized to cope with the work load placed upon it, the backlog of work from the early period hindered its performance well into 1949. By 1950, however, it had developed into a highly efficient machine, which functioned consistently well.

Auditing duties were at first entrusted to a private firm, but in view of the organization's peculiar statutory position it was considered more appropriate that the auditors be appointed by the state. Consequently, in March 1948 a special audit commission was appointed by state decree.

PERSONNEL

The main functions of the personnel department were to represent the organization in its relations with the local officials of the Ministry of Labor and the trade unions, to maintain personnel records and to deal with the complicated system of national health insurance payments for the workers. Personnel recruiting, evaluation and counseling were undertaken by other administrative units and were not the responsibility of this branch.

By custom and by law, the distinction between the day laborer, paid by the day, and the salaried employee, paid by the month, is more sharply defined in Italy than in the United States.

Reference has been made in the previous chapters to the number of day laborers employed by the various field services.

The combined figures for these are shown in figure 21. The number of workers engaged in the administrative services—that is, drivers, mechanics, porters, storekeepers, guards and others— is shown in figure 22. The number of salaried workers engaged in the administrative services, together with the number that served with the field services are shown in figure 23.

The remuneration of personnel merits special attention, representing as it did 77 per cent of the total cost of the project. For workers paid by the day, wage rates were established after discussions between ERLAAS and the local representatives of the Ministry of Labor. For salaried personnel, rates usually paralleled those of state employees. These basic pay rates were augmented by the complicated series of cost-of-living bonuses, family allowances, and national health and unemployment insurance required by Italian law.

ERLAAS wage rates were consistently higher than those prevailing elsewhere in Sardinia for similar categories. In 1948 the difference for field laborers was considerable, but from late 1948 onwards, as Sardinian pay rates rose to more realistic levels, the difference became and remained comparatively slight. For specialist workers, such as mechanics and drivers, ERLAAS rates were substantially greater. These increments were justified by the necessity of attracting and keeping the better type of skilled worker.

Since ERLAAS was a temporary agency it was thought reasonable that salaried personnel be paid more than persons in similar positions in the permanent government services. A given position received a higher rating in ERLAAS than in permanent services and in addition, ERLAAS increased the basic salary for each rating by 20 per cent. On the other hand, holiday periods were shorter, hours were longer, and certain bonuses given to permanent officials were not paid. As a general rule no extra pay was given for overtime.

An obvious danger inherent in the temporary nature of the organization was that its key personnel might drift away into other employment as the end of the project approached. This

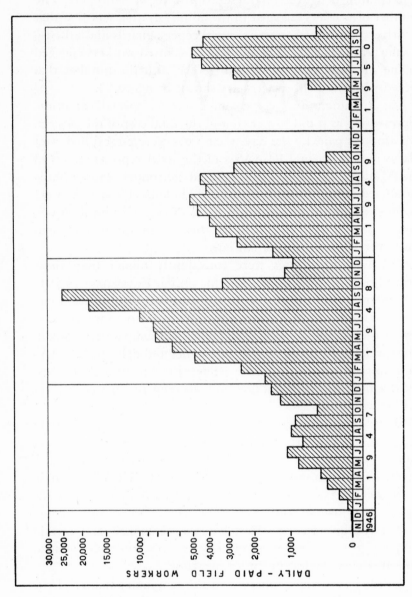

FIGURE 21. Average number of day laborers in the field services, by months, 1946 to 1950.

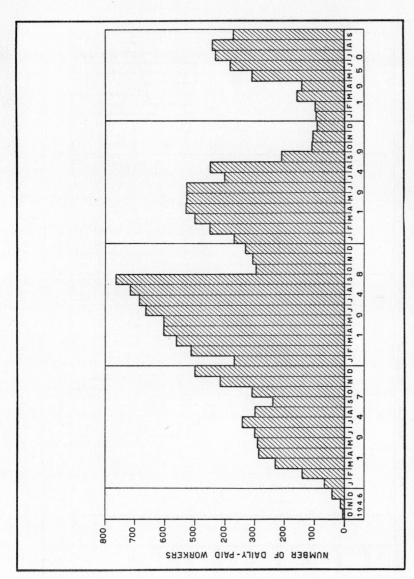

FIGURE 22. Average number of day laborers in the administrative services, by months, 1946 to 1950.

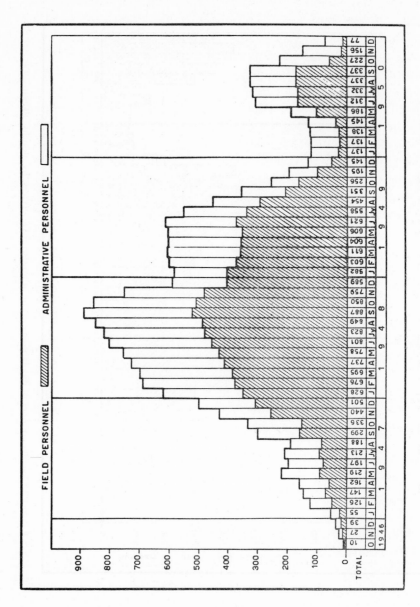

FIGURE 23. Number of salaried personnel employed, by months, 1946 to 1950.

danger was almost entirely averted by the establishment, in 1950, of a bonus system. A weekly bonus, increasing in size as the year advanced, was awarded to all satisfactory salaried personnel on the condition that they remain with the organization until its termination. The device served as an incentive for the men to remain with ERLAAS in the crucial concluding months and provided a constant encouragement to good work, as the weekly increment was withheld if a job was poorly done. The bonuses also gave the employees a measure of security, in that they could count on an extra sum of money to help them through the period of unemployment following their dismissal.

Certain other special bonuses were given, the most notable of which were the sleeping-out and travel allowances. Schedules A and B in the financial summaries show that these two items formed a substantial part (350,000,000 lire) of the total costs. The former was given to day laborers whose work required them to sleep away from home. The amount varied according to the worker's rating. In 1949 claims on this allowance were made rather too readily, so that in 1950 it was paid to salaried personnel and to certain categories of specialized day laborers. Normal government practice was followed fairly closely, except that ERLAAS rates were somewhat lower in this instance. To eliminate much of the bookkeeping involved in calculating these allowances, salaried field workers in 1949 and 1950 were paid fixed monthly sums in lieu of the usual fluctuating allowance based upon actual periods away from base.

Besides these cash payments, ERLAAS provided its permanent field workers with boots, trousers and in some cases jackets and raincoats. This equipment was not generally issued to casual labor, although rubber or leather boots were usually provided for work in water. Residual spray workers were not issued clothing. The men who did receive clothing were expected to keep it in reasonable condition, but major repairs, particularly of boots, were made by the organization. The direct issue of clothing was considered preferable to a clothing allowance, which probably would have been used for other purposes. The total cost of this during the ERLAAS campaign was 53,000,000 lire (Schedule C).

The Italian labor code requires the employer to pay day laborers for the first three days, and salaried workers for the first three months, of any period of illness. A medical certificate is required, but local doctors are inclined to take a generous view of alleged indispositions and issue certificates rather freely. In consequence, most daily workers fell ill at some time or other during the ERLAAS campaign but consistently recovered on the third day of their absence. Sickness was most widespread in the sowing, harvesting or threshing periods.

In addition to their right to three months sick leave per year with pay, salaried personnel could not be dismissed during a period of illness. Consequently, all periods of staff reductions were accompanied by an increase in illness. The rather ambiguous " nervous exhaustion " was a popular complaint. In June 1950 this technicality was overcome by employing most of the personnel for a fixed period and by withholding the special termination bonus from all personnel who had been absent for more than 15 days. The remarkable improvement in health which followed is clearly demonstrated in figure 24. Records of illness were not kept on day laborers, but the figures for salaried personnel alone represent a direct loss to the organization of approximately 45,000,000 lire. In addition, there must have been a large incalculable factor of indirect loss resulting from the absence of supervisory personnel in the field at these times. This somewhat cynical view of sickness rates should not obscure the fact that much illness was perfectly genuine.

Most of the laborers were agricultural workers and shepherds. Students and young men previously unemployed, except perhaps for military service, formed a good-sized minority, particularly in the scouting service. Salaried personnel came from all ranks

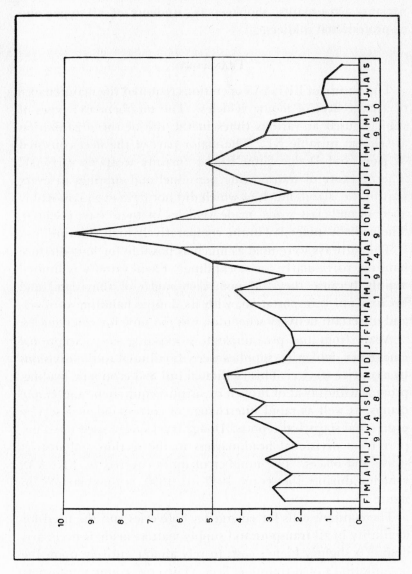

FIGURE 24. Per cent of total workdays lost by salaried personnel due to illness, 1948 to 1950.

of life and included lawyers, schoolteachers, farmers, veteri-
narians, accountants, shopkeepers, students of all types and
ex-professional soldiers.

TRANSPORT

The nature of ERLAAS operations required the maintenance
of a large fleet of motor vehicles. The numbers and types of
vehicles used at various times in the life of the organization
are shown in table XL. The major part of the fleet consisted
of jeeps and Dodge $\frac{3}{4}$-ton trucks (mainly weapons carriers).
The necessity of transporting personnel and supplies to every
part of the island, much of which did not have even reasonably
good second-class roads, made vehicles of their type essential.
Their disadvantage lay in the comparatively high running cost.

The railways were used as much as possible for long-distance
hauling, particularly for stockpiling. Their value was limited
mainly because they did not reach much of the island and
because rail transportation, with its double handling of goods
and uncertain delivery schedules, was too slow for emergencies.

Apart from the pre-campaign stockpiling and exceptional
emergency deliveries, supplies were distributed to the divisions
by a courier service. This facilitated full and economic loading,
prompt withdrawal of broken or surplus equipment and empty
drums, as well as rapid interchange of correspondence, service
orders and statistical reports. Dodge trucks were used for transport from divisional headquarters to the section and district
stores and offices. The number of miles covered by ERLAAS
vehicles during the years 1947 to 1950 is summarized in
figure 25.

The constant calls for emergency deliveries and the need for
flexibility in all transport and supply matters made it necessary,
despite a slightly higher cost, to rely almost entirely upon the
organization's own transport fleet. The cross-country transport
for which jeeps and Dodge trucks were normally used was
beyond the capacity of private firms, although by 1949 these

TABLE XL

TYPES AND NUMBERS OF MOTOR VEHICLES USED BY ERLAAS, BY QUARTER, 1947 TO 1950

Year and quarter	Jeeps	¾-ton Dodge trucks	3-ton trucks	Miscellaneous trucks	Heavy Diesel trucks	Passenger cars	Motor-cycles	Total
1947								
February	16	10	1			1		28
May	29	52	6			2		89
August	29	38	2			6		75
November	42	87	14	1		6		150
1948								
February	67	115	15	1		5	2	205
May	73	133	17	1		5	2	231
August	84	149	18	1	10	5	2	269
November	37	98	10	1	2	4		152
1949								
February	46	107	13	1	2	6	2	177
May	67	136	16	1	3	9	2	234
August	52	108	14		2	9	2	187
November	6	7	6		1	10		30
1950								
February	6	6	8			8	1	29
May	32	92	11	1		12	1	149
August	44	122	12	13	3	12	2	208
November	4	2	6			7	2	21

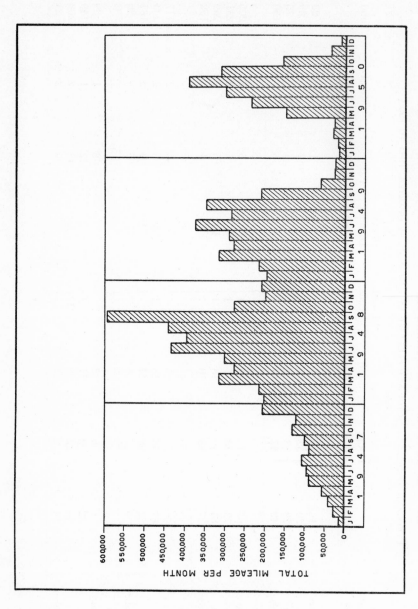

FIGURE 25. Total mileage of ERLAAS motor vehicles, by months, 1947 to 1950.

32. Larviciding in cleared breeding place.

33. Larviciding, using hand pump.

34. Larviciding, using shoulder pump.

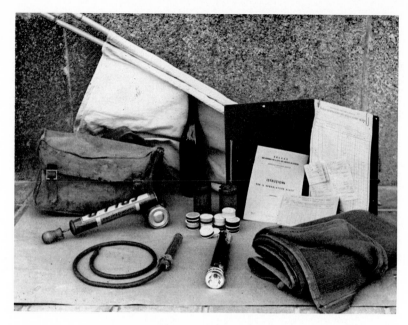

35. Adult scouting equipment.

36. Larviciding in swamp area near Elmas, using extension cane.

concerns had recovered sufficiently from the disruptive effects of the war to be seriously considered for this work.

In some special instances private transportation was used. Within villages, for example, insecticide for residual spray work was usually transported by donkey cart. This mode of transportation was particularly suitable because the distance traveled each day was short and the standing or " out of service " time was relatively high. Pack horses, donkeys or oxcarts were used for the transport of larvicide in zones where motor vehicles either were unavailable or could not pass. Horses were hired for use in reconnaissance and supervisory work, particularly in 1948. Bicycles proved impractical for general use because of the long distances to be traveled, the mountainous terrain, the scarcity of good roads and the hazard of theft.

The operation and maintenance of the transport fleet was a considerable undertaking. A central garage and repair shop was located at Cagliari in the main supply and equipment depot to facilitate the coordination of supply and transport. The efficiency of the garage could have been increased with the purchase of more capital equipment, such as lathes, but this was not done due to the uncertain duration of the project. Nevertheless the garage made possible the periodic overhaul of all vehicles, and only a relatively small amount of repair work had to be turned over to outside firms.

Smaller workshops were established at Sassari and Nuoro, and three mobile workshops (converted three-ton General Motors trucks) constantly toured divisional headquarters to take care of on-the-spot repairs and maintenance. The divisions and sections were each allowed a small monthly expenditure for repairs by private garages.

Almost all motor vehicles were procured from war surplus. They had already had considerable wear and tear, and ERLAAS also gave them extremely hard use. The consumption of spare parts was therefore high, and some difficulty was encountered in buying replacements, particularly in 1948. The purchase of large stocks from army surplus dumps—and a good deal of improvisation—helped to overcome this problem and reduced to a low level the time lost through breakdowns. In fact, the longer the vehicles were used, the less time was lost.

Gasoline was distributed to the divisions by private oil companies and redistributed from the divisions to the sections by ERLAAS transport. Difficulties sometimes arose from the failure of the companies to lay in sufficient stocks to meet the organization's needs. The worst hold-up, which might have had grave consequences, occurred in August and September 1948 because of a 40-day strike by oil company workers. The situation was fortunately saved by loans of oil from the Italian Navy.

Despite a rigid disciplinary code and the careful selection of all drivers, the number of serious accidents was high. The main reasons were probably the treacherousness of the twisting, narrow Sardinian roads and the long hours worked by the drivers.

An analysis of transport expenditures, which represented about 20 per cent of the total cost of ERLAAS operations, is given in Schedule O.

SUPPLIES

The main supply depot was located in Cagliari. From this depot supplies went out to the divisional stores. These allocated the supplies to the sections, which in their turn allotted them to the districts and other field work units.

Unlike the transport department, which was able to develop from the existing, although smaller, UNRRA organization, the supply department had to start from scratch. The early handling of supply matters was inefficient because of personnel difficulties and underestimation of the magnitude of the program. It cannot be sufficiently stressed that in programs of this nature supply procedures should receive their proper emphasis.

With regard to the handling of supplies in the field, the following points are worthy of mention:

(a) Each store, whatever its size, needed at least one store-keeper. Attempts to economize by eliminating this man from the smaller stores almost always resulted in an administrative confusion which outweighed the economy effected by the saving in pay.

(b) Each division had a supply chief who was responsible for the receipt and distribution of supplies within his division.

(c) Supplies were always transferred to individuals who were held personally responsible for proper accounting. Thus the division supply man was responsible for all stocks within his division; the section clerk for those within the section; field storekeepers for those within the work unit; and the individual worker for those directly issued to him. Losses and damage through negligence had to be paid for by the individual concerned.

(d) Minor equipment repairs were made in either the section or the division, larger repairs in Cagliari. It was important to keep sufficient reserve stock to allow for the immediate replacement of damaged equipment.

(e) Sometimes one division had an excess of certain tools while another had a shortage. Supplies, particularly of tools, had to be kept mobile.

(f) Experience showed that each piece of equipment should be standardized. Some difficulty resulted, for example, from the fact that the flashlights used different types of bulbs and the wrong type of replacement was sometimes issued.

(g) ERLAAS established standard outfits for each worker and each work unit. Renewals and replacements were, if possible, based upon these standard outfits.

(h) The distribution of basic supplies had to be completed before the initiation of the campaign. This required detailed staff work some months in advance.

ERLAAS undertook a wide range of repair and maintenance work in its own workshops. The workshops manufactured and adapted a large quantity of tools, equipment and furniture at a cost considerably lower than the normal market. Producing and distributing the necessary larvicide and insecticide was a major operation in itself.

LEGAL

The legal department was set up for counsel in regard to both internal administration and outside controversies. As far as possible, claims were settled by agreement with the parties concerned, but in a minority of cases it was necessary to take the disputes to court. To help in the evaluation of these claims, a special committee of outside experts in technical and administrative affairs was appointed to assist the legal advisor.

The disputes which arose fall into the following main groups: (a) disputes with employees over terms of employment; (b) disputes regarding toxicity of larvicide to animals, fish and bees; (c) disputes regarding damage to land; (d) disputes regarding damage to premises; (e) criminal actions; (f) motor accidents.

Disputes with employees over terms of employment. The unusual constitution of ERLAAS made its contractual position with its employees complicated. Italian labor law has two codes for salaried personnel—one for state employees and one for privately employed workers. The ambiguous position of ERLAAS as a semigovernmental organization meant that neither of these codes was strictly applicable. Attempts to clarify the situation by means of a special statute failed because of disagreement over terms of the statute. As it turned out, contracts were decided on a pragmatic basis by applying whichever of the two codes appeared to be more appropriate and equitable for the case in question. This ambiguity was the main cause of the few disputes with salaried personnel which could not be settled out of court. In all these cases the court ruled in favor of ERLAAS. As far as day labor was concerned, the number of disputes was small and all cases were of minor importance. The difficulties were, in general, confined to the specialist workers and were easily settled.

Disputes regarding toxicity of larvicide. From the first days of larviciding, ERLAAS received complaints from farmers and fishermen that the larvicide was poisoning bees, domestic animals and fish. The reports were grossly exaggerated; bees were alleged to die by thousands, sheep and goats were supposed either to die in large numbers or else to suffer grave intestinal disturbances, and fish ponds were allegedly covered with dead fish. Despite this obvious exaggeration, it was clearly of importance to test even the partial veracity of the charges; to that end three separate studies—on bees, on fish and on livestock —were undertaken by local experts. These studies resulted in the following conclusions:

(a) The bees allegedly killed by DDT had acaraiasis, which was responsible for the deaths.

(b) The larvicide was not toxic to domestic animals at dosages considerably higher than normal.

(c) The larvicide was not toxic to fish in the dosage normally used, except to young eels and a few other species, and then only under special laboratory conditions rarely found in nature.

On the basis of these findings, ERLAAS rejected all claims concerning toxicity of the larvicide.

Practical demonstrations were also conducted to prove to livestock owners that the larvicide was not toxic. The results were encouraging; only one farmer among those who witnessed them proceeded with his court action.

Two claims for damage to fish were heard by the courts. In one of these a partial judgment was awarded to the plaintiff. Although the case has been appealed, only minor sums, if any, will have to be paid on this account.

Disputes regarding damage to land. Drainage and clearing operations inevitably resulted in certain damage: that essential for the successful outcome of the campaign and therefore deliberately caused, and unnecessary damage occasioned by negligence or poor work. In general the land was improved, not damaged. In a few cases, however, there was a genuine clash of interests, as, for example, when the elimination of a marsh dried up fodder crops. All such disputes were settled amicably for a total sum of 382,536 lire. Accidental damage due to negligence or poor work by employees was more frequent, particularly that resulting from field fires. In such cases, the damage (totaling 1,286,500 lire) was admitted and an equitable settlement reached.

Disputes regarding damage to premises. Two major fires caused damage to premises; one was the result of the imprudence of an ERLAAS worker, the cause of the other was unknown. Other claims for injury to premises were made, usually for the wear and tear occasioned by occupancy. All these claims were settled amicably for approximately 1,000,000 lire.

Criminal actions. While there were a few cases of theft by ERLAAS employees, these were unusually rare in view of the very large sums of money and quantity of goods handled. On the other hand, thefts by outsiders were more numerous, particularly in the " bandit " zone of Nuoro Province. The total amount lost in such robberies was 3,501,669 lire.

In the Nuoro area, and indeed in various other parts of the island where there were no banks, the payrolls had to be sent out in cash. After the first holdup, cash was replaced by checks wherever possible and messengers who had to carry large sums of cash were given a police escort. The situation improved considerably by 1949 and in that year there was only one holdup. In September 1950, however, when it was generally supposed that banditry had been eliminated, a pay truck in the vicinity of Nuoro was held up and its three-man *carabinieri* escort cold-bloodedly murdered. The bandits took almost 2,000,000 lire from the pay truck.

Where farmers believed that larvicide was toxic to their livestock, a certain amount of sabotage took place. Its most usual form was punching holes in larvicide drums or destroying the numbers and signs indicating breeding places. In some instances workers were threatened or attacked. Such cases were reported to the police, but persuasion combined with practical demonstrations of the harmlessness of the larvicide proved the best means of overcoming antagonism.

Another type of opposition was encountered in several mountain zones which were used as hideouts by bandits. In certain areas brigands warned ERLAAS workers to stay out, particulary after a rumor that *carabinieri* were circulating disguised as members of the organization. As these threats were occasionally backed by firearms, scouts and larviciders expressed a natural reluctance to work in such areas. The resistance of the banditry was taken care of by private negotiations and the guarantee that ERLAAS uniforms were not being loaned to disguise *carabinieri*.

Motor accidents. The extensive transport involved in ERLAAS activities resulted in a considerable number of road accidents (33 in 1942; 91 in 1948; 64 in 1949; and 31 in 1950). At first it was thought that accidents would be sufficiently infrequent to enable the organization to meet damage claims without insurance. Two serious accidents in the early months demonstrated the inadvisability of this policy and insurance was taken out. An accident in June 1950 in which 16 men lost their lives made it evident that the insurance coverage was not extensive enough; it would have been prudent to insure against all possible claims, no matter how remote they might have seemed.

ERLAAS Contribution to National Insurance Agencies

In any calculation of the cost of ERLAAS, the very considerable amounts that were returned to the Italian Government in the form of customs duties, taxes and national insurance contributions must not be overlooked.

The insurance contributions (in lire) may be summarized as follows:

(a) Contribution to the Istituto Nazionale Previdenza Sociale (INPS) for tuberculosis, old age and unemployment assistance (paid by ERLAAS) 372,966,091

(b) Contribution to the Istituto Nazionale Assicurazioni Infortuni sul Lavoro (INAIL) for accident insurance (paid by ERLAAS) 105,334,622

(c) Contribution to the Istituto Nazionale per l'Assicurazione contro le Malattie (INAM) for insurance against sickness (paid by both ERLAAS and the individual worker) 131,844,829

(d) In addition, a tax (INA-CASA) for the financing of the state housing program, paid by the ERLAAS organization, was initiated early in 1949 5,660,947

Total expenditure by ERLAAS for these purposes was 615,806,-489 lire. This sum represents 9 per cent of the total budget and 12 per cent of the payments to personnel.

EFFECT OF INFLATION

The cost of labor and supplies rose steadily until the fall of 1948, when the deflationary policy of the government began to take effect. In 1946 and early 1947 the dollar-lira exchange was fixed at 225 lire per dollar but this rose until it was stabilized, in 1948, at a rate of 625 lire to the dollar. Wage rates did not increase as much as the exchange. If wages, including insurance, in January 1947 are taken as a base, increases in the different categories varied from 110 to 150 per cent by 1950; on the same basis gasoline and kerosene costs had increased over 200 per cent by June 1950.

Fuel oil was a special case; although its price increased in the same general way as gasoline and kerosene, oils used for larviciding had for years been exempt from the normal oil tax. Each exemption had to be obtained, however, by the passage of a special decree. The existence of this law was overlooked in the first year of operation, and when an attempt was made to rectify the situation, months passed before it could be made applicable to ERLAAS. Over 68,000,000 lire could have been saved if the law had been applied during the early part of the campaign.

TABULATION OF EXPENDITURES

The schedules that follow are divided into two main groups:

I. A general financial summary of income and expenditure
   (Schedules A, B, C and D).
II. An allocation of costs by department and campaign
   (Schedules M, N, O, P and Q).

It will be noted from Schedule A that the main sources of income were the UNRRA and ERP lire funds. These were counterpart funds established by the Italian Government from the proceeds of the sale of supplies brought into Italy, first by UNRRA and later by ECA.

In addition to its contribution through the lire fund, UNRRA made the following direct grant of supplies:

Insecticides and solvents	109,125,000 lire
Vehicles and spare parts	56,250,000 lire
Other supplies and equipment	9,675,000 lire
Total	175,050,000 lire

The values given here are artificially low because of the nominal value of the vehicles and because the cost of the insecticides was converted at the exchange rate of 225 lire to the dollar existing in 1946. As a result, the insecticide costs of the first two residual spray campaigns, which were supplied almost entirely with DDT emulsion concentrate imported by UNRRA, were below normal, even for those periods of lower general costs.

The contribution of The Rockefeller Foundation was $576,000. This sum has been converted at the 1950 rate of 625 lire to the dollar. It does not include the services of visiting Foundation consultants.

On the expenditure side of the first group of schedules (the general financial summary) the following points are of interest. Payments in one form or another for personnel accounted for 77 per cent of the total cost of operations. (Twelve per cent of these payments to personnel were contributions to the national insurance agencies, which therefore benefited very considerably by the existence of ERLAAS.) Workers in the administrative services received approximately 22 per cent of the total expenditures for personnel, and workers in the field services received 78 per cent (Schedule B).

As analyzed in Schedule C, approximately 21 per cent of the total ERLAAS expenditures went toward equipment, insecticides and supplies of all sorts (including transport). The largest single items in this account, apart from transport supplies and fuel, are the costs of residual insecticides and larvicides. The amounts involved (303,317,405 lire for insecticides and 347,110,980 lire for larvicides) are, however, fairly small in comparison with the total ERLAAS costs. The printing of various types of forms, a supposedly minor item, cost the rather surprising sum of approximately 24,000,000 lire.

The general overhead and other sundry expenses were comparatively low, representing only 2 per cent of the total costs. They are analyzed in Schedule D.

The expense of closing down the organization, which includes the writing and publishing of the final report, is indicated in Schedule A, but has been excluded in computing the total operational cost.

The stock on hand as of June 30, 1951 has been valued at approximately 197,924,058 lire. It has not yet been determined whether this will be transferred to other agencies or sold. In the latter case, the stock will probably be found to be worth considerably more than the estimate.

ERLAAS did not keep detailed cost accounts, and consequently the figures given in the second group of schedules

(M, N, O, P and Q) must be considered as approximate. But in all likelihood they are sufficiently correct to give a reasonable and fair view of the cost of the various departments and campaigns.

General administrative expenses and overhead (Schedule M) represented 12.5 per cent of the total expenditures. Payments to personnel, mainly clerks in the accounting and personnel departments and guards of premises and stores, made up over half of this sum.

The supply services accounted for 6.1 per cent of the total cost of ERLAAS (Schedule N). Here again, the two main items were personnel and transport. Personnel includes the relatively large staff employed in the central warehouse and the various categories of storekeepers distributed throughout the island. Wages for workshop and mixing plant personnel are not included but have been allocated to the particular supply concerned. Thus, for example, the cost of clothing has been increased by the cost of repairs, and that of larvicide by the cost of the mixing plant operations. The figure for transport reflects the cost of the distribution of supplies to the main field centers and their collection either for repairs or at the end of a campaign; also included is the cost of inspection trips by the supply service staff.

As previously noted, the cost of the transport department operations (Schedule O) was very high, representing no less than 20.5 per cent of the total expenditures. Once again the largest single item was that of payments to personnel, but this was almost equaled by the cost of gasoline and oil. An arbitrary allocation of one-half the salaries paid to transport personnel has been made to the repairs and maintenance section. The figure for the actual repairs does not appear to be excessively high, in view of the age of the vehicles and the constant rough treatment to which they were subjected. Depreciation may seem unduly low under the circumstances, but the initial value placed by UNRRA on the majority of the vehicles was also comparatively low. Transport by other agencies was a small item.

The necessity of considering transport costs while planning general strategy is evident from the fact that transport costs for the scouting service in 1948 were almost 100,000,000 lire higher than they were in 1950 (Schedule P), despite the fact that the personnel costs of scouting in the two years were almost the same. This is a strong financial argument for employing a larger number of scouts for a shorter period of time.

Schedules P and Q analyze the total expenditure by the various campaigns and services. In Schedule P the items have been arranged according to campaigns, and in Schedule Q according to the various types of field services. Schedule P shows, as might be expected, that the island-wide antilarval campaign of 1948 accounted for the greater part of the total expenditure (about 47 per cent). If the 1947-48 winter residual spray campaign is included with this main operation, the percentage is approximately 52. The mop-up work of 1949 came next in cost with about 27 per cent, 1950 third with almost 14 per cent and the experimental campaign of 1947 fourth with a little over 2 per cent.

Schedule Q and figure 26 show the total costs of the various types of work, which may be summarized as follows:

Larviciding	31.74%
Drainage and clearing	25.17%
Scouting	24.40%
Residual spraying	11.12%
Logistics	6.22%
Other field services	1.35%
	100.00%

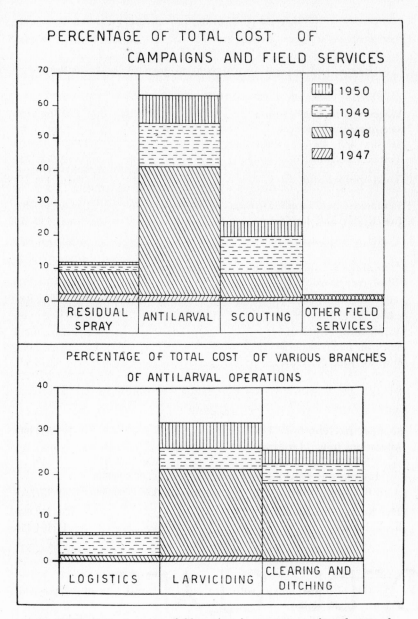

FIGURE 26. Cost of various field services in percentage of total costs of field services.

I. GENERAL FINANCIAL SUMMARY

Schedule A

Income and Expenditure Account to June 30, 1951 (in lire)

EXPENDITURE

Wages and national insurance	3,516,902,192
Sleeping-out allowances	225,116,102
Salaries and national insurance	1,298,758,127
Travel allowances	124,717,792
Total (per Schedule B)	5,165,494,213
Equipment and supplies (including transport)	780,452,894
Insecticides and larvicides	651,433,478
Total (per Schedule C)	1,431,886,372
Administrative and other miscellaneous expenses—	
Total (per Schedule D)	144,352,365
Total Cost of Operations	6,741,732,950
Terminating expenses	76,970,746
Stock on hand, June 30, 1951	197,924,058
Surplus, June 30, 1951	6,914,621
	7,023,542,375

INCOME

Supplies received from UNRRA *		175,050,000
Allocations from " Lire Funds "		
UNRRA Lire Fund	2,594,337,925	
Interim Aid (ERP) Lire Fund	500,000,000	
ERP Lire Fund	3,386,500,000	6,480,837,925
The Rockefeller Foundation **		356,250,000
Bank interest		11,404,450
		7,023,542,375

---

* Value of dollar import converted at the 1946-47 rate of exchange of 225 lire to the dollar.

** $576,000 converted at the 1950 rate of exchange of 625 lire to the dollar.

I. GENERAL FINANCIAL SUMMARY

Schedule B

Personnel: Analysis of Salaries, Wages, Insurance and Allowances (in lire)

	Salaries and National Insurance	Travel Allowances	Wages and National Insurance	Sleeping-out Allowances	TOTAL	Per Cent of Total
ADMINISTRATIVE SERVICES						
Transport Department	92,174,563	6,506,109	338,221,634	28,190,147	465,092,453	9.00
Supplies Department	91,036,094	6,456,828	59,102,015	1,007,902	157,602,839	3.05
General Administration, Accounting and Personnel Departments	362,246,035	15,527,869	65,380,500	—	443,154,404	8.58
Drafting and Statistics Offices	25,136,197	1,221,537	—	—	26,357,734	0.51
Public Relations Office	20,350,000	1,080,000	—	—	21,430,000	0.41
Total	590,942,889	30,792,343	462,704,149	29,198,049	1,113,637,430	21.55
FIELD SERVICES						
Entomological and Scouting	245,828,521	30,934,600	724,676,219	71,136,352	1,072,575,692	20.76
Logistical	120,607,242	17,837,919	150,220,867	8,884,099	297,550,127	5.76
Residual Spray	51,286,548	6,341,249	143,010,680	5,040,336	205,678,813	3.99
Antilarval	257,926,584	37,471,681	2,024,930,137	110,329,210	2,430,657,612	47.06
Quarantine	12,002,593	800,000	11,360,140	528,056	24,690,789	0.48
Medical	20,163,750	540,000	—	—	20,703,750	0.40
Total	707,815,238	93,925,449	3,054,198,043	195,918,053	4,051,856,783	78.45
Total: All Services (see Schedule A)	1,298,758,127	124,717,792	3,516,902,192	225,116,102	5,165,494,213	100.00

I. GENERAL FINANCIAL SUMMARY

Schedule C

Analysis of Equipment and Supply Costs (in lire) *

A. ADMINISTRATIVE SERVICES

General Administrative Services

Printing and stationery	17,470,426	
Equipment and general supplies	7,465,810	
Forms of accounting and personnel departments	8,575,450	33,511,686

Supplies Department

Equipment and general supplies	545,411	
Forms	3,300,947	3,846,358

Drafting and Statistics Offices

Sundry supplies	6,236,092

Public Relations Office

Sundry supplies	3,820,734

Transport Department (see Schedule O)	575,202,710
Total: Administrative Services	622,617,580

B. FIELD SERVICES

Entomological and Scouting

Equipment and sundry supplies	16,900,238	
Forms	5,170,285	22,070,523

Residual Spray

Insecticides	303,317,405	
Equipment and sundry supplies	16,665,648	
Forms	2,065,537	322,048,590

Logistics †

Sundry supplies	7,296,679
Carried forward	351,415,792

* This schedule includes the cost of insecticides and larvicides.

† In this schedule and the others, the term " logistics " signifies the work of subdividing the island into sectors, establishing offices and warehouses, and the listing and numbering of foci.

	Brought forward	351,415,792
Larviciding		
Larvicides	347,110,980	
Equipment and sundry supplies	16,527,602	
Forms	5,074,842	
	368,713,424	
Airplane and helicopter fuel	7,337,101	
Airplane and helicopter spare parts	1,561,193	377,611,718
Draining and clearing		
Dynamite	9,924,898	
Tractor spare parts and depreciation	650,826	
Tractor fuel	1,069,054	
Equipment and sundry supplies	13,071,655	
Forms	50,000	24,766,433
Quarantine		
Insecticides	1,005,093	
Sundry supplies	500,000	1,505,093
Clothing and repairs		53,164,867
Medical		804,889
Total: Field Services		809,268,792
TOTAL: ALL SERVICES (see Schedule A)		1,431,886,372

I. GENERAL FINANCIAL SUMMARY

Schedule D

Analysis of Administrative and Other Miscellaneous Expenses (in lire)

Rent and repairs to premises	24,315,976
Repairs and maintenance of office furniture	3,070,389
Lighting, heating, insurance and cleaning	14,607,810
Postal, telephone and telegraph charges	12,129,038
Bank charges	1,819,048
Legal and audit charges	2,388,290
Claims by outside parties not covered by insurance	19,179,036
Losses due to banditry	3,501,669
Miscellaneous expenses	8,606,706
Total: Administrative Expenses (see Schedule M)	89,617,962
Transport Department: Various expenses (see Schedule O)	54,734,403
TOTAL (see Schedule A)	144,352,365

II. COST BY DEPARTMENT AND CAMPAIGN

Schedule M

Cost of General Administrative Expenses and Overhead (in lire)

Salaries and wages: general administration, accounting and personnel departments	427,626,535
Travel allowances: general administration, accounting and personnel departments	15,527,869
	443,154,404
Public Relations Office: salaries, wages and general expenses	25,250,734
Drafting and Statistics Offices: salaries, wages and general expenses	32,593,826
Transport: general administration, accounting and personnel departments	217,593,759
Various supplies and equipment	33,511,686
Miscellaneous expenses (per Schedule D)	89,617,962
Total (12.5 per cent of total expenditure)	841,722,371

Schedule N

Cost of Supply Service (in lire)

Personnel salaries and wages	150,138,109
Travel and sleeping-out allowances (per Schedule B)	7,464,730
	157,602,839
Transport: administration of service and supply to central warehouses	203,129,382
Various supplies and equipment	3,846,358
	364,578,579
General overhead charges	45,499,506
Total (6.1 per cent of total expenditure)	410,078,085

II. COST BY DEPARTMENT AND CAMPAIGN

Schedule O

Cost of Transport Service (in lire)

Fuel and oil		457,275,024
Drivers' wages and allowances		283,810,687
Repairs and maintenance		
Salaried personnel (Repairs Section)	49,340,336	
Mechanics' wages and allowances	82,601,094	
Spare parts, general supplies and electric power	81,205,468	
Repairs by private agencies	11,320,922	224,467,820
Insurance and taxes		6,150,391
Depreciation of vehicles		35,229,296
Depreciation of bicycles		2,100,101
Transport: administration of service, delivery of vehicles, breakdowns, etc.		79,509,815
Transport by private agencies		35,515,828
Cost of forms relative to service		1,140,083
Salaries and allowances of personnel		
All salaried staff	98,680,672	
Less: Repairs Section as above (50 per cent)	49,340,336	49,340,336
		1,174,539,381
General overhead and supply charges		210,007,641
Total (20.5 per cent of total expenditure)		1,384,547,022

II. COST BY DEPARTMENT AND CAMPAIGN

Schedule P

Cost of Various Campaigns *(in thousands of lire)*

Campaign	Wages and salaries	Travel allowances	Insecticides and larvicides	Equipment, supplies & clothing	Transport services	Supply services, administrative overhead	TOTAL	Per Cent
Entomological Survey (1946)	6,111	239		250	568	1,243	8,411	0.12
Malaria Control Residual Spray (1946-47)	35,877	1,766	46,452	6,308	20,062	19,155	129,620	1.92
Experimental Antilarval (1947)	77,190	5,087	2,929	8,838	40,054	23,253	157,351	2.33
a) Scouting	11,221	626		4,972	15,441	5,594	37,854	0.56
b) Larviciding	56,893	3,913	2,929	3,366	22,506	15,538	105,145	1.56
c) Drainage and clearing	9,076	548		500	2,107	2,121	14,352	0.21
Island-wide Residual Spray (1947-48)	110,692	7,203	126,516	11,103	60,048	54,720	370,282	5.50
Island-wide Antilarval (1948)	1,927,017	133,016	247,171	60,454	318,570	465,807	3,152,035	46.75
a) Logistics	81,436	7,671		4,760	7,622	17,599	119,088	1.77
b) Scouting	206,080	19,103		9,788	135,844	64,301	435,116	6.45
c) Larviciding	755,667	51,190	186,472	26,708	92,255	192,878	1,305,170	19.36
d) Drainage and clearing	870,150	54,872		17,356	73,971	176,241	1,192,590	17.69
e) Residual spray	13,684	180	60,699	1,842	8,878	14,788	100,071	1.48
Labranchiae Zone Residual Spray (1948-49)	16,436	1,067	34,633	2,126	8,770	4,925	67,957	1.01
Mop-up Antilarval (1949)	1,019,394	103,136	115,363	44,003	267,618	274,700	1,824,214	27.07
a) Logistics	179,281	18,706		7,717	39,024	42,437	287,165	4.26
b) Scouting	519,721	61,154		15,700	127,780	125,607	849,962	12.61
c) Larviciding	141,505	10,179	87,631	12,036	32,980	49,305	333,636	4.95
d) Drainage and clearing	164,820	12,305		7,931	61,281	42,716	289,053	4.29
e) Residual spray	14,067	792	27,732	619	6,553	14,635	64,398	0.96
Final Antilarval (1950)	506,082	34,461	77,364	23,198	160,008	139,266	942,379	13.97
a) Logistics	10,111	344		100		1,831	12,386	0.18
b) Scouting	207,684	20,950		6,950	37,800	47,407	320,791	4.76
c) Larviciding	182,027	9,984	70,079	7,915	65,875	58,244	394,124	5.85
d) Drainage and clearing	102,718	4,810		7,980	54,670	29,510	199,688	2.96
e) Residual spray	3,542	373	7,285	253	1,663	2,274	15,390	0.22
General Entomological Services	19,688			250		3,457	23,395	0.35
Quarantine Services	23,363	1,328	1,005	500	3,087	5,078	34,361	0.51
Medical Services	20,163	540		805	5,531	4,689	31,728	0.47
All Campaigns	3,762,013	289,843	651,433	157,835	884,316	996,293	6,741,733	100.00

II. COST BY DEPARTMENT AND CAMPAIGN

Schedule Q

Cost of Various Types of Operations

		Thousands of lire	Per Cent
Residual Spray			
Malaria control 1946–47		129,620	1.92
Island-wide 1947–48		370,282	5.50
Summer 1948		100,071	1.48
Labranchiae zone 1948–49		67,957	1.01
Summer 1949		64,398	0.96
Summer 1950		15,390	0.23
	TOTAL	747,718	11.10
Antilarval: Logistics			
Island-wide 1948		119,088	1.77
Mop-up 1949		287,165	4.26
Final 1950		12,386	0.18
	TOTAL	418,639	6.21
Antilarval: Drainage and Clearing			
Experimental 1947		14,352	0.21
Island-wide 1948		1,192,590	17.69
Mop-up 1949		289,053	4.29
Final 1950		199,688	2.96
	TOTAL	1,695,683	25.15
Antilarval: Larviciding			
Experimental 1947		105,145	1.56
Island-wide 1948		1,305,170	19.36
Mop-up 1949		333,636	4.95
Final 1950		394,124	5.85
	TOTAL	2,138,075	31.71
Scouting			
Experimental 1947		37,854	0.56
Island-wide 1948		435,116	6.45
Mop-up 1949		849,962	12.61
Final 1950		320,791	4.76
	TOTAL	1,643,723	24.38

	Thousands of lire	Per Cent
Other Services		
General entomological service	23,395	0.35
Entomological survey 1946	8,411	0.12
TOTAL	31,806	0.47
Quarantine	34,361	0.51
Medical	31,728	0.47
TOTAL	97,895	1.45
TOTAL COST OF OPERATIONS	6,741,733	100.00

CHAPTER VIII

QUARANTINE SERVICE

It was recognized that in the event of the eradication of *labranchiae* from Sardinia, further preventive measures would be necessary to guard against reinfestation of the island by this or other malaria vectors from neighboring regions. The possibility of reinfestation was increased by the proximity of the island to Corsica, continental Italy, Sicily and the coast of Africa. From these areas ships, and to a lesser extent airplanes, arrive regularly in Sardinian ports. Accordingly, in December 1947, ERLAAS established an Inspection and Quarantine Service to investigate methods for the disinsectization of ships and aircraft, and to study the national and international legal provisions for quarantine operations.

AUTHORIZATION OF QUARANTINE MEASURES

Early in 1948, conferences were held with the Inspector-General of Quarantine of the Italian High Commission for Hygiene and Public Health and with WHO consultants. As a result of these meetings the Italian Government issued two ordinances (Gazzetta Ufficiale, 1948) making ERLAAS responsible for the inspection and disinsectization of all national ships and aircraft entering Sardinian ports. In the case of foreign carriers, it was decided that the best way to secure authorization was by international agreements cleared through WHO.

A study was also made of the International Sanitary Conventions of 1926 and 1933, as amended in 1944. The original intention was to adapt these conventions, which dealt with the control of infectious diseases carried by sea and air traffic, to include anophelines. This expedient proved unsatisfactory, and an " Interim International Agreement Regarding the Prevention

249

of the Introduction of Anophelines into Sardinia " was drafted. The proposed agreement was submitted to the Italian High Commission, and by that organization to the Interim Commission of WHO with a request that the technical aspects of the regulations be considered by the Expert Committee on International Epidemic Control. This committee was reluctant to endorse any interference with international carriers which was not already covered by the International Sanitary Conventions and referred the proposed agreement to the Expert Committee on Malaria, with a request that the latter committee communicate its opinion directly to the First World Health Assembly. The following are the recommendations of the Expert Committee on Malaria (WHO, 1948 a) :

" 1. The Expert Committee on Malaria emphasizes the necessity of preventing the introduction of anophelines, by sea or by air, into areas where a campaign of species eradication has been completed or is in progress, as in Sardinia.

" 2. Experience has shown that inspection of a ship for the presence of mosquitoes is unreliable in that even after lengthy search it is impossible to be sure that none is present. The committee recommends, therefore, that the local authority be empowered to carry out immediate disinsectization of any ship which does not possess a valid disinsectization certificate.

" 3. The committee, however, is of the opinion that the production of a valid disinsectization certificate should not preclude a subsequent inspection of the ship by the local authority while the vessel is in port.

" 4. The committee considers that ships which in the opinion of the local authorities require disinsectization on arrival in Sardinian ports should be treated by the most rapid methods available such as aerosols, but suggests that the technical questions relating to the best methods of disinsectization of sea or aircraft be referred to the Sub-Committee on Insecticides proposed in Section V of this report.

" 5. The committee recommends that whenever regulations be enforced regarding the disinsectization of seacraft or aircraft, rigid antimosquito sanitation should be, as far as practicable, maintained within the mosquito flight range of ports and airports of the country to be protected, so that no imported mosquitoes will be able to survive.

" 6. With the above reservations, the committee approves in general the provisions of the drafted International Sanitary Agreement and recommends to the World Health Assembly that steps be taken to effect immediately the measures contemplated in the draft."

On the basis of this report, the Committee on Programme recommended, and the First World Health Assembly adopted, a resolution recognizing the right of the Italian Government to apply measures of disinsectization beyond those authorized by existing international sanitary conventions (WHO, 1948 b).

PRELIMINARY INSPECTIONS

Beginning in March 1948, the ERLAAS Quarantine Service carried out a detailed survey, classifying the coast of Sardinia and its islands into 163 ports, bays and anchorages. All of these were visited by an inspection party in a chartered 25-ton boat in order to obtain information on the type of littoral, the use made of the port or anchorage, and the type and size of the vessels in port. All craft were examined for mosquitoes but no anophelines were found. Potential anopheline breeding places were located and mapped; 833 possible breeding places were examined, none of which harbored anophelines.

The most probable source of anopheline reinfestation was the island of Corsica, which at its nearest point is only 12 kilometers from Sardinia. Consultation with the Corsican public health authorities indicated that this danger was greatly lessened by the malaria control program in effect in Corsica; however, the Corsican Government agreed to carry out special measures in ports used by vessels plying between Corsica and Sardinia. Another hazard with respect to the importation of *labranchiae* from Corsica lay in the contraband traffic between the two islands. It would obviously be impossible for a quarantine service to cover all of the bays and anchorages available to boats engaged in this activity. Here again, the danger was less than had been supposed. Most of the exchange of smuggled goods appeared to take place between boats in the fishing grounds, so that the Corsican vessels did not ordinarily land at points on the Sardinian shoreline.

From April to September 1948, ship inspections were made in the Sardinian ports of Sant'Antioco and Cagliari. No anophelines were found, although many culicines were collected. Aircraft inspections carried out at the same time at Elmas airport (Cagliari) disclosed no mosquitoes of any kind.

In view of this negative evidence and the work of the ERLAAS residual spraying and larviciding program, the effectiveness of the barrier against reinfestation seemed assured. The danger of reinfestation was not deemed sufficient to justify undue interference with shipping, and, accordingly, one of the original regulations of the quarantine service was changed. Ships anchored at buoys some distance offshore were no longer required to pass inspection while at anchor, but were permitted to dock first.

Other modifications were also suggested and, on the basis of the original Italian Government proposal, new ERLAAS quarantine regulations were drafted. These were submitted and approved in substance by the First Session of the WHO Expert Committee on Insecticides, held in Cagliari May 10-15, 1949 (WHO, 1950 a).

QUARANTINE REGULATIONS

Under the ERLAAS quarantine regulations, Sardinian seaports were classified as to port activity and tonnage of ships berthed. There were seven Class I ports (major ports receiving ships of more than 1,500 tons) and 18 Class II ports (smaller ports receiving ships of less than 1,500 tons) (figure 27). Permanent quarantine stations were not provided for the many lesser ports listed in the coastal survey; most of these were merely anchorages, without docks or port facilities, which were used by small craft engaged in coastal voyages or fishing. Treatment and inspection in these ports were carried out from the nearest Class I or Class II station.

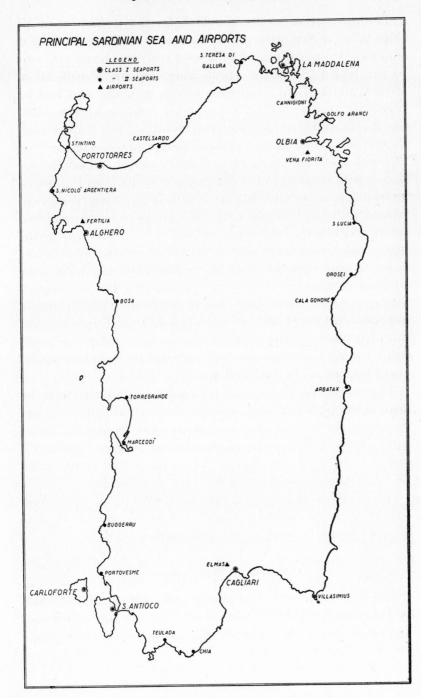

FIGURE 27. Location of ERLAAS quarantine stations.

The quarantine service provided for the inspection of all ships entering Sardinian ports. All insects discovered on board ship were collected, placed in labeled specimen boxes and sent to the ERLAAS entomological laboratory for identification. If mosquitoes of any kind were found, or if the ship had no certificate verifying that it had been sprayed with residual insecticide within the previous two months, it was disinsectized. Pyrethrum aerosol bombs or hand pump sprays were used for the bridge, officers' quarters, passengers' cabins and other locations where damage to furniture might result from the use of a residual spray. Full holds inaccessible to spraying crews were treated with DDT smoke canisters. All other living quarters, galley and mess halls, storage and utility rooms, empty holds, spaces and passageways were treated with residual insecticide. A 5 per cent solution of DDT in kerosene or a 5 per cent aqueous emulsion of DDT, at 2 grams of DDT per square meter, was used. Any dead insects found after the treatment were collected for identification. A certificate of disinsectization was then issued. This was valid for two months, but the vessel was retreated if mosquitoes of any kind were found on subsequent inspections in the interim.

The corresponding regulations relating to aircraft were in force at the principal Sardinian airfields. All aircraft of extra-insular origin were treated with pyrethrum aerosol bombs or hand pump sprays after disembarkation of passengers. All insects found after the spraying were collected and sent to the ERLAAS entomological laboratory for identification.

Other ERLAAS activities, such as larviciding, scouting and residual spraying, carried out in the vicinity of sea and airports, complemented the work of the quarantine service.

Scope of Operations

The quarantine service began operations in April 1949 and by June was functioning in all ports. During June, July and August, the period of peak operation of the service, the volume of work per month averaged as follows: inspection of 858 ships totaling 304,000 tons, residual spraying of 488 ships totaling 227,000 tons, and inspection and treatment with pyrethrum spray of 186 aircraft.

No anopheline mosquitoes were found in ships or airplanes, although there were many culicines. The service was therefore reduced in scope after September 30, 1949. All spraying of ships was stopped, except in the event of finding anophelines. However, the inspection of ships, including the collection and identification of insects, was continued in the four principal ports of Cagliari, Portotorres, Olbia and Sant'Antioco. Aircraft inspection, with the collection and identification of insects, was retained only at Elmas, the principal airport of the island. Pyrethrum spray treatment of all aircraft arriving at this airport was continued, because of the relative ease and cheapness of this measure.

These operations proceeded unchanged until July 1, 1950, when the inspection of ships was resumed at the port of Santa Teresa Gallura because of the inauguration of a daily boat service to Corsica. The quarantine service itself was terminated on September 30, 1950, when virtually all ERLAAS activities ceased. The volume of operations carried out by the service during the 18 months of its existence is summarized in table XLI.

Personnel

Ship operations in 1949 were directed by a port chief assigned to each of the 25 seaports, Class I ports having an assistant chief as well. Disinsectization personnel were assigned to each seaport on the basis of the amount of traffic handled. The airport service was operated by one man at each of the three airports. During the three-month period of peak operations, a total of 56 persons handled all inspections and treatments in the 25 seaports and three airports. After September 30, 1949, when operations were confined to inspection at the four major seaports and inspection with treatment at one airport, only eight persons were employed. Two more were added with the resumption of inspections at Santa Teresa Gallura.

Cost

The average monthly cost of operating the service with 56 employees in 28 ports during the three months of maximum

TABLE XLI

Summary of ERLAAS Quarantine Service operations during 1949 and 1950

	April 1– December 31, 1949	January 1– September 30, 1950	Total April 1, 1949– September 30, 1950
Number of ships			
Inspected			
Class I ports	3,627	3,140	6,767
Class II ports	773	146	919
Total	4,400	3,286	7,686
Treated			
Class I ports	1,717	0	1,717
Class II ports	416	0	416
Total	2,133	0	2,133
Tonnage of ships			
Inspected			
Class I ports	2,075,660	2,480,703	4,556,363
Class II ports	26,598	25,553	52,151
Total	2,102,258	2,506,256	4,608,514
Treated			
Class I ports	929,007	0	929,007
Class II ports	11,271	0	11,271
Total	940,278	0	940,278
Number of aircraft			
Inspected and treated	1,038	579	1,617

operations was 2,560,000 lire: of this, 2,300,000 lire, or 90 per cent, represented expenditures for labor; 220,000 lire, or 8.5 per cent, the cost of insecticide; and 40,000 lire, or 1.5 per cent, miscellaneous expenses.

On an annual basis the estimated cost of the complete quarantine service as it operated during the three months was therefore 30,720,000 lire. This represents the direct operating cost of the service, not including expenditures for purchase, maintenance and depreciation of equipment which was supplied from ERLAAS stocks. Detailed cost data are given in Annex 4 to the Report on the Second Session of the WHO Expert Committee on Insecticides (WHO, 1950 b).

ANALYSIS OF FINDINGS

Of the 7,686 ships inspected between April 1, 1949 and September 30, 1950, 422 or 5.5 per cent were positive for mosquitoes and 744, or 9.7 per cent, for other arthropods. Of 1,617 aircraft, 19 or 1.2 per cent were positive for mosquitoes and 156 or 9.7 per cent were positive for other arthropods. Many culicine mosquitoes were captured on vessels of all sizes down to 15 tons; no mosquitoes were found on boats smaller than 15 tons. No anophelines were found in the course of either ship or aircraft inspections until the end of September 1950, when four *algeriensis* were collected from three ships in the harbor of Portotorres. Two of these ships had arrived from the Italian ports of Genoa and Savona and the third from Bastia, Corsica. *Algeriensis* occurs in the region of Portotorres, and larvae were later located in the Mannu River, 600 meters from the port area. The anophelines may therefore have originated locally.

Mosquitoes were not found in the few airplanes arriving from foreign airports, but only in those originating in continental Italian airports. Aircraft from Sardinian airports were not inspected.

Of the 422 ships positive for mosquitoes, 304 had arrived from Italian ports, 30 from foreign ports and 88 were engaged in local coastwise trade.

All arthropods found in the course of ship inspections are classified in the appended list, with the number of ships positive in each case. The corresponding data for aircraft inspections are also given. The mosquitoes specifically identified are all known to occur in Sardinia.

As a result of the experience gained in 1949 and 1950, the ERLAAS quarantine regulations were again modified. Routine treatment of ships and aircraft was replaced by routine inspection with treatment only in the event of positive anopheline findings. These modifications were submitted to the Second Session of the WHO Expert Committee on Insecticides (WHO, 1950 b) and approved for submission to the WHO Expert Committee on International Epidemiology and Quarantine.

LIST OF ARTHROPODS FOUND IN THE COURSE OF SARDINIAN SHIP INSPECTIONS.

Organism	Number of ships positive
Class Myriapoda	2
Class Arachnida	
Order Araneida	2
Class Insecta	
Order Thysanura	
Family Lepismidae	1
Order Blattaria	
Family Phyllodromiidae, *Blatella germanica*	103
Blatta orientalis	1
Order Ephemerida	9
Order Hemiptera	
Family Cimicidae, *Cimex lectularius*	36
Family Lygaeidae	1
Family Hydrometridae	1
Order Neuroptera	1
Family Chrysopidae	2
Order Lepidoptera	7
Family Tineidae	1
Order Coleoptera	11
Family Dermestidae	1
Family Cerambycidae	1
Order Hymenoptera	3
Family Evaniidae	1
Family Ichneumonidae	1
Family Formicidae	4
Order Diptera	7
Family Mycetophilidae	4
Family Tipulidae	4

37. **ERLAAS** fleet of aircraft.

38. Larval scouting equipment, using dip net.

39. Examining the contents of a large dip net.

40. Training larval scouts in the use of the dip net.

41. Larval scouting in horizontal vegetation, using dipper.

	Number of ships positive
Organism	
Family Culicidae, *Anopheles algeriensis*	3
Culex pipiens	133
Culex sp.	250
Culiseta sp.	13
Aedes vexans	1
Aedes caspius	15
Aedes detritus	16
Aedes sp.	21
Family Chironomidae	36
Family Ceratopogonidae	2
Family Sciaridae	2
Family Dolichopodidae	2
Family Syrphidae, *Eristalis* sp.	1
Family Cordyluridae, *Cordylura* sp.	2
Family Piophilidae, *Piophila casei*	12
Family Drosophilidae	3
Family Anthomyiidae	5
Fannia sp.	30
Family Muscidae	1
Musca domestica	566
Musca sorbens	1
Musca autumnalis	1
Muscina stabulans	4
Family Stomoxyidae, *Stomoxys calcitrans*	9
Lyperosia irritans	1
Family Sarcophagidae, *Sarcophaga* sp.	1
Family Calliphoridae	3
Lucilia sp.	1
Family Tachinidae	2

LIST OF ARTHROPODS FOUND IN THE COURSE OF SARDINIAN AIR INSPECTIONS.

	Number of aircraft positive
Organism	
Class Arachnida	1
Class Insecta	
Order Blattaria	
Family Phyllodromiidae, *Blatella germanica*	2
Order Orthoptera	
Family Locustidae	1

Organism	Number of aircraft positive
Order Dermaptera	2
Order Ephemerida	2
Order Hemiptera	2
Order Neuroptera	
Family Myrmeleonidae	1
Order Lepidoptera	
Family Tineidae	1
Order Coleoptera	12
Family Carabidae	1
Order Hymenoptera	8
Family Vespidae	1
Family Formicidae	1
Order Diptera	3
Family Bibionidae	1
Family Tipulidae	1
Family Culicidae, *Culex* sp.	14
Culiseta sp.	1
Aedes caspius	3
Aedes sp.	3
Family Chironomidae	15
Family Stratiomyidae	1
Family Tabanidae	3
Family Rhagionidae	1
Family Syrphidae	1
Family Piophilidae, *Piophila casei*	1
Family Muscidae, *Musca domestica*	138
Musca sorbens	1
Muscina stabulans	2
Family Stomoxyidae, *Stomoxys calcitrans*	1
Family Calliphoridae, *Calliphora* sp.	2
Family Sarcophagidae, *Sarcophaga* sp.	2

CHAPTER IX

HOUSEFLY CONTROL

Houseflies are a serious problem in Sardinia due to the lack of screens on doors and windows, to the unsanitary methods used for disposing of refuse and excreta and, in rural areas, to the practice of sheltering animals close to or inside houses. During the warm months, flies are present in houses in such great numbers that, apart from their undoubted importance as vectors of disease, they cause great inconvenience to the occupants. This fact is of considerable significance with regard to public acceptance of residual spraying of houses. Since anopheline mosquitoes usually enter houses at night, are rarely seen and are usually not annoying, the public judges the effectiveness of a residual spraying campaign on the basis of the amount of fly control provided. The householder is willing to be put to the trouble of having his house sprayed if he is able to see immediate benefits in the control of flies.

Control Campaigns with DDT

The first Sardinian residual house-spraying campaign with DDT was carried out from November 6, 1946 to June 28, 1947 and covered 281 of the 326 communes in the island. Although the campaign was directed primarily against overwintering mosquitoes, excellent control of flies was obtained.

Detailed checks were made in two treated sections in Cagliari, in two treated farmhouses and in an untreated village near Cagliari. Flypapers were placed in rooms and animal shelters and left in place for 48 hours; then the flies caught were counted. The Sant'Avendrace quarter of Cagliari, near the municipal garbage dump, had been treated with 2 grams of DDT per square meter on November 11, 1946. On May 29,

261

1947, more than six months after treatment, fly counts in 27 counting stations showed an average of 2.3 flies per station. On July 30, eight and a half months after treatment, the average count was 11.3 flies per station. The Is Mirrionis quarter, consisting of abandoned barracks used as temporary housing for poor families, had been treated with 2 grams of DDT per square meter November 12-15, 1946. Fly counts on June 23, 1947, more than seven months after treatment, gave an average of 0.4 flies per shelter; on July 30, eight and a half months after treatment, the average was 1 fly per shelter.

The two farms outside Cagliari had been treated with 1 gram of DDT per square meter on May 19 and 25, 1947. This was an experimental method of treatment in which the same 5 per cent aqueous emulsion used for applying 2 grams per square meter was employed, but the spraying time was halved in order to halve the amount of DDT applied. Fly counts in these farms averaged 22 per shelter on May 29 (ten and four days, respectively, after treatment), and 25 per shelter on June 23, approximately one month after treatment. The degree of control thus appeared to be less than in Cagliari. This may have been due to the smaller dosage of DDT applied, to less careful application or to less complete coverage resulting from the rapid spraying.

Fly counts in the nearby untreated village of San Sperate averaged 294 per shelter on May 29 and 385 per shelter on June 23. This comparison count was not repeated on July 30 because by this time the village had been treated.

These figures demonstrated that fly control was still good almost nine months after treatment in districts of Cagliari where flies were ordinarily numerous; the figures also indicated good control one month after treatment in farms outside the city where, in the absence of treatment, fly counts would be expected to approximate those in the untreated village.

In August 1947, flies began to reappear in some sections of Cagliari. To find out whether this was due to the development of DDT resistance in flies or to the loss of the residual effect, an experiment was carried out in two villages near Cagliari.

Direct fly counts, made in 41 rooms in one village and 25 rooms in the other, averaged 39 and 16 per room, respectively. All buildings were then sprayed with 2 grams of DDT per square meter. Two days later, the average counts in the same rooms were 4 and 3 per room for the two villages, a reduction in density of 90 and 81 per cent, respectively. There were many dead flies in all the rooms. This seemed to indicate that the flies in the region of Cagliari were still susceptible to DDT.

The second residual spraying campaign, again primarily directed against mosquitoes, was carried out from October 8, 1947 to February 28, 1948, and included the entire island except the three cities of Cagliari, Alghero and Sassari. DDT was applied at the rate of 2 grams per square meter to all man-built structures, including bridges and culverts, capable of sheltering anophelines. Flies began to appear with the onset of warm weather in April, and were apparently not controlled by DDT. It was thought at first that the treated surfaces had lost their residual effect, since the spraying had been completed several months earlier than in the preceding winter. However, colorimetric testing demonstrated the persistence of DDT on walls treated six months previously, and later, after the campaign was extended to include Cagliari, Sassari and Alghero, flies continued to increase in the sections of these cities which had been treated in April and May. It was then concluded that Sardinian flies had become resistant to DDT, an opinion confirmed by releasing 98 flies caught in the town of Muravera into a room which had recently been heavily treated with DDT. After 24 hours, 50 per cent of the flies were still alive, without any evidence of DDT intoxication. No additional flies were dead at the end of 48 hours.

In August 1948 an experiment was performed to determine whether a suspension of DDT wettable powder would yield better results than the DDT emulsion hitherto used. The farm of Sa Illetta was treated with 5 per cent aqueous suspension of 50 per cent DDT wettable powder in a dosage of 2 grams of DDT per square meter, and Machiareddu was treated with a 2.5 per cent suspension in a dosage of 1 gram per square meter. For comparison Dolianova was treated with 5 per cent DDT emulsion at the rate of 2 grams per square meter. Fly-paper strips were placed in kitchens and stables, and counts were made after 24 hours. Post-treatment counts were higher in all cases than pretreatment counts, and no effective control was obtained (table XLII).

TABLE XLII

24-HOUR FLY COUNTS IN VILLAGES TREATED WITH DDT IN AUGUST 1948

Village	Treatment	Number of stations	Average 24-hr. fly counts per station			
			Before treat-ment	Weeks after treatment		
				2	4	6
Sa Illetta	5 per cent wettable powder 2 grams per sq. meter	5	93	527	126	354
Machiareddu	2.5 per cent wettable powder 1 gram per sq. meter	5	46	80	45	99
Dolianova	5 per cent emulsion 2 grams per sq. meter	17	118	119	170	254

The failure of DDT to control flies created serious problems for the residual spraying operations. It was therefore decided to undertake an antifly program with chlordane. A field trial was carried out in June 1948 in the village of Muravera and in part of the San Benedetto quarter of Cagliari. A 2 per cent aqueous emulsion of chlordane was applied at the rate of 0.8 gram of chlordane per square meter, and the numbers of flies caught on papers over 24-hour periods were counted on three occasions. There was immediate control of flies, as shown in table XLIII. Although pretreatment counts were not done in the eight San Benedetto stations, flies were observed to be numerous there.

TABLE XLIII

24-HOUR FLY COUNTS AFTER TREATMENT WITH 2 PER CENT CHLORDANE
EMULSION IN JUNE 1948

Location	Number of stations	Average 24-hour fly counts per station			
		Before treatment	Weeks after treatment		
			2	4	6
Muravera	30	277	1.6	0.8	1.9
San Benedetto	8			0.75	2.25

CONTROL CAMPAIGNS WITH CHLORDANE

From June to October 1948, 165 communes, which included about 70 per cent of all human habitations in the island, were treated with chlordane. The basic preparation was 33.9 per cent emulsifiable concentrate, consisting of 5 parts by weight of chlordane, 9 parts of kerosene and 0.75 parts of Triton X-100. Immediately before use, this concentrate was diluted with water to give a 2 per cent chlordane emulsion, which was applied to walls in a dosage of 0.8 gram of chlordane per square meter. Kitchens, toilets or latrines, and all animal shelters were treated; other rooms in houses were omitted because they harbored many less flies. Walls were sprayed only to a height of four meters, ceilings only if less than four meters from the floor. As almost all ceilings in village homes are less than four meters high, in practice the rooms were completely treated. In addition to houses and animal shelters, public buildings, such as hospitals, barracks, orphanages, markets and all food-handling establishments, were treated.

Again, a high degree of fly control was achieved. Flies virtually disappeared from the treated centers and remained absent throughout the summer. Fly counts made in Alghero before and during treatment illustrated the extent of treatment necessary to reduce the fly population throughout the city. On July 24, two weeks before treatment was started, 48-hour fly counts in 18 stations scattered throughout the city gave an average of 121 flies per station. On August 23, when one-third of the city had been treated, counts in five treated buildings gave an average of 21 flies per station, while the counts in three untreated shelters, located less than 150 meters from the treated area, averaged 101 flies per station. Thus, the spraying was already effective in the treated area, although no effect was apparent as yet in the untreated area. A shortage of chlordane interrupted the spraying from August 23 to September 6. On September 11, when approximately three-fourths of the city had been treated, 48-hour fly counts in 26 treated and 8 untreated shelters averaged 19 and 17 flies per station, respectively. Apparently, treatment of three-quarters of the shelters sufficed to reduce the fly population not only in the treated area, but also in the untreated area. On September 22, four days after completion of the city-wide spraying, 48-hour counts in 36 shelters gave an average of 3.5 flies per station; comparison 24-hour counts made at the same time in a nearby untreated village gave an average of 256 flies per station.

While this 1948 chlordane campaign was in progress, two towns were partially sprayed with various formulations of benzene hexachloride on an experimental basis. Twenty-four-hour counts were made in the village of Assemineddu, treated in August with benzene hexachloride emulsion in a dosage of 100 milligrams of gamma isomer per square meter. The pre-treatment counts for five shelters gave an average of 187 flies per station. Counts in the same shelters at two, four and six weeks after treatment averaged 13, 52 and 260 flies per station, respectively, demonstrating that the control was of short duration.

A limited fly control program was planned for the summer of 1949 in response to pressure from the public and from the provincial health authorities. Budgetary limitations did not permit an island-wide program. Forty-seven communes with a total population of 285,000 persons were selected by the provincial health officers for treatment. ERLAAS supplied the insecticide and the supervisory personnel, as well as the general direction of the campaign. Labor and transportation within the villages were provided by the communes concerned. An additional 38 communes with a total population of 110,000 organized campaigns for themselves, supplying their own labor, transport and insecticide. ERLAAS loaned the necessary spray pumps, accessories and mixing equipment, and provided technical direction to the spraying crews. Chlordane was used in 2 per cent aqueous emulsion, again prepared from a 33.9 per cent concentrate as in 1948. Kitchens and animal shelters of all houses were treated up to a height of four meters from the floor; ceilings were treated if they were under this height. Public buildings of the same types treated in 1948 were also sprayed. Small quantities of benzene hexachloride dust were used in the treatment of refuse dumps in two communes. In a part of Cagliari benzene hexachloride emulsion was used for the treatment of some animal shelters because of a temporary shortage of chlordane. As in 1948, a high degree of fly control was obtained.

In addition to the campaigns described, many other communes were protected against flies by the chlordane residual spraying carried out in the anopheline eradication campaign.

FIELD EXPERIMENTS WITH CHLORDANE, BENZENE HEXACHLORIDE AND DDT

For future fly control work, information was needed as to the optimal amount of chlordane to apply and the duration of the residual effect. Field trials with this compound were therefore begun in a group of villages in 1949; field trials were also made with benzene hexachloride, to obtain similar information concerning this insecticide, and with DDT, in order to see if resistance to DDT still existed.

It was decided to treat entire villages for these experiments, and to use untreated villages in the same locality for comparison, rather than to spray part of a village and to measure the effect of the insecticide by comparison with untreated houses. The disadvantages of the latter method were that the spraying effect might extend to untreated houses, or that flies from untreated houses might invade treated houses, thus partially masking the effect of the treatment. However, the method chosen did not permit a direct comparison between the numbers of flies present in treated and untreated villages, since the pretreatment fly populations in different villages were obviously not identical. Estimation of the effectiveness of the insecticide therefore depended upon the comparison of the trends of the fly counts in the treated and untreated villages.

Preliminary experiments were carried out to determine the best method of estimating fly densities in houses. Cylindrical metal-screen fly traps with the entrance at the apex of a conical base, placed over honey as bait, gave low and variable counts in relation to the observed number of flies present. This was also true of the fly grill (Scudder, 1947). Pyrethrum spraying of rooms, with counts of flies killed, gave an accurate estimate of the number of flies, but measured only the flies present at the moment of spraying. Thus the count depended entirely upon the circumstances present at the time when the spraying was carried out. For example, a count made after a kitchen had been cleaned, and exposed food put away, would be low in relation to the average number of flies present over a longer period of time. It was found that the use of flypaper, as previously described, was the most satisfactory method of determining fly densities. The strips were left in place for a week, the trapped flies were counted to obtain an estimate of the average density of flies present over this period, and a new strip was then put in place.

Since flies were present in much greater numbers in kitchens than in other rooms, the fly strips were hung in kitchens, one strip being fastened to the center of the ceiling. Counting stations were distributed in all sections of the village, with one station for each 100 inhabitants. The mean of the counts from all stations in a village was taken as the fly count for the village. Most of the villages varied from 700 to 1,500 in population, so that the village counts represented the findings of from seven to fifteen stations.

The great majority of the flies caught by the strips were *Musca domestica*. During April, when the counts were relatively low, *M. domestica* averaged from 50 to 60 per cent of the total flies caught. This proportion increased rapidly when the weather became warmer, reaching from 90 to 98 per cent in the summer, from May through October. The relative incidence of *M. domestica* was low and much more variable during the winter months, but the total numbers of flies caught then were also very low. Other species of flies were almost entirely *Fannia canicularis* and *Piophila casei*. On rare occasions flies belonging to other genera, such as *Drosophila, Muscina, Calliphora, Lucilia, Stomoxys, Sarcophaga, Tipulidae* and *Lyperosia*, were found.

Spraying was carried out in all food-handling or food-processing establishments in the villages. All kitchens, animal shelters, toilets and latrines were treated. Walls were sprayed only to a height of four meters and ceilings if they were under this height, as they are in most village homes. Other structures were not treated.

DDT was used as a 5 per cent solution in kerosene. With chlordane, the standard 33.9 per cent emulsifiable concentrate was sent to the villages and the aqueous emulsion prepared on location immediately before use. Benzene hexachloride was used as an aqueous suspension of a 6.5 per cent gamma isomer wettable powder.

All the experimental villages had been routinely treated twice previously with DDT in the course of the eradication campaign. The first treatment (1 or 2 grams per square meter) was done in the first half of 1947, the second (2 grams per square meter) seven to ten months later, the most recent being in January 1948.

Controls. Five villages (Donori, Gonnoscodina, Simala, Ussaramanna and Baradili) in the same general area, with a total population of approximately 4,000, served as controls. Forty-one counting stations were established, and the fly counts for the control villages represent the mean weekly counts from all 41 stations.

DDT. The villages of Bauladu and Soleminis (total population 1,700, 17 capture stations) were treated with DDT. Bauladu, which had been treated with DDT in February 1949 in addition to the two earlier sprayings, was treated with 4 grams per square meter to determine whether control could be achieved with this higher dosage. Soleminis was treated with 2 grams per square meter. No control was obtained, although in Soleminis the count for the week after treatment fell slightly, while the count in the comparison villages was increasing. This experiment demonstrated that local flies were still resistant to DDT, and that their resistance could not be overcome by using larger doses of DDT.

Chlordane. Four villages (Tramatza, Siddi, Baressa and Soleminis) with a total population of approximately 4,000 were used for the chlordane experiment. Thirty-nine counting stations were established. Tramatza had been treated with 1 gram of chlordane per square meter in August 1948, and Soleminis had been treated with DDT one month previously. For this field trial, Baressa was treated with 2.5 grams of chlordane per square meter, while the other three villages received 1 gram per square meter. A marked diminution in the numbers of flies caught on the papers occurred in all four experimental villages, in comparison with the numbers caught in the control villages. The effect lasted approximately 20 weeks in Tramatza; fly counts began to rise in September, corresponding to the trend in the untreated villages. In Siddi control lasted for about 16 weeks, the counts beginning to increase in August. In Baressa, which received the highest dose of chlordane, control lasted approximately 12 weeks;

counts began to increase late in September. The effect of the treatment was somewhat delayed in Soleminis, which was treated early in July at a time when the fly population had already built up to a high level. The counts fell slowly for four weeks, after which control was reasonably good for eight weeks. The number of flies then increased slowly, beginning at the end of September, but did not reach the very high levels seen in the untreated villages.

An interesting phenomenon was noted in the treated villages in November, when cold weather sets in and flies enter houses in increasing numbers. Despite the fact that in this month the indoor fly population reached its peak for the year, as shown by the counts for the untreated villages, the counts in the treated villages decreased sharply from the high levels previously reached. The counts then remained lower than those in the untreated villages for four to five months, although the difference was relatively much less marked beginning in January, since the counts in the untreated villages also fell to low levels at this time. The probable explanation for this phenomenon is that after the initial period of good control in the chlordane-treated villages, the residual film deteriorated to the point where the remaining insecticide was insufficient to exert control. However, as the weather became colder in late October and November, the flies became much more sluggish and spent more time resting on walls. This considerably longer exposure to the chlordane resulted in renewed control, despite the small amount of insecticide left. With the return of warm weather in May, and the progressive deterioration of the residual chlordane film, control was again lost.

Benzene hexachloride. Three villages (Serdiana, Collinas and Gonnostramatza) with a total population of 3,900 were used for the benzene hexachloride experiment. Forty-one counting stations were established. Collinas had previously received only the 1947 and 1948 DDT treatments, but in the summer of 1948 Gonnostramatza had been sprayed a third time with DDT and Serdiana had been treated with 1 gram of chlordane per square meter. For the benzene hexachloride trial, Collinas was treated with 80 milligrams of gamma isomer per square meter, Serdiana with 110 milligrams per square meter and Gonnostramatza with 400 milligrams per square meter. The last dosage, about five times that recommended for mosquito control, was the maximum possible with the formulation used, as the extreme heaviness of the suspension caused difficulty in spraying. No worthwhile degree of control was achieved in either Serdiana or Collinas, where only slight decreases in the fly counts were obtained for two to three weeks, after which the counts began to rise again, while the counts in the untreated villages remained fairly constant. In Gonnostramatza, which received the highest dosage, control lasted for about eight weeks.

It should be noted that the Ministry of Agriculture used large quantities of benzene hexachloride dust from 1946 to 1949 in an island-wide campaign against grasshoppers. Although the Ministry confined the treatment to fields, flies might possibly have had sufficient contact with the insecticide to develop resistance. Bruce and Decker (1950) offer another possible explanation: on the basis of experiments with resistant strains of *M. domestica*, these authors consider that flies highly resistant to one insecticide usually show a noticeable tolerance for other insecticides.

THE DEVELOPMENT OF CHLORDANE RESISTANCE IN SARDINIAN FLIES

Field experience. Because of chlordane's success in controlling flies in 1948 and 1949, the Regional Government of Sardinia passed a law requiring all communes to control houseflies and other domestic insects by means of insecticide treatment (Regional Law No. 2 of February 3, 1950). Early in 1950, ERLAAS began another field trial with chlordane. Its purpose was to define the minimum treatment necessary for good fly control and thereby reduce the cost of the regional program. Five villages (Donori, Simala, Gonnoscodina, Collinas and Ussaramanna), all in the same general area, were used for the experiment. Fifty-two counting stations were set up. The methods of making counts and of spraying were the same as those described previously. All five villages had been treated twice (1947 and early 1948) with DDT. In addition, Gonnoscodina and Simala had received a third DDT treatment in the summer of 1948, and Collinas had been used for the benzene hexachloride trial in 1949.

Kitchens and animal shelters in Collinas were treated with 2 grams of chlordane per square meter. In Donori, all interior walls of houses and animal shelters were treated with 1 gram per square meter. This dosage was also used in Simala, where only kitchen walls were sprayed, and in Gonnoscodina, where only animal shelters were treated. Ussaramanna served as the untreated control.

In Donori, the first village to be treated, the control obtained was slight. The treatment did not keep flies from increasing rapidly when the warm weather began in May, in marked contrast with the effect previously obtained with chlordane. The emulsion concentrate used in Donori had been prepared in the previous September, and it was at first thought that it might have deteriorated. However, chemical analysis showed that the estimated amount of unaltered chlordane was present.

A new stock of emulsion concentrate used for the treatment of Simala, Gonnoscodina and Collinas also had virtually no effect. Counts in these villages did decline after treatment, but the drop coincided with a downward trend in Ussaramanna, the untreated village. A new shipment of chlordane was obtained to make up a third supply of concentrate and Donori was treated a second time in May. Still the fly counts rose uninterruptedly, leading to the conclusion that the flies in the experimental villages had become resistant to chlordane.

This opinion was confirmed by an experiment in which flies from the village of Soleminis were exposed to panels treated with a preparation of chlordane from Rome, which was giving good control of flies in the Province of Latina. Almost all the Soleminis flies were knocked down by a 30-minute exposure to the panels, but all recovered by the end of 24 hours. In a second experiment, the whitewashed interiors of five wooden beach cabins were treated with a kerosene solution of chlordane. Two cabins were treated with 2 grams per square meter and three cabins with 1 gram per square meter. Forty-eight hours after treatment, 200 flies caught at the Cagliari garbage dump were released in each cabin. At the end of eight hours of exposure, 350, or 35 per cent, of the total 1,000 flies released were dead or knocked down. At the end of 22 hours of constant exposure to the insecticide, 814 flies (81.4 per cent) in the five cabins were dead or knocked down, while 186 flies (18.6 per cent) survived this intensive exposure. No difference was observed in the mortality produced by the two concentrations of chlordane. Considering the cabins individually, the percentages that survived 22 hours of exposure were 19, 18 and 19.5 for the cabins treated with 1 gram per square meter, and 17.5 and 19 for those treated with 2 grams per square meter. It thus appeared that approximately one-fifth of the flies from the Cagliari garbage dump were able to resist far greater exposure to chlordane than would ordinarily occur. Of 300 flies released into an untreated control cabin, 285 (95 per cent) survived and only 15 (5 per cent) were dead at the end of 22 hours.

It should be noted that none of the villages used in the field trial had previously been treated with chlordane. Chlordane had been used, however, in nearby villages in the same area. Hence, it would appear that resistant strains from chlordane-treated villages may have spread to the five trial villages, giving rise to resistant populations in these villages also. Another possible explanation is the evidence of Bruce and Decker (1950) quoted previously.

Professor A. Missiroli's laboratory at the Istituto Superiore di Sanità in Rome had demonstrated that there was a high mortality rate when Sardinian flies were placed in glass cages, half of whose surfaces had been treated with DDT and half with chlordane. Accordingly, this technique was tried in the village of Villanovaforru. Chlordane emulsion was applied to half the interior wall surfaces at the rate of 2.5 grams of chlordane per square meter and the other walls were treated with a suspension of DDT wettable powder at 2 grams of DDT per square meter. For control purposes the village of Baradili was sprayed with 5 per cent DDT in kerosene solution at 2 grams of DDT per square meter and the village of Gonnostramatza was again sprayed with benzene hexachloride, using an aqueous suspension of wettable powder in a dosage of 400 milligrams of gamma isomer per square meter. The results showed that none of these insecticides provided any control. The same dosage of benzene hexachloride had furnished some control in Gonnostramatza in the experiments of the previous year.

A further experiment was carried out in groups of isolated farmhouses in an agricultural development near Sanluri. The insecticides used were 5 per cent aqueous emulsion of chlordane at 2 grams of chlordane per square meter; 5 per cent aqueous emulsion of DDT at 2 grams of DDT per square meter; 2 per cent aqueous suspension of heptachlor 50 per cent wettable powder at 0.5 gram per square meter; 7.7 per cent aqueous suspension of 6.5 per cent gamma isomer benzene hexachloride wettable powder at 225 milligrams of gamma isomer per square meter; and 5 per cent aqueous emulsion of methoxychlor at 2 grams per square meter. Kitchens and animal shelters of five houses were sprayed with each insecticide, and five untreated houses were observed for comparison. The means of the fly counts for each group of five houses are given in table XLIV.

None of the insecticides had any apparent effect and, at the time of the weekly counts, no dead flies were seen on the floors of the houses. Heptachlor and methoxychlor had not previously been used in Sardinia.

Benzene hexachloride in aqueous emulsion was applied at weekly intervals for four weeks to all obvious fly-breeding

TABLE XLIV

EFFECT ON HOUSEFLIES OF RESIDUAL SPRAYING WITH VARIOUS INSECTICIDES
IN FARMHOUSES NEAR SANLURI, 1950

Weeks after spraying	Number of flies (mean of weekly counts from 5 counting stations)					
	Chlordane 2 grams per sq. meter	DDT 2 grams per sq. meter	Hepta-chlor 0.5 gram per sq. meter	Benzene hexachlo-ride 225 mg. gamma per sq. meter	Methoxy-chlor 2 grams per sq. meter	Un-treated
1	634	772	498	494	814	845
2	606	723	463	539	663	725
3	912	917	737	878	1,020	995
4	1,160	1,180	1,133	1,000	1,140	1,375
5	1,380	1,433	1,450	1,300	1,520	1,400

places, such as manure piles and refuse heaps, in the village of Soleminis. No reduction was noted in the fly counts, which continued at a high level.

A new insecticide (Geigy Compound no. 23383) was tested near the village of Villarios. This compound, a methylated pyrazolone, is entirely different in chemical structure from other residual insecticides. A small group of houses on the edge of the town, about 400 meters from the center, was treated with the formulation supplied by the manufacturers—a 5 per cent kerosene solution with 5 per cent DDT added (it was known that DDT alone did not control flies in Villarios). Ten houses were treated with 1 gram of the pyrazolone per square meter and six houses with 2 grams per square meter. Using flypapers, counting stations were established in these 16 houses and in three untreated houses in the village center. The fly counts before and after treatment are given in table XLV.

A considerable degree of fly control was obtained, particularly in the houses that received the higher dosage, and the effect persisted for three months after the spraying. The experiment was discontinued following the count made 111 days after treatment because of the beginning of winter and a sharp

TABLE XLV

EFFECT ON HOUSEFLIES OF RESIDUAL SPRAYING WITH GEIGY COMPOUND
NO. 23383 NEAR VILLARIOS, AUGUST 1950
(Data of the Sardinian Domestic Insect Control Service)

Days after treatment	Number of flies (mean of 24-hour counts from all counting stations)		
	10 treated houses 1.0 gram per sq. meter	6 treated houses 2.0 grams per sq. meter	3 untreated houses
	208*	162*	132
10	39	24	175
20	18	5	143
32	98	30	291
40	61	20	305
54	80	16	390
70	175	61	650
90	190	60	590
98	158	47	660
111	60	2	170

* Treatment applied three days after this count was made.

decrease in the number of flies in the untreated houses. It should be noted that the counts given are 24-hour catches.

A second village, San Pietro Pula, was partially treated with a solution of the insecticide containing 3 per cent of the pyrazolone and 5 per cent DDT. There was not enough material to spray the entire village, so that only kitchens and animal shelters in about one-third of the houses were treated. Under these conditions, no worthwhile degree of fly control was achieved, although numbers of dead flies were found on the floors of the treated rooms on each visit, and the mean counts were somewhat lower in the treated houses than in the untreated dwellings.

Laboratory experiments. Strains of flies from four Sardinian villages and one strain of normal flies (i. e., never exposed to insecticides) from the Istituto Superiore di Sanità were maintained in colonies in the laboratory. Experiments on these strains confirmed the insecticide resistance of Sardinian flies.

Measured amounts of standard acetone solutions of insecticide were pipetted into 500 cc. Erlenmeyer flasks. While the flask was being rotated to wet the entire interior surface with the solution, a current of air was passed through it to evaporate the acetone. Approximately 35 flies were introduced into each flask and exposed to the film of insecticide for 20 minutes. The flies were then transferred to cardboard cylinders closed with mosquito netting at each end, held there for 24 hours and the percentage mortality recorded. A control was run for each experiment, in which flies were exposed to flasks treated only with acetone, and thereafter handled in the same way. (Mortality was always low in the control flies, and was usually zero.) Five concentrations of each insecticide were tested. Each concentration was run in triplicate and the numbers of dead flies from all three flasks were pooled, so that the percentage mortality at a given concentration represented the experience with approximately 100 flies. By constructing a curve on which per cent mortality was plotted against concentration, the concentration giving 50 per cent mortality was interpolated and the LD_{50} for Sardinian flies compared with that for normal flies.

Preliminary results indicated that the Sardinian strains of flies were from 12 to 16 times as resistant to DDT as normal flies, more than 25 times as resistant to benzene hexachloride, from 10 to 12 times as resistant to methoxychlor and at least 15 times as resistant to chlordane and heptachlor. The exact degree of resistance to the latter two compounds was probably much greater, since in repeated experiments with local Sardinian strains there was virtually no mortality with a dose of 40 milligrams per flask, or 1.2 grams per square meter, the highest concentration which could be applied to the flasks without breakdown of the residual film into discrete oily droplets. These differences are of the same order of magnitude as those reported in areas where failure to control flies in the field has been attributed to resistance to insecticides (March and Metcalf, 1949). They are also comparable to those reported by Busvine (1951) for Sardinian and normal (Rome) flies.

CHAPTER X

CRITICAL REVIEW

The ERLAAS project was established to investigate the feasibility of the eradication technique as a means of malaria control in the Mediterranean area. It was also hoped that if eradication proved possible, the project would benefit Sardinia by the permanent elimination of both the malaria vector and malaria itself.

On the close of operations in 1950, malaria transmission had been eliminated. However, after an intensive effort over a five-year period, *labranchiae* still existed and it was evident that eradication had not been attained.

It will be the purpose of this chapter to review the project critically in an attempt to point out why eradication was not accomplished and to indicate, where they have been evident, the lessons that have been learned.

GENERAL

It has been shown that the eradication of an indigenous species under Sardinian conditions is much more difficult than dealing with an invading species such as *gambiae*. It was originally believed that the use of DDT together with the eradication techniques developed in Brazil and Egypt would be equally effective against *labranchiae*, one of the best known of the anopheline mosquitoes. This confidence failed to take adequate cognizance of the fact that in Sardinia the mosquito, the insecticide and the terrain were different. Although much of the Egyptian and Brazilian eradication experience was applicable to Sardinia, some of it was not only irrelevant but misleading. These differences were generally recognized only after they had shown up in operations. As a result, certain

279

basic data were found to be lacking and certain new procedures were found necessary. Some of these points were:

(a) Insufficient knowledge of *labranchiae*, specifically:
   (1) the life span of the adult at various seasons of the year, at different temperatures and humidities, and in the presence or absence of control measures;
   (2) its ability to survive away from man;
   (3) its reproductive potential;
   (4) its ability to survive at low densities;
   (5) the presence of strains having special characteristics such as estivation, special egg laying habits, or the ability to live without blood meals.
   (While all of this information was probably not necessary, the failure to eradicate may have been due to some unknown characteristic, the knowledge of which would have altered the campaign.)

(b) Insufficient knowledge as to what constituted an effective larvicide.

(c) The original failure to appreciate the effect of the terrain, the size of the island and the lack of communications.

(d) Failure to appreciate the need to prepare larval habitats by clearing and draining before treatment could be effective.

(e) The need for numbering breeding places and for clearly delimiting sector boundaries, in order to obtain a systematic method of checking treatment and scouting.

(f) The impossibility of eliminating certain habitats from treatment (as was possible in Brazil and Egypt) and, conversely, the need for larviciding all collections of fresh water in Sardinia.

(g) The advantage of designing treatment areas (sectoring) on a watershed basis.

(h) The difficulty involved in recognizing the presence of *labranchiae* at low population levels.

(i) The difficulties resulting from the time and financial limits placed on the completion of the project.

(j) The original failure to recognize the importance of the human factor in operations, particularly in areas which were difficult of access.

(k) The underestimation of the time required for effective larviciding (1949 and 1950).

It is not, however, suggested that the project should have been postponed until all of the available knowledge had been tested for relevancy, or until the gaps had been filled. Such a policy would have meant indefinite postponement, as many of the answers and, more important, many of the problems themselves could not have been determined except by the initiation of large-scale operations. A certain amount of risk is inherent in the eradication concept and the pioneer nature of ERLAAS made this risk unusually high. Eradication might have been attained if the organization had been able to isolate and solve certain key problems more rapidly than proved to be possible. However, although a greater knowledge of the biology of *labranchiae* and the techniques of eradication in the beginning would have been of great value, the lack of this information did not automatically doom the project to failure.

Eradication was apparently achieved in some parts of the island and not in others. Success or failure in eradication evidently depended on a combination of factors, both environmental and technical. The analysis of this situation, then, would require the examination of such factors both separately and in relation to one another. This applies not only within the island, but to comparisons between the Sardinian project and similar undertakings in other parts of the world.

BASIC PLANNING

The early difficulties in setting up the organization resulted in a full year's delay in starting the project, and changes in the over-all plan produced further delays. As a result, the island-wide larviciding program originally scheduled for 1946 was not carried out until 1948. As labor rates and prices increased by 30 per cent during 1947 alone, these postponements proved costly. If this money could have been saved, considerable operational improvements, such as an extension of eradication activities for a further four to six weeks at the end of the island-wide larviciding campaign, would have been possible.

Furthermore, the delays in starting the 1946-47 winter residual spraying campaign made it irrelevant to the general eradication plan. Instead of that campaign being followed by an island-wide larviciding program, larviciding was confined to a trial project in the southwest corner of the island. It would have been more logical (if less advisable from a public health point of view) to have postponed the 1946-47 residual spray campaign to the following year, or to have restricted it to the experimental area. As it was, the campaign greatly reduced malaria transmission, but it had no major effect on eradication, and it reduced the available funds. Even more important, it distracted attention and facilities from the planning of the larviciding experiment and from studying the island to develop a sectoring system and to plan the logistics of future campaigns. To further aggravate the situation, the first spray program was not completed in March 1947, as scheduled, but carried on until the end of June, and, as a result, the experimental larviciding project was late in starting. The planning of this work, which should have begun in January at the latest, did not begin until April, and larviciding was not generally started until June. The area chosen was too large and should have been reduced in size when the lack of supplies and trained personnel became apparent.

Mistakes in an experimental project were inevitable and the important thing was that lessons learned should have been well learned. But while valuable experience was obtained, important points were not appreciated or were overlooked until the 1948 campaign was under way.

It was originally planned to follow the experimental larviciding program by two residual spray programs (1947-48 and 1948-49), an island-wide larviciding program (1948) and a season devoted to checking the results obtained (1949). In retrospect this was not realistic, for these reasons:

(a) The semisylvatic nature of *labranchiae* reduced the importance of residual spray work (the value of residual spraying, particularly after the first campaign, was, and remains, a controversial point).

(b) It was unlikely that eradication could have been obtained by one larviciding campaign alone.

(c) The tendency for *labranchiae* to persist at low densities (which were not always detected) during, and the year after, larviciding should have indicated the necessity of continuing observations for at least two years after the final larviciding program.

These points were recognized during the course of the campaign, and, as far as possible, the policy was changed accordingly, but in a project with a limited life and budget, the opportunity to make changes was restricted. The ideal policy often had to be rejected in the face of what was possible under the circumstances.

During the 1947-48 residual spray campaign, all man-built structures on the island were given a complete treatment with DDT at a rate of 2 grams per square meter. The work started in November and was completed by February 15, prior to the general initiation of the spring oviposition period of *labranchiae*. Assuming that the work was necessary to eradication, the campaign would appear to have been satisfactory, both in its timing and technique.

The design of the sectors and the training of larviciding personnel was carried out contemporaneously with the 1947-48 winter residual spraying campaign. The layout of the sectors may be criticized as follows:

(a) Although in a general way, the island subdivisions were based on watersheds, more use could and should have been made of this principle.

(b) Sectors were, in general, too large and later had to be reduced in size.

(c) Breeding-place numbering and boundary marking were not originally recognized as being necessary and standardization of these was not developed until after the general larviciding program was under way.

The 1948 larviciding campaign was apparently successful over a part of the island. Failure in the remaining areas is assumed to have been due, in part at least, to a complex of environmental and perhaps biological variations, as in general the eradication effort was equally distributed.

While the use of residual spraying was directed specifically against *labranchiae* and the initiation of the 1948 larviciding program was based on the estimated time of the first *labranchiae* spring ovipositions, it was not until early in 1949 that the policy of defining *labranchiae* as not just the principal but as the only objective was adopted. Should this differentiation have played a greater role during 1948? In the first place, it was believed that the inclusion of all anophelines in the eradication plan provided a valuable margin of safety. Also, in 1948 the difficulties of *labranchiae* eradication were not appreciated, and it appeared that the inclusion of all anophelines would not seriously complicate the problem and would make the results more significant. It is apparent from the later scouting returns that those zones in which *labranchiae* was found in 1948 were not the only ones in which *labranchiae* existed; the presence of other anophelines (and other mosquitoes) served as the only guide to the areas needing extra treatment, and it was necessary that some guide be used. If all species had not been included, the non-*labranchiae* anophelines would have been so abundant that they would have masked the presence of *labranchiae*, as apparently happened in 1949 and to a greater extent in 1950.

The winter of 1948-49 was used to revise the sectoring and breeding-place numbering and for the residual spraying of those areas of the island in which *labranchiae* had been found after August 1, 1948. Assuming the need for residual spraying, the policy of concentrating on areas which were considered dangerous would appear logical. In practice, however, it was impossible to say which zones contained *labranchiae*, and almost half of the zones subsequently found positive were not considered dangerous at the time the residual insecticide was applied. It would seem, therefore, that if residual spray work was considered essential, the original plan of treating the whole island should have been followed; if it was not essential, no work at all should have been done.

It was believed that the 1948 larviciding campaign had eliminated most of the *labranchiae*, and that the problem in 1949 would be to detect the survivors. The main emphasis, therefore, was placed on the scouting services. Because of the time needed to carry out the eradication treatment cycle, it was considered that the chance of eradication after August 1 was slight and that scouting after this date was also of limited value, but the difficulty of finding larvae at low densities was not realized. During the early months of the year, the *labranchiae* population would, in any event, have been normally low. In those areas, however, where the species still remained, the 1948 campaign had reduced it to very small numbers. In consequence, the return from the large scouting force employed during the early months of the year was very low. Instead of starting scouting in March, as was done, it might have been better to have started, for example, on April 15 in the lowlands and on June 1 in the mountains. This would have released a considerable sum of money for other purposes and would probably have made no practical difference in the results obtained. Postponing the start of scouting operations would not, however, have solved the problem of detecting the residual *labranchiae* early enough to ensure eradication. In view of this, four alternative lines of action appear to have been possible. They are:

(a) To have started larviciding in those zones in which *labranchiae* was found before, say, July 1, and after that date to carry out "prophylactic" larviciding in all other zones suspected of being positive.

(b) To have based larviciding on the scouting returns, but to have considered that all *labranchiae* infestation found in zones after July 1 could not be eradicated in 1949 and to have automatically continued eradication measures in these zones throughout 1950.

(c) To have continued island-wide larviciding as in 1948.

(d) The program as carried out (i. e., larviciding all *labranchiae* positive zones regardless of the date found, as well as a limited number of other areas which were considered dangerous).

Of these alternatives, the third now appears preferable, but was not considered possible at the time because of its cost.

ORGANIZATION

The ERLAAS decree (appendix 3) proved, on the whole, satisfactory. The Advisory Committee established by the decree was valuable, not only for consultation, but because of the active participation and collaboration of the agencies which were represented. A serious omission in the decree was, however, the failure to provide for certain tax exemptions such as import duties and the tax on petroleum products, which would have saved the organization hundreds of millions of lire.

The project obtained both advantages and disadvantages from its temporary nature and the fact that it was established as a separate entity and not as a part of an existing malaria control organization. It was seriously handicapped at the beginning because no permanent malaria control group was available from which key personnel could be drawn, and on the conclusion of operations there was no continuity of employment for the staff. However, as a new organization ERLAAS had complete freedom to organize and plan for the work at hand and was not limited by the rules and regulations which would have been associated with an established agency.

As a new organization, it was necessary for ERLAAS to find and train large numbers of both field and office personnel. Due to the widespread unemployment in Sardinia, there was an excess of available candidates, but not always of the caliber desired. The speed at which it was necessary to develop the organization accentuated this problem, and provides an argument in favor of carrying out projects of this nature in successive steps, as in Cyprus, rather than on an island-wide basis. The temporary nature of the work made it difficult to hold the better workers, as there was always a desire on their part to find permanent employment. This difficulty was met, in part at least, by extra pay and allowances.

Emphasis on training was extremely important, especially during the early part of the project. The amount and type of training varied considerably, depending on the worker category. The technique of larviciding, for example, was essentially simple, whereas scouting required a much longer period of training for efficiency. There were men available for such work as truck driving, ditching, warehousing and bookkeeping, but it required the time-consuming process of elimination to select the men who were satisfactory. It was more difficult and also more important to select the staff for the higher posts in the organization, and a great deal of inefficiency resulted in the early months while the weeding-out process was going on. This was unfortunately true not only in the case of field workers engaged in eradication activities, but also in such normal occupations as accounting. These early difficulties emphasized the importance of developing an efficient administrative staff.

The time limitations which existed, the necessity of developing the organization from the ground up, together with the problem of isolating and solving the many technical questions which arose, emphasized the need for trained scientific personnel. Insufficient numbers of persons of this category proved to be a constant handicap to the project. This lack was overcome to a certain extent by the use of consultants, whose visits varied in length from a few days up to several months. Although they proved extremely helpful, such visits could not take the place of additional full-time staff, the lack of which prevented investigational work on a number of important problems. A separate research laboratory, operating continuously from the beginning of the project, should have been established.

As for the organizational structure itself, a legitimate criticism of the early years was the failure to distinguish sufficiently between the functions of administration, in the policy-making sense, and "administrative services." In practice, this failure was reflected in the misplacement of the statistics, budget control and legal departments, which, instead of reporting directly to the Superintendent, formed a part of "administrative services." The statistics office furnished much of the evidence on which policy had to be made, and the budget control and legal departments were of direct interest in formulating future plans. By working only indirectly with the Superintendent's office, delays and misunderstandings arose which might have been avoided. A gradual improvement in this relationship was made, until by 1950 it was considered that an ideal arrangement had been developed. With this exception, the organization was generally satisfactory.

The Value of Residual Spraying

The original plans for the project were made in the belief that residual spraying was essential to eradication. By 1950 it was apparent that its value, as far as eradication was concerned, was debatable. The importance placed on residual spraying was due largely to the results obtained with DDT house spraying on the Italian mainland (Aitken, 1946; Soper et al., 1947b; Missiroli, 1947), where a high reduction in the larval populations of not only labranchiae but also of sacharovi, melanoon and messae was obtained. The amount of reduction of labranchiae larvae in Sardinia was, in general, disappointingly low, apparently because of the semisylvatic nature of the species.

In any event, it would appear that a high rate of kill would be necessary to make residual spraying economically justifiable as a tool in eradication. The problem does not lie in the initial reductions in population density, which are comparatively easy to bring about, but in eliminating the small residue once the first large reductions are obtained. A killing rate of 60 per cent would, for example, show considerable apparent results in the early stages of a campaign, but would be of slight value in the later stages of eradication when matched against the normal biotic potential of an indigenous species.

The funds and knowledge spent on house spraying might, therefore, have been more usefully employed on either increasing the efficiency and lengthening the period of larviciding or strengthening the scouting service. The inclusion of residual spraying, besides its cost and the time it consumed, had other disadvantages:

(a) it complicated the supply and administrative problem;
(b) workers had to be trained in two techniques instead of one;
(c) the value of adult scouting was reduced.

For these reasons, ERLAAS can be criticized for its lack of decision in this regard, particularly in 1949 and 1950. If residual spraying was an essential part of the eradication technique, it was not used to its full extent in these two years. If, on the other hand, the arguments against its use in eradication are valid, there was not much reason for the work which was done (particularly the sporadic treatment of the later years), except for public health and public relations.

ERADICATION TECHNIQUE

The main clearing and drainage effort should have been made in the spring of 1948 instead of the summer. Although a planned campaign of clearing and ditching was carried out, the sharp rise in anopheline collections experienced in June of that year demonstrated the need for further operations, with the result that much more work was done in the later months of the campaign than in the early months, when its effect would have been greater. The failure to determine the precise need for breeding-place preparation was one of the failures of the 1947 experimental campaign, and is probably the most obvious single reason for the amount of residual anophelism found in 1949.

It is argued that neither in Brazil nor in Egypt, nor in the eradication project in Cyprus, was any particular need shown for clearing and drainage. In fact, Professor G. Macdonald, after a visit to Sardinia in July 1950, wrote: " Some clearing may be necessary to reduce water area or to make breeding places visible to the workers, but it should not be necessary to remove vegetation in order to enable larvicide to make contact with the larvae. Trials and general experience else-where show that an effective larvicidal DDT solution in oil can be developed which will penetrate through vegetation by its own spreading power." (Macdonald, 1950a). He believed that " a moderate efficiency of 99 per cent or more destruction could be attained in all breeding places " without such clearing, and that this efficiency would be sufficient, provided that larviciding was continued over a period of, say, three or four months. " If emphasis on the importance of using a highly effective larvicide is kept in mind, it is possible to question the economic utility of some of the associated clearance. Some is very necessary; some reduces water area so greatly that it is an economy in itself, and some is necessary so that the worker can see the breeding place to be treated. With these qualifications, some of it could be greatly reduced. An effective DDT solution in a spreading oil will penetrate through vegetation by virtue of its own spreading pressure and will destroy larvae amidst the vegetation. In any continued eradication program I would therefore urge . . . the simplification of the eradication tech-nique by omission of much of the clearing and the prolongation of the period for which work is carried out."

The crux of this matter would appear to be whether " an efficiency of 99 per cent or more " could be obtained by the restricted type of clearing suggested by Professor Macdonald. In the experience of ERLAAS, it could not. In many breeding places the vegetation was so abundant and extensive that, even if the larviciders could have worked in them, very high appli-cations of insecticide as well as a great deal of time would have been required. Even then there would have been no assurance that complete coverage had been attained. The same conditions prevented efficient scouting. The more conspicuous examples of this type of vegetation existed in such large swamps as Uta (Cagliari), Mare Foghe (Oristano) and Colustrai (Muravera),

42. Squad scouting in the Cixerri River near Siliqua.

43. Collecting larvae from an examination plate.

44. Laboratory instruction of field personnel in mosquito identification.

45. Inspector giving instructions on the use of the " umbrella " in adult scouting.

46. Using an "umbrella" for adult scouting in a pigsty.

47. Searching for adult mosquitoes in a natural shelter in a stream bed.

but smaller breeding places with similar characteristics could
be found over the entire island. Even with less dense vegetation, however, satisfactory results could not always be obtained.
For example, in 1950, in the Codaruina swamp (Sassari),
various irrigation canals with a medium heavy vegetation were
deliberately left uncleared and were heavily treated twice
weekly, using shoulder pumps. After 17 weeks of such treatment the area was found still to harbor *labranchiae*, apparently
because of the failure to clear the vegetation. Border-line cases
certainly existed where vegetation was cut despite its being
sufficiently sparse to have allowed larvicide penetration and
expansion. It was difficult, however, to establish a standard
and the tendency to provide a margin of security led to doing
more than was necessary rather than taking a chance on doing
less.

There was a gradual increase in the rate of application of
larvicide from the beginning of the project. If the average rate
of application for September 1948 had been applied throughout the year, an increase in the *labranchiae*-free area would
probably have resulted. An increase in consumption to that
of either 1949 or 1950 would not, however, have been justified.
These high application rates were deliberately undertaken in
areas which had resisted the 1948 treatment, and would not
necessarily have been advisable for the island as a whole.

The radius of the eradication zones was theoretically three
kilometers, but in practice it was usually increased. Although
three kilometers may be considered low, there is little, if any,
practical evidence to indicate that *labranchiae* had a longer
flight range. There appeared to be, in general, a tendency for
the species to stay very near to those habitats in which it was
first located. There were, however, enough exceptions to this
to suggest the possibility of fall dispersal flights.

In both 1949 and 1950, the period of larviciding was undoubtedly too short. In 1949, the period of effective treatment
was even shorter, owing to the policy of carrying on clearing
and ditching simultaneously with larviciding, and this limited

treatment period appears to have been an important factor in the failure to attain eradication in many of the treatment zones that year. Even with the modifications adopted in 1950, the failure to achieve eradication in a higher percentage of the zones must have been due partially, at least, to the limited period of treatment. Other factors were the inefficiency of treatment and supervision, the inefficiency of the larvicide and the possibility that *labranchiae* possess certain survival characteristics of which we are not aware.

Scouting Technique

Although scouting has a number of obvious limitations, the methods used in finding larvae in Sardinia appeared in the long run to be effective. They were less so in the case of adult mosquitoes, which were fewer in number and had a greater opportunity to escape detection in their natural habitats. Both in 1949 and 1950, the scouts were apparently able to establish the location of most of the existing *labranchiae* infestations with a fair degree of accuracy. Two essential difficulties, however, affected the value of the scouting and in turn adversely affected eradication:

    (a) The difficulty in detecting the species when present in very low numbers, particularly in 1950 when the abundance of other anophelines tended to mask the presence of *labranchiae*.

    (b) The resulting delay in being able to declare a given area as either positive or negative.

These factors, as well as the relative values of adult and larval scouting, have already been discussed in previous chapters.

Altitude and Temperature

In Sardinia these factors are fairly closely related and may conveniently be considered together. Considerable variations of temperature may exist, however, both locally and at the same elevation in different parts of the island. For example, dry ravines which are protected from the wind and which have been stripped of trees and other vegetation are much hotter during the summer months than nearby forested river valleys. Even within a confined area differences occur, as between a sheltered damp cave and an open shed standing nearby. However, no attempt was made to record either microclimates or even the grosser changes between one valley and another, and all references to climate have been based on the available records from government stations.

Previous to ERLAAS operations, it is reasonable to suppose that *labranchiae* occupied the entire island and existed in most of the sectors which were subsequently established. It now appears that they were less firmly established in the higher and cooler areas than in the warm lowlands, as in the former the breeding season of the species was shorter and its densities were generally much lower. Figure 11 shows the deadlines established by the entomological service for the initiation of larviciding in 1948, based on an estimation of the first spring *labranchiae* ovipositions; a map showing the onset of overwintering would be similar in appearance and would show overwintering commencing in the highest areas first. This map illustrates in a general way, therefore, the variations in the length of the *labranchiae* breeding season. Table LI shows the decrease in *labranchiae* larval density with altitude.

It appears that shorter breeding periods and lower normal densities favor eradication. However, the shortness of the breeding season reduces the period in which larviciding can be undertaken; thus, for example, during the 1948 island-wide larviciding campaign some of the higher areas were treated for only 18 to 25 weeks, whereas lower areas received from 36 to 40 weeks of treatment. If the length of treatment is, as is believed, one of the most important factors in eradication, altitude would work against success in that the period of treatment decreases inversely with elevation. Table XLVI shows, however, that eradication measures were, in general, more successful in the higher than in the lower areas. It is not certain whether this was due to the indirect effects of altitude

TABLE XLVI

RELATIONSHIP BETWEEN ALTITUDE AND THE ERADICATION OF *Anopheles labranchiae*

Altitude in meters above sea level	Area			1949			1950		
	Number of sectors	Square kilometers	Per cent of total	Sectors positive	Per cent of total positive sectors	Per cent of sectors in given contour	Sectors positive	Per cent of total positive sectors	Per cent of sectors in given contour
0– 300	2,700	12,436	51.7	252	83.5	9.3	142	94.1	5.2
300– 500	1,233	5,680	23.6	33	10.9	2.7	8	5.3	0.6
500–1,000	1,172	5,400	22.4	17	5.6	1.4	1	0.6	0.1
1,000–1,500	117	540	2.2	0	0	0	0	0	0
Above 1,500	7	30	0.1	0	0	0	0	0	0
Total	5,229	24,086	100.0	302	100.0		151	100.0	

and temperature or to other factors. The question is further complicated by the fact that one of the most successful areas in 1948 was the Oristano division, which is both low and hot.

RAINFALL

Considerable differences in the total rainfall exist from one part of the island to another. It should be noted, however, that these differences are less pronounced during the summer. This is important, as it is the rain which falls during the breeding season (late spring, summer and early autumn) which has the greatest effect on eradication. In other words, both timing and quantity are important, and rains in June, which may be slight in comparison with those of December, may be much more significant. Timing must also be considered in relation to altitude, as March rains in Cagliari, on the southern coast where breeding starts early, are far more dangerous than similar rains in Desulo, one of the highest villages in Sardinia. Furthermore, both timing and quantity must be related to the relative permeability or runoff factor in a given locality, which depends not only on the soil, vegetation and slope but also on the saturation effects of previous rains.

Although the flooding which follows heavy rainstorms might be helpful in a control program, it is relatively unimportant as an aid to eradication. It is unlikely that 100 per cent kills result from such flooding, and at best no more effect would be obtained than that provided by an additional larviciding treatment. However, flooding may have an important adverse effect in carrying larvae from an infected to a cleared area.

NUMBER AND TYPE OF BREEDING PLACES

In order to study the effect of the number and type of breeding places present in a given area on the ease or difficulty of eradication, data were analyzed for 200 " eradication " zones, of which 100 had apparently been successfully " eradicated " in 1948, while the second 100 were positive in 1949 or 1950 or in both years. It was found that, in general, eradicated zones were "wetter" than noneradicated ones, and that the success of eradication was not directly associated with a relative scarcity of breeding places. The comparative figures are summarized in table XLVII.

TABLE XLVII

NUMBER AND TYPE OF BREEDING PLACES PER SQUARE KILOMETER IN
100 ZONES APPARENTLY ERADICATED IN 1948 COMPARED WITH
100 ZONES NOT ERADICATED

Type of breeding place	Median number of breeding-place units	
	100 zones not eradicated in 1948	100 zones apparently eradicated in 1948
Swamps	0.7	0.4
Rivers	6.5	9.9
Streams	5.7	10.3
Springs	0.8	3.9
Wells	2.5	2.5
Water holes	4.9	2.5

RELATIVE HUMIDITY

The effect of relative humidity on the longevity of anophelines is well known. It has been impossible, however, to find any direct correlation in Sardinia between the relative humidity of a given area and eradication. Wide variations in humidity do exist from place to place and from year to year, and it would appear reasonable to suppose that they have affected the ease or difficulty of eradication in the areas in question. For example, based on Freeborn's data for *maculipennis* in California (Freeborn, 1932), it was estimated that the survival time of *labranchiae* in 1948 in Olbia (northeastern noneradicated area) may have been approximately twice as long as that in Oristano (west-central eradicated area). It proved, however, impossible to work out any general correlation between eradication and humidity.

WIND

No data are available on the effect of wind on *labranchiae*. The winds in Sardinia are strong enough in some areas to prevent the growth of trees, and it is possible that this would have some effect on oviposition, feeding habits or the destruction of adult or larval life, and, therefore, on eradication.

Wind action had a pronounced influence on larviciding, both in increasing the difficulty of application and in rapidly breaking up the larvicide film. Strong winds greatly restricted the use which could be made of air-spraying, both as to the time of day and the location. Of the 200 eradication zones studied in 1950 to determine the reasons for success or failure to eradicate, 10 per cent of each category reported considerable difficulty due to wind action.

OTHER FACTORS

The ecological factors affecting *labranchiae* varied considerably from one part of the island to another, and many of these were changed by ERLAAS operations. It is not possible, however, either to evaluate the original factors or their modifications, or to say whether some of them helped or hindered eradication.

The more obvious changes in the environment, such as the drying up of areas by ditching, had the effect of entirely eliminating *labranchiae* and it is believed that other radical changes, such as those caused by cutting the vegetation from a swamp, hastened the destruction of the species which normally inhabited the area. The effect of reducing the numbers of other aquatic insects, animals and plants is, however, unknown.

The fact that *labranchiae* was found in 1949, 1950 and again in 1951 almost exclusively in the same areas and often in the same foci, even after repeated and intensive eradication measures, raises the question of what essential information, if any, was lacking in our knowledge of the species which prevented eradication. Why did the particular areas where the species was able to hold out provide the special conditions which favored survival? As none of the obvious factors such as humidity, temperature, type of habitat, distance to man-built structures and terrain were common to a significant number of these areas, it might be possible that the remaining *labranchiae* were a special strain which possessed some characteristic, such as a method of estivation, which has protected the species. The nature of strains is discussed in Trapido's article in appendix 2 and is suggested in a general way in a recent article by Senior White (1948). Even if strains exist, however, the difference in "strains" of scouts and larviciders was undoubtedly a more important factor.

Relation of Foci to Human Habitations

In 1949 the average distance of all *labranchiae* collections from village centers was about 4.1 kilometers, while in 1950 the distance had increased to 4.4 kilometers. In the 200 eradication zones studied, however, there appeared to be no indication of a significant correlation between the success of eradication and the number of buildings in the eradication zone.

Recommendations

While it is believed that eradication might have been accomplished by a continuation of "attrition" tactics over a period of years following the completion of the project in 1950, this is by no means certain. Also, with our present knowledge of *labranchiae* and of insecticides, it is not apparent that eradication could have been accomplished by other tactics during the life of ERLAAS. However, it is clear that the results which were obtained could have been accomplished at a lower cost, hence, more efficiently. If, therefore, the project was being repeated, several general rules would be followed:

(a) No residual spraying would be undertaken. (Opinion on this point was divided, but it was unanimously agreed that the value of residual spraying fell rapidly after the first island-wide treatment.)

(b) The existence of extremely low densities would be expected in the year following larviciding, and the inability to establish success or failure in that year would be recognized.

(c) Adequate provisions would be made for both biological and chemical investigations, including the establishment of a *labranchiae* colony, and routine chemical and biological tests on the larvicide.

(d) Larviciding would be started after larval habitats were first prepared for treatment by clearing and draining and would be extended over two seasons.

Discussion of an ideal program does not necessarily imply that it is the type of program which should have been adopted in 1946; previous eradication experience and the particular circumstances which existed in Italy after the war made it advisable to plan a short project. Based on the ERLAAS experience, however, and assuming that no emergency existed, the ideal program would be carried out over a longer period than that actually taken. As species eradication and agriculture have a common interest in water management, the ideal project might profitably be a combination of agriculture and eradication, and these two could form a basic part of a broad conservation and development plan. A joint drainage department would be established to lay out land improvement operations on a long-term basis; permanent, semipermanent and temporary ditching projects would be planned.

The first year of the project would be devoted to a start on obtaining the essential entomological data, to a general logistical survey of the island and basic planning for drainage. The project could be operated in stages and, at the end of this year, the size and number of the stages would be decided. There would be a number of advantages (as well as some disadvantages) in carrying out the project in stages:

(a) less capital, such as transport, would be required;

(b) a smaller organization would be employed which would have a longer tenure and could be more efficiently selected and trained;

(c) a longer period of operations would remove the sense of urgency and would provide more opportunity to profit by experience.

Assuming that the project was to be carried out in three stages (i. e., dividing the island into three areas), two complete larviciding campaigns in each area would be advisable, followed by patrol-type scouting for a minimum of two years after the discovery of the last positive. The two-year larviciding program in a given area should be completed before initiating the work in a new zone. This would mean that basic larviciding would take six years, which, together with the preliminary year of study and preparation, would mean a minimum life of nine years for the project.

GENERAL

While recommendation for an ideal project for Sardinia is based on the subdivision of the island into three areas, the number of such divisions, if any, in another country would depend on local circumstances. Working in stages has obvious disadvantages, such as the time in which key personnel are involved, the necessity of establishing barrier zones against the reinfestation of cleared areas, the difficulty in maintaining the high standards of efficiency which are required, and so forth.

While certain key scientific and administrative personnel are clearly indispensable, it should be kept in mind that it would be inefficient to use them where local people could be trained. A trained malariologist should not be required, for example, to act as supervisor of residual spraying operations, provided that he is available to train other personnel. However, the provision of training and supervision is likely to be a full-time occupation and arrangements would have to be made to provide personnel for research and investigation in addition to those required for administrative duties. A legitimate criticism of the ERLAAS campaign was that, due to the shortage of key personnel, an attempt was made to have these carry out both technical and administrative duties. Due to the pressure of the campaign, administration had to receive first priority to the detriment of investigations.

Another factor which would have to be considered in carrying out stage operations is that while supervisory personnel are fairly mobile, daily workers are not. Supervisors can be transferred from one part of a project to another, but laborers are usually not prepared to leave their homes for any considerable period of time unless they are paid exorbitantly high wages. It would not be possible, therefore, to count on moving the best workers from one part of an eradication project to another, and a campaign would have to be planned on the basis of placing reliance on local residents for most of the needed manpower.

Conclusion

From the evidence furnished by ERLAAS, the eradication of an indigenous anopheline, such as *labranchiae*, is a difficult and expensive proposition. In Sardinia, from the standpoint of malaria control, the residual spraying method would have been both cheaper and easier to operate. The use of eradication may, nevertheless, offer some advantages under certain special conditions, particularly when it is incorporated in a general conservation and development program, where part of the cost of eradication could be charged to rehabilitation. Aside from its application in malaria control, the technique as used in Sardinia, or some modification of it, may have a limited field of use against other insects in both the medical and agricultural fields, and it remains, therefore, as a potent though expensive possibility in any situation where man is engaged in raising living standards by the suppression or elimination of harmful insects. Eradication should be based on an accurate knowledge of the biology of the vector involved and provision should be made to utilize any equipment or method which seems advisable under the circumstances. The project should not be rigidly confined by time, finance or methods.

In preparing Sardinia for larvicidal treatment by clearing and draining, it has been estimated that over 30,000 hectares of land were reclaimed. Unfortunately, not all of this has been put to productive use, but as it was normally rich bottom land it is hoped that the excellent results obtained in those parts now being cultivated will encourage other landowners to do the same. The nature, extent and possibilities of this drained land were investigated by a special ERLAAS survey, carried out during the winter of 1949-50.

As ERLAAS operations were carried out in every part of the island, it was necessary to consider the island as a geographic whole, and this made it possible to examine Sardinia's potentialities in their proper perspective. From this consideration the extent of uncultivated and unused land, the sparseness of the population and the lack of knowledge concerning the island's social and economic resources were evident. With the pressure of excess population existing on the mainland, it seemed logical that a study should be made to examine the possibility of Sardinian development over a long-range period, with particular reference to its ability to absorb people from the continent. As ERLAAS made it possible, for the first time, to live and work in safety anywhere on the island, opportunities for development existed which had never before been present.

A social-economic survey of the island along lines suggested by Lord John Boyd-Orr was proposed to determine its problems and potentialities, the abilities, needs and desires of the people, and to chart a long-range plan for development. This principle was accepted by both the Regional and Federal Governments and the survey is now under way. ERLAAS has meant, therefore, more to Sardinia than just malaria control; it has been, in essence, a rehabilitation project. As such, much was accomplished that could not have been achieved by malaria control alone, and the additional expenditure represents, therefore, an investment in the future of the island.

THE ANOPHELINE FAUNA OF SARDINIA

T. H. G. Aitken

During the period 1946 to 1950, seven species of anophelines were identified in the Sardinian fauna. These were:

(1) *Anopheles labranchiae labranchiae* Falleroni, 1926

(2) *Anopheles melanoon melanoon* Hackett, 1935
   (Hackett and Missiroli, 1935)

(3) *Anopheles claviger* (Meigen), 1804.

(4) *Anopheles algeriensis* Theobald, 1903

(5) *Anopheles marteri* Senevet and Prunnelle, 1927

(6) *Anopheles plumbeus* Stephens, 1828

(7) *Anopheles hispaniola* (Theobald), 1903

All but the last three of these species had previously been reported from the island by various authors, including Missiroli (1927, *maculipennis* = *labranchiae* in all probability; *bifurcatus* = *claviger* and *algeriensis*) and Spanedda (1940, *melanoon*). These four species, and also *marteri*, were encountered during the entomological survey of 1946 prior to the start of ERLAAS operations. *Plumbeus* and *hispaniola* were not found until 1947.

Six other anophelines are reported in the literature on Sardinia, but intensive scouting over the five-year period 1946 to 1950 failed to confirm their presence. These species are: *A. sacharovi* Favr (Hackett, 1929 and Spanedda, 1940, as *elutus*), *messeae* Falleroni and *maculipennis maculipennis* Meigen (Hackett and Missiroli, 1935), *labranchiae atroparvus* (Spanedda, 1940), *hyrcanus pseudopictus* Grassi (Senevet, 1935) and *superpictus* Grassi (Missiroli, 1944). It is strange that these anophelines did not show up in the ERLAAS collections, especially as intensive search was made for them by literally thousands of scouts. Possibly the *superpictus* record refers to *hispaniola,* a very similar species. The *messeae* and *atroparvus* records were based on egg identifications and might well have been confused with aberrant forms of *labranchiae* or *melanoon.* There appears to be little doubt about the *sacharovi* records, as the eggs of this species are quite distinctive.

It is possible that the above species were present in small numbers in the island prior to ERLAAS activities and that they were quickly eliminated by eradication measures. All six have been encountered in Corsica in small numbers. Sardinia and Corsica are on the periphery of the distribution of these species, and it may well be that their position was so precarious that anti-anopheline measures caused their rapid disappearance.

What little has been published on Sardinian anophelines refers largely to *labranchiae.* In the twenties, Missiroli and Hackett studied this species (called *maculipennis* in their earlier papers) in connection with investigations on the control of malaria. This work started in 1925 in Portotorres and later was extended to include Oschiri, Olbia (Terranova), Siniscola, Posada and Torpè, all low-lying towns in the northern part of the island. Studies were conducted on the seasonal history of *labranchiae,* its flight habits and larval habitats (Missiroli, 1927, 1928 and 1930).

In the course of an epidemiological study of malaria in the two foothill villages of Loiri and Montelitu (near Olbia), Pampana and Casini (1940) made some interesting observations on the seasonal history of *labranchiae.* Attendant to the general study of the European *maculipennis* complex, observations were made in Sardinia by Hackett and Missiroli (1935). Identifications were made by the examination of eggs laid by captured females. *Labranchiae* was the dominant form in the few localities visited (198 ovipositions during 1932 and 1933). Other eggs identified belonged to the following species: *sacharovi* (four ovipositions), *messeae* (four ovipositions) and typical *maculipennis* (one oviposition). More recently Spanedda (1940), investigating the *maculipennis* complex in the southern portion of the island, found *labranchiae, sacharovi, atroparvus* and *melanoon.*

Maculipennis (*labranchiae*) was considered the only important vector of malaria in the island (Missiroli, 1927). *Sacharovi* had an extremely limited distribution (it was recorded from Portotorres, Siniscola and Porto Corallo near Villaputzu) and was **never** abundant; nevertheless, it may have been responsible for a certain amount of transmission (Spanedda, 1940; Putnam and Hackett, 1946). *Claviger* and *algeriensis* were both considered innocuous species, and little reference was made to them except that the adults rarely entered houses and that the larvae preferred shaded habitats and were most frequently encountered in the spring and fall months (Missiroli, 1927).

PRELIMINARY SURVEY (SUMMER OF 1946)

Prior to the initiation of eradication activities, a three-man team undertook an anopheline survey of the island during the summer of 1946. This investigation began on May 13, with Cagliari serving as a base of operations until June 27. Later, temporary headquarters were established in other towns to facilitate inspection of the surrounding countryside.

Because it was necessary to cover a large amount of territory in the three and one-half months, the custom usually was to make roadstops only; an attempt, nevertheless, was made to check all marshy areas indicated on the maps even if these were some distance from the road. Not every water collection was inspected, particularly if the same type of habitat was seen repeatedly within a short distance. On an average, 14 possible larval breeding places and three possible adult shelters were inspected every day.

Larval inspections received most attention because they offered opportunity for a more rapid and more selective survey in the limited time available. Not only were the immature stages of the various species found more frequently than adults, but there were extensive areas of the island where suitable man-made shelters for adult anophelines were few and far between or nonexistent. Of constant interest was the presence of anopheline eggs in natural habitats (Aitken, 1948). The fact that eggs were recovered from approximately 80 per cent of the positive foci was of great help in evaluating the findings, since larvae of the *maculipennis* group are difficult to identify.

Anophelines of the *maculipennis* group, consisting largely of *labranchiae*, were found in practically every part of the island. In the course of the survey, it seemed that almost every water collection harbored the immature stages of this species. It was found from sea level, in rock-pool seepages ten feet from the Mediterranean at Porto Ferro (the Nurra), to an altitude of 1,060 meters in the Ogliastra; larval densities at different altitudes are shown in table XLVIII. *Labranchiae* adults predominated in the collections from human dwellings and domestic animal shelters. Larvae of this species were not found in either of the large hydroelectric impoundments on the Tirso and Coghinas rivers, although the latter was a prolific source of *maculipennis* (*labranchiae*) at the time of its inception (Missiroli, 1928). Only a few of the small islands bordering the coast could be visited within the time allowed for the survey. Inspections of Sant'Antioco and San Pietro in the southwest confirmed the presence of *labranchiae*, although the species did not appear to be abundant. No anophelines were found in the island of Tavolara just east of Olbia.

TABLE XLVIII

DENSITY OF LARVAE OF *Anopheles labranchiae* AT VARIOUS ALTITUDES DURING 1946

Altitude (meters)	Number of collections	Number of dips	Average number of larvae per dip
0–99	171	898	7
100–199	62	318	8
200–299	64	292	10
300–399	57	259	9
400–499	48	270	4
500–599	31	142	8
600–699	35	147	11
700–799	11	63	5
800–899	13	55	3
900–999	4	18	1
1,000 and over	1	5	1
All altitudes	497	2,411	8

Note: Collections positive for eggs only are excluded, but pupae are included.

Claviger was widespread in the island but was never abundant in the collections. Had more inspections been made in springs, fountains and rivulets, the recovery rate for *claviger* would have been greater. About 20 per cent of all the inspections were made in these habitat types, but only 13 per cent were positive for the species. The question has been raised as to whether the data obtained in the survey were a true portrayal of the facts, particularly in the light of later experience which showed *claviger* to be very abundant. Possibly the many small larval habitats of *claviger* would balance or outnumber the larger and more extensive watercourse type of habitats characteristic of *labranchiae*. This is difficult to estimate. Nevertheless, it was quite evident that larval densities of *labranchiae* were much the greater of the two. On the basis of the number of larvae per dip, *labranchiae* larvae were three times as abundant as the shade-loving *claviger*; on only one occasion were larvae of the latter species taken at the rate of 50 per dip. Usually the number was very much less, whereas *labranchiae* was frequently found in such densities.

Of the remaining anophelines, *algeriensis* was widespread, but always at low altitudes. With the exception of one record from the north near Castel Sardo, all *melanoon* collections were made in the southern part of the island in the vicinity of Ales (Assolo and Curcuris), Muravera and Osteria (near Muravera). The few collections of *marteri* came from Domus de Maria, Cantoniera Genna Cassa (Seulo), Riu de Berissai (Seulo) and Punta Lacasse (Meana Sardo).

DISCUSSION OF THE VARIOUS SPECIES

The following pages deal largely with the biology, so far as it is known, of each of the Sardinian anopheline species. Included in the discussion are brief descriptions of the various life-cycle stages, based on Sardinian specimens unless otherwise indicated.

Anopheles labranchiae labranchiae FALLERONI

It was not possible to distinguish first instar larvae and pupae of this species from those of *melanoon*. This is likewise true of the adults, although differences may exist in the wing-scale structure (Ungureanu and Shute, 1947; Laven, 1950).

Egg: Broad and fat in appearance. Dorsal exochorion pale to dark gray with lateral darker cuneiform spots or with one to six irregular bands. Poles dark. Floats small, not extended onto dorsal surface, occupying less than 20 per cent of egg length and averaging about 14 ribs. Intercostal membrane rough, i. e., with transverse folds and secondary striations forming fine reticulum.

First instar larva: Subantennal hair asymmetrically pinnate.

Fourth instar larva: Frontal hairs with well-developed shaft, pinnately branched. Outer clypeal hairs multiply branched. Inner clypeal hairs apically branched. Antennal hair arising from basal fourth of antenna. Antipalmate hair of abdominal segments IV and V generally with two branches (Bates, 1939).

Pupa: Lateral hair of abdominal segment VIII short and multiply branched. Lateral hair of segment VII in form of blunt spine. Paddles with few minute serrations restricted to apical half of external edge and extending slightly beyond terminal hair.

Adult: Generally dark brown in color. Head with tuft of upright pale scales medianly and black scales laterally. Thorax with mesonotum having central pale stripe and dark lateral bands; tuft of pale hair-like scales on anterior margin of mesonotum. Wings with dark scales, forming four spots at junction of first and second veins, at forks of second and fourth veins and on the cross vein.

World distribution. *Labranchiae* is restricted to the western and central Mediterranean region. It occurs in a restricted area near the sea in the Spanish provinces of Murcia and Alicante (Hackett, 1949). It is the most frequently encountered anopheline in Morocco, where it is known as *sicaulti*. It has been found as far south as Foum Zguid and Tagounit on the edge of the Sahara Desert and from sea level up to 1,900 meters at Tizi n'Tchka in the Atlas Mountains. Elsewhere in North Africa, the species occurs along the coastal belt of Algeria and Tunisia (Gaud, Faure and Maurice, 1949). *Labranchiae* is known to inhabit the islands of Corsica, Sardinia and Sicily, as well as the Italian mainland where its distribution is restricted to the coastal area as far north as the Tuscan Maremma in the west and Foggia in the east (Missiroli, 1939).

Distribution in Sardinia. The 1946 survey disclosed the presence of *labranchiae* in practically every part of Sardinia, including the islands of Sant'Antioco and San Pietro. Subsequent observations confirmed this widespread distribution of the species in the lowlands as well as in the mountain areas. Collections were made in the wilder portions of the island where villages are few and far between and houses rare or nonexistent. *Labranchiae* was also reported from the island of Maddalena in the north and the island of Mal di Ventre, approximately nine kilometers from the western coast near Oristano.

Seasonal cycle—the late winter period. Labranchiae overwinters in the adult state, but it is incorrect to assume that the species hibernates, for many individuals take blood meals and thus remain in a semiactive condition. Observations in the Cagliari and Nuoro areas during 1947 pointed to an astonishingly high degree of activity on the part of overwintering females (figure 28). In January, 59 per cent of the females examined contained developing or mature ovaries. For the sake of brevity these two conditions have been combined in the graph, but actually 40 per cent of the females had mature ovaries during this month. This activity may not have been so pronounced earlier, for observations did not start until the middle of January and were restricted to the Cagliari area, where the mean outdoor temperature for the month was 8.4° C.

Upon further investigation it was found that this phenomenon was not confined entirely to lowland areas. In February, of 734 females collected in areas over 500 meters in elevation, 568 (77 per cent) contained active ovaries and 18 (3 per cent) of these were mature; an additional 77 (10 per cent) showed evidence of recent blood meals. While active females were thus present in the higher mountain areas, they were not so common as in the lowlands and lower temperatures undoubtedly retarded development from two to three weeks.

In general, pronounced ovarian activity is apparent in the early months of the year. It is a dynamic phenomenon, as evidenced by the relatively high oviposition rates obtained in the laboratory during these two months: 20 per cent in January and 35 per cent in February (figure 28). Ovipositions took place much sooner among females observed in the Cagliari laboratory at sea level than among those in the Nuoro laboratory situated in the interior highlands at an elevation of 553 meters. In January and February

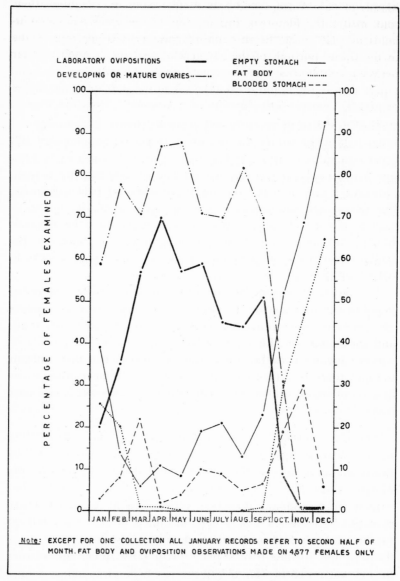

FIGURE 28. Abdominal condition of 8,501 female *Anopheles maculipennis* group (largely *labranchiae*) collected in Sardinia during 1947.

approximately 50 per cent of the Cagliari females deposited their eggs within the first two days of capture, whereas at Nuoro in February (no studies were made in January) 50 per cent of the ovipositions occurred during the second and third weeks. Lower temperatures in that area (5.7° C. mean for February as compared with 15° C. in the Cagliari laboratory) were undoubtedly responsible.

The incidence of recently fed females (figure 28) during the latter half of the winter was not great (3 per cent in January and 8 per cent in February). At first this seems to be contrary to what one would expect when the incidence of ovarian activity is high. However, it may be that blood meals are taken infrequently during this period and the digestive processes in general are slower. A high proportion of females feed, but they digest their blood meals slowly, and their ovaries mature accordingly. Judging by the Cagliari laboratory, an increase in temperature would appear to hasten the process.

The incidence of inactive, or empty, females (without ingested blood or developing ovaries) was not particularly great in January (38 per cent) but dropped rapidly in February (to 14 per cent) and even more in March (to 6 per cent). With the passing of winter, females with fat body also become increasingly difficult to find (figure 28). La Face (1933) observed similar manifestations of activity among *labranchiae* collected in the Agro Romano near Ardea.

The spring period. With the coming of spring, overwintering females become increasingly active. Oviposition is followed by death, as is evident from the small number of females found during March (figure 29). The incidence of recently fed females (but without active ovaries) increased during March (to 22 per cent) as might be expected (figure 28) but then unexpectedly fell off rapidly in April (to 2 per cent) and May (to 4 per cent). A slight drop in the incidence of females with developing and mature ovaries was noted in March (72 per cent) but was followed by a sharp rise in April (to 87 per cent) and May (to 88 per cent). This rise was also generally reflected in the rate of laboratory

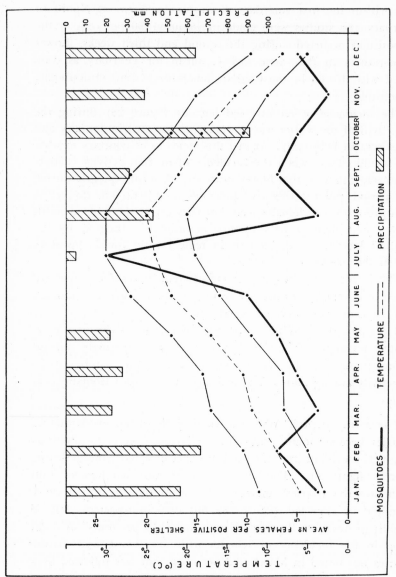

Figure 29. Densities of female *Anopheles maculipennis* group (largely *labranchiae*) in untreated shelters by months compared with mean precipitation and maximum, minimum and mean temperatures averaged for Cagliari, Nuoro and Sassari during 1947.

ovipositions (figure 28) during this period (57 per cent in March, 70 per cent in April and 57 per cent in May) ; a corresponding shortening of the gestation period was also noted.

During January and February careful search was made for the immature stages of *labranchiae*; approximately 6,000 dips were made in a variety of aquatic habitats in the Campidano, Trexenta, Cixerri Valley and the Baronia without finding a single immature stage. It was not until March 4 that the first larvae were found (18 first, one second and one third instar). All collections came from the southern portion of the island near Siliqua in the Cixerri Valley and the Palmas Valley in the Sulcis. On March 10 fourth instar larvae were collected in the southeast coastal area near Muravera. Midday water temperatures at this time varied between 11° C. and 17° C., averaging 16° C. Corradetti (1931) gives evidence that the developmental period (egg to adult) of *maculipennis* in the environs of Rome is the 45 days from March 1 to April 15, when water temperatures average 13.9° C. Using these figures as a guide, it can roughly be estimated that the first ovipositions of the season in southern Sardinia occurred during the first week of February.

Larvae, including fourth instars, were not encountered in the north (Baronia) until the end of March, suggesting that ovipositions in this area were about a month behind those in the southern portion of the island. On the other hand, in 1948 ovipositions were much earlier in the Baronia, being comparable to those further south in 1947. On February 6, 1948, first instar larvae were found at Torpè (Baronia), indicating egg-laying activity around the first of the month. On February 12, two fourth instars were found (water temperature 15° C.), and again on February 14, first, second and third instars were collected at Torpè, suggesting that the first ovipositions may have taken place even earlier, possibly during the third week of January. This activity may have been the result of unseasonably high temperatures in late January and early February.

In the higher reaches of the eastern central mountain mass, it would appear that first ovipositions generally occur about a month to a month and a half later than in the lowlands. These may even be delayed until early April. For instance, the first larvae (third instar) were found at Orgosolo (elevation 700 meters) on April 15, at Austis (elevation 737 meters) on April 16 (second, third and fourth instars), and on the Nuoro Plateau (elevation 560 meters) on April 21 (fourth instars).

With the advance of spring, there is an increase in the incidence of the immature stages of *labranchiae* and likewise in the density of these populations (figure 30). In March, 13 per cent of the habitats inspected were positive. By April this figure had jumped to 29 per cent, and by May 54 per cent were positive.

The summer period. The peak of adult densities generally occurred in June or early July, depending on temperatures and other meteorological conditions. In 1947 maximum densities (averaging 24 adults per positive station) were observed during July (figure 29). Pampana and Casini (1940) reported a peak in adult captures during the first week of June, followed by a rapid decline in numbers early in July and remaining low during August. The curves plotted by Missiroli (1927, 1928 and 1930) for Portotorres show the peak usually occurring during the last two weeks of June; July also was a fairly high month, but by August adult densities were reduced to very low figures. A similar trend was noted by the same author in other Sardinian towns (Oschiri, Olbia and Siniscola).

This decline, which may occur in either July or August, appears to be a reflection of high temperatures and saturation deficiencies. It has been studied by Freeborn (1932), who worked with a California member of the *maculipennis* complex (*Anopheles freeborni*).

During the summer of 1947 the incidence of females with developing and mature ovaries dropped somewhat in June (to 71 per cent) and July (to 70 per cent) but was followed by a secondary rise in August (to 82 per cent). Laboratory ovipositions demonstrated a corresponding fluctuation (figure 28).

Larval densities continued to increase throughout the 1947 summer period (figure 30), corroborating the findings on adults. The larval counts did not, however, reflect the August decline in adults, suggesting that the majority of the females were living only long enough to obtain a blood meal and oviposit.

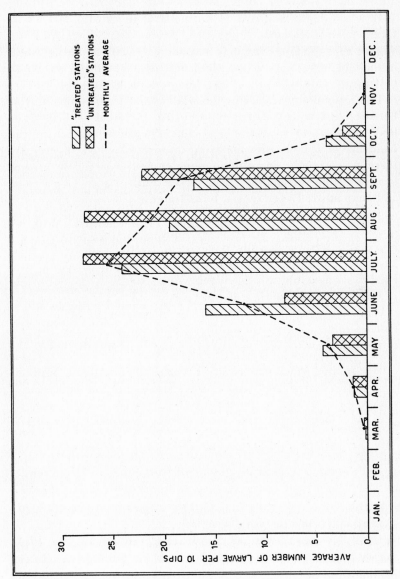

FIGURE 30. Monthly larval densities of Sardinian *Anopheles maculipennis* group (largely *labranchiae*) close to and distant from DDT residually sprayed structures during 1947.

The fall and early winter period. With the cooler fall temperatures, there is a brief resurgence of *labranchiae* activities. During 1947 adult densities increased during September, dropped off in October and November, but rose again slightly in December (figure 29); the latter rise may be caused by females concentrating in shelters preparatory to overwintering. Such a tendency was noted by Pampana and Casini and to a lesser extent by Missiroli.

The September increase in the adult population would seem to be correlated with a higher reproductive potential as a result of lower temperatures. While a decline during September in the incidence of females with maturing ovaries was noted (figure 28), there was a slight increase in females with completely mature ovaries during this month (July, 17 per cent; August, 15 per cent; and September, 17 per cent). In addition, a temporary rise in the oviposition rate (to 51 per cent) was noted in September. Subsequently, ovipositions dropped off rapidly in October (to 9 per cent) and were practically nonexistent by the end of the year. In October the average gestation period of Nuoro females lengthened to six days, but this slowing down in activity was not noticeable in Cagliari females until a month later.

With the general fall drop in the number of sexually active females came a corresponding increase in the numbers of inactive forms, which with the approach of winter completely dominated the mosquito population. The incidence of females that had taken recent blood meals rose sharply in October and November, but dropped to almost zero by December. This increased feeding activity at first glance appears incongruous in conjunction with decreased ovarian and oviposition rates, but, as suggested by La Face (1931), it would seem that the mosquito utilizes blood meals taken during this period to develop fat body which tides it over the winter. Fat body was first noted in a specimen collected September 23 from the mountain area near Bitti (elevation 400 meters); ten days later it was observed in lowland females from the Campidano near Samassi. The incidence of fat body rose sharply in October (to 31 per cent) and by December had reached 65 per cent. Sexually inactive females taking blood meals in the late fall suggests the phenomenon of gonotrophic dissociation as observed in *atroparvus* by Dutch workers. If the Sardinian *labranchiae* does undergo such a phenomenon it would appear to do so for a short time only (possibly two months) because sexual activity was renewed at least by the middle of January.

What is the fate of the final larval populations of the season? Pampana and Casini noted a secondary rise in larval densities during September, but their observations terminated at the end of the month. Missiroli (1928) mentions that following the cessation of Paris green larviciding on September 30, first instar larvae may appear during the first week of October. A few of these may develop into second instars, but only under very exceptional conditions will any mature to the adult state. During 1947 the sharp August drop noted by Pampana and Casini was not discerned. Instead, larval densities remained fairly high through September (figure 30), then fell off sharply in October; by the end of November larvae had disappeared completely.

Field observations on immature stages in October and November are summarized in table XLIX. It will be seen that egg laying was still occurring as late as the fourth week in October; one collection of eggs was made during the week in question, and two collections of second instar larvae came two weeks later from both the northern and southern portions of the island. In general, however, ovipositions fell off sharply after the first week of the month, and larvae became increasingly difficult to find. A few adults emerge even in late November, but only in very small numbers.

Larval habitats. Water courses were found to be the principal larval habitat of *labranchiae* during the 1946 survey. This observation was amply confirmed in subsequent years (figure 31). This type of habitat did not assume any degree of importance, however, much before late April or early May. Prior to this, streams were generally flowing too swiftly, and low temperatures were not conducive to a rapid development of vegetation in deeper waters. On the other hand, the winter and spring rains created many shallow ground pools which generally had a short existence. Some of these were very large and have been classified as swamps; nevertheless, they were shallow and their waters were readily warmed by the weak rays of the vernal sun. Vegetation consisting of short, fresh meadow grass and water buttercup (*Ranunculus aquatilis*) developed rapidly in such places and provided an ideal environment for the first two larval generations.

TABLE XLIX

INSPECTIONS FOR IMMATURE STAGES OF Anopheles maculipennis (LARGELY labranchiae) IN SARDINIA DURING OCTOBER AND NOVEMBER, 1947

Week	Number of foci visited	Foci positive		Number of dips	Number of foci positive by stage					
		Number	Per cent		Egg	1st instar	2nd instar	3rd instar	4th instar	Pupa
9–29 to 10–5	68	44	65	1,088	20	26	33	34	33	11
10–6 to 10–12	62	28	45	1,321	1	9	18	23	17	5
10–13 to 10–19	56	14	25	2,041	0	1	4	9	11	1
10–20 to 10–26	68	11	16	3,723	1	2	5	8	8	2
10–27 to 11–2	30	8	27	2,231	0	0	6	6	7	2
Total for October	284	105	37	10,404	22	38	66	80	76	21
11–3 to 11–9	62	5	8	1,629	0	0	2*	1	3	2
11–10 to 11–16	34	3	9	735	0	0	0	2	3	0
11–17 to 11–23	38	4	11	1,012	0	0	0	0	4	0
11–24 to 11–30	42	1	2	1,263	0	0	0	0	0	1
Total for November	176	13	7	4,639	0	0	2	3	10	3

* Posada 11-3-47 and Senorbi 11-5-47.

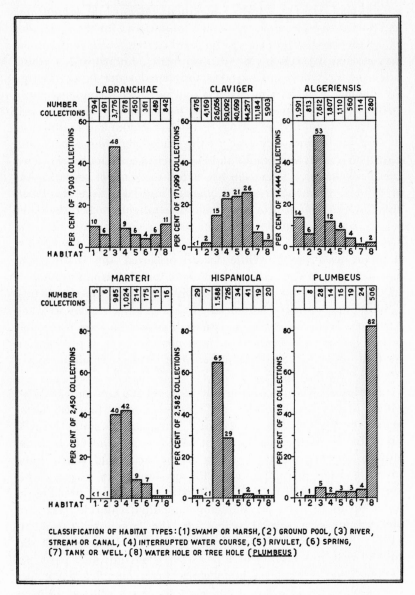

FIGURE 31. Percentage of total collections of each Sardinian anopheline found in various types of aquatic habitats during the period 1946-50.

By mid-April the drying-up process had begun, and by June ground pools were practically nonexistent. Meanwhile, *labranchiae* had started to leave these temporary habitats and for the remainder of the season selected principally water courses which had become slow-moving or stagnant or, in many cases, interrupted, forming what are for tabulation purposes considered water holes. During the summer months, tiny rivulets flowing from springs became a fairly important *labranchiae* habitat, particularly if they were well exposed to the sun. The springs themselves seldom harbored larvae, presumably because they were usually shaded and their waters cold. Earth- or cement-lined tanks and even wells occasionally supported larval development if the sun had access to them for several hours of the day. Permanent swamps, marshes and lakes were also favorable for *labranchiae*, providing sufficient sunlight reached the water surface and horizontal vegetation had an opportunity to grow. *Labranchiae* also developed readily in the rice fields of the Arborea Bonification Project. While larvae preferred the ditches and exposed edges of the paddies, a few were found during midsummer in the centers of the fields completely shaded by the rice plants.

While the Sardinian *labranchiae* has been successful in adapting itself to a wide variety of aquatic habitats, it appears to exhibit certain preferences. Perhaps the most noteworthy is its predilection for fresh water. In Sardinia, *labranchiae* larvae were almost never found in brackish waters.

Contrary findings in continental Italy, by Hackett and Missiroli (1935, p. 74), indicate that the species prefers "brackish water marshes and lagoons along the coast." These authors state, however, that "In the southernmost part of its range, *labranchiae* is found also in the interior fresh waters as in Sicily and south Italy, where it is not in competition with any other race except *elutus* (*sacharovi*)." Further (p. 75), "In nature it is found breeding in water up to 10 parts per thousand of sodium chloride (Hackett, observations over several years). In the laboratory Corradetti (1934) found that *labranchiae, atroparvus* and *messeae* all did equally well at a salinity of 3 parts per thousand; at 5 parts per thousand the percentages of imagines were: *labranchiae*, 68 per cent, *atroparvus*, 45 per cent and *messeae*, 35 per cent; at 10 parts per thousand *messeae* were all dead on the second day, 28 per cent of *atroparvus* and 70 per cent of *labranchiae* were bred out. *Labranchiae* larvae will, however, develop perfectly well in fresh water in the laboratory." Elsewhere Hackett (1949, p. 794) says, " On the islands of Corsica, Sardinia and Sicily, and along the Barbary Coast of North Africa from Tripolitania to Morocco, where it has no fresh-water competitors such as *A. messeae* or *A. melanoon*, *A. labranchiae* breeds in fresh and saline waters alike, and in both rivers and marshes." It is safe to say that during the five years of work in Sardinia, over 99 per cent of the *labranchiae* collections were made in fresh water.

Labranchiae larvae were generally found in clear, still, sunny waters containing horizontal vegetation in the form of algae, *Ranunculus, Chara, Myriophyllum, Ceratophyllum* or *Potamogeton.* Vertical vegetation was tolerated, if not too dense. While larvae usually inhabited still waters, considerable numbers were encountered in slowly moving streams and on occasion in rapidly running water. Observations made during 1947 on the characteristics of the aquatic environment of *labranchiae* are summarized in figure 32.

Water temperatures for March through November of 1947 were taken in 1,061 *labranchiae* habitats. The mean temperature was 24° C. (S.D. ± 4.72). Average mountain water temperatures tended to be slightly lower than those in the lowlands, although they became high during the hot summer months. The average water temperatures of *labranchiae* habitats recorded during this study were similar to those observed during the survey of 1946. During that year 70 per cent of the breeding places registered temperatures between 20° C. and 28° C., the over-all average being 23° C. It is obvious from these observations, as well as from those mentioned previously regarding illumination, that *labranchiae* is predominantly a heliophilous species. Maximum larval development occurs in the higher average temperature bracket (23° C. to 25° C.), with maximum temperatures about 36° C.

Species association. *Labranchiae* was not commonly found occupying the same aquatic habitat with other anopheline species, only 4 per cent of all collections being mixed. These mixed collections are summarized in table L. It will be seen that *labranchiae*'s most frequent associations were with *algeriensis* and *claviger*. Both of these species preferred well-shaded habitats char-

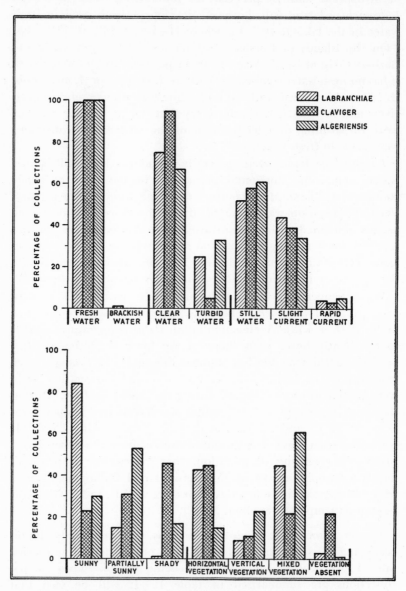

FIGURE 32. Characteristics of aquatic habitats of *Anopheles labranchiae,*
A. claviger and *A. algeriensis* in Sardinia during 1947.

48. The use of the smoke method in searching for adult mosquitoes in a well.

49. Searching for adult *labranchiae* in prehistoric rock tombs, *domus de janas*.

50. Searching for adult *labranchiae* in *nuraghi*.

51. ERLAAS motorcycle patrol checking on truck itinerary.

52. Motor vehicles awaiting overhauling in Cagliari depot.

53. Transporting larvicide by oxcart to district headquarters.

54. Pack donkey being used for transporting larvicide and equipment
in hilly country.

TABLE L

Mixed larval collections of *Anopheles maculipennis* (largely *labranchiae*)
by habitat type, Sardinia, 1946 to 1950

Habitat type	Number of mixed collections							
	M-C	M-C-A	M-A	M-A-H	M-H	M-Ma	M-Me	Total
Lake and swamp	7	0	20	2	0	0	0	29
Ground pool	5	0	10	0	0	0	0	15
River, stream and canal	43	7	81	1	10	2	8	152
Interrupted water course	10	1	20	0	1	1	0	33
Rivulet	19	0	9	0	0	0	0	28
Spring and fountain	9	0	0	0	0	0	0	9
Tank and well	3	0	4	0	0	0	0	7
Water hole	18	0	13	0	2	0	3	36
Total	114	8	157	3	13	3	11	309

Note: M = *maculipennis* (largely *labranchiae*), C = *claviger*, A = *algeriensis*,
H = *hispaniola*, Ma = *marteri* and Me = *melanoon*.

acterized by cool waters; *marteri* was also a cool water species. *Hispaniola*, on the other hand, exhibited preferences more closely resembling those of *labranchiae*. Its larvae were collected in shallow flowing water of gravelly stream beds, around stones and in mats of spirogyra. *Labranchiae* was also found abundantly in such algal mats. In spite of this similarity in choice of habitat, the number of mixed collections of the two species was small, possibly because *labranchiae* was a more aggressive species and dominated the habitat. Certainly the small numbers of *melanoon* collected during the five-year period, and always associated with *labranchiae*, indicate that this particular species provided little competition. Unfortunately, the figures cited do not portray the situation very accurately, as they were influenced by eradication operations.

Adult resting places. The principal known shelters of *labranchiae* adults have been pigsties, stables and houses; these shelters harbored 78 per cent of the 11,101 mosquitoes collected during this period.

In order to obtain a more accurate idea of shelter preference, the 1947 collections made in untreated shelters have been summarized in table LI. On the basis of percentage of shelter positivity, *nuraghi* were the most common diurnal resting places of female *labranchiae*. Because of the relatively small number of visits to these structures, the significance of *nuraghi* as preferred resting places must be discounted. Pigsties and stables, on the other hand, were important sources of mosquitoes, as shown by the relatively high average number of mosquitoes per positive shelter. Houses did not show up so favorably when the number of inspections was

TABLE LI

INCIDENCE AND DENSITY OF 4,494 ADULT FEMALE AND 551 ADULT MALE
Anopheles maculipennis (LARGELY *labranchiae*) IN UNTREATED
SARDINIAN SHELTERS DURING 1947

Type of shelter	Number of shelters inspected	Adult female *A. maculipennis*			Adult male *A. maculipennis*		
		Shelters positive		Number of mosquitoes collected	Shelters positive		Number of mosquitoes collected
		Number	Per cent		Number	Per cent	
House	3,485	214	6	977	18	0.5	32
Stable	818	185	23	1,481	13	1.6	33
Pigsty	479	115	24	1,029	4	0.8	9
Shed	426	37	9	355	4	0.9	34
Hen house	315	28	9	79	5	1.5	7
Bridge	300	60	20	367	49	16.3	386
Grotto	147	31	21	137	15	10.2	50
Nuraghe	65	22	34	65	0	0.0	0
Church	6	1	17	2	0	0.0	0
Rabbit hutch	6	1	17	2	0	0.0	0
All types	6,047	694	11	4,494	108	1.8	551

Notes: 1) All inspections were made in areas not affected by antilarval operations.
2) The first male was collected on March 24 and the last on November 25.

taken into consideration. This can be explained by the fact that many of the inspections were made early in the year, before residual spraying operations had started, but when the incidence of mosquitoes in such structures was low; at that season more mosquitoes were found in animal shelters than in houses.

The relatively high incidence of mosquitoes in grottoes and under bridges is significant as it indicates that a good portion of the *labranchiae* population was capable of living away from immediate contact with man. These structures were the principal source of the male mosquito collections. Such collections were most abundant during the summer and fall months. Included in the category of grottoes were overhanging banks along streams, rock fissures, undersides of boulders in stream beds, caves, and mine shafts or galleries.

Inspections early in 1947 made it clear that overwintering *labranchiae* were not abundant in village centers. On the contrary, *labranchiae* was more commonly encountered in isolated rural houses. It is reasonable to suppose that in rural areas many mosquitoes preparing to overwinter were attracted to isolated houses, whereas the mosquito population drawn to a village scattered among the greater number of houses.

During 1947 the relative incidence and abundance of *labranchiae* in inhabited and uninhabited shelters were recorded. Although only one-fourth of the inspections were made in uninhabited shelters, this was enough to get some idea of shelter preference. Interestingly enough, it turned out to be about the same for the two types of shelters. Eleven per cent of the inhabited shelters were positive and 12 per cent of the uninhabited; over-all mosquito densities were also about the same.

Feeding habits. While *labranchiae* feeds on a variety of hosts, man is one of the most common. Van Thiel (1938) considered the species anthropophilic. Hackett (1937, p. 58) states, " In southern Italy and Sardinia, where *labranchiae* prevails, from 10 to 20 per cent live on human blood, while in Greek Macedonia every third *elutus* (*sacharovi*) captured will have been biting a man." And again (p. 65), " We know that *typicus* (*maculipennis s. s.*), *melanoon* and *messeae* are deviated by stabled animals to a far greater extent than *elutus* (*sacharovi*) or *labranchiae*, and that *atroparvus* comes somewhere between. We do not yet know of any region in which *elutus* (*sacharovi*) or *labranchiae* are not associated with an intense malaria. These two forms, so much alike in instinct and physiology, persistently try to enter bedrooms even in the presence of an abundance of animal blood. They wander back and forth between house and stable biting man and cattle indifferently."

In Sardinia, precipitin tests were not run on *labranchiae*, yet from the large numbers of adults collected in domestic shelters and the high incidence of malaria, it was evident that the species frequently fed on humans.

While the resting place of the female is not necessarily the location where it obtained its blood meal, it is believed that a high proportion of Sardinian *labranchiae* fed on domestic animals (largely pigs, horses and oxen). This appeared to be particularly true in the winter. At that time *labranchiae* was rarely found in houses but recently fed females were frequently encountered in animal shelters. Mention has been made previously of the great amount of activity noted among overwintering females during January and February (activity in the sense that they were feeding and showing signs of a high degree of ovarian development).

Not all Sardinian *labranchiae* were so closely associated with the shelters of man and his domestic animals. *Labranchiae* was widespread over many areas of the island which were completely uninhabited except for occasional shepherds leading nomadic lives with their flocks of sheep, pigs or goats in the mountain areas. Contact with such animals could only have been sporadic, and *labranchiae* must have maintained itself on blood from other sources; the logical alternative was the wild mammalian population. Certain birds likewise may have acted as suitable hosts. Furthermore, it is not too much to suppose that at times the species was capable of tiding itself over periods of famine by feeding on plant juices. While the reproductive potential may have been reduced under such conditions, the species could survive.

Flight activities. Marking experiments conducted at Portotorres and Oschiri (Missiroli, 1927) indicated that *labranchiae* is capable of flying a distance of three to three and one-half kilometers. Under very favorable circumstances in June or July, the species proved able to invade a protected area about six and one-half kilometers away. A radius of three kilometers, however, was considered adequate for establishing a control zone.

It has been suggested that longer flights may occur in the fall, but little information is available regarding the phenomenon. Although Missiroli (1927) stated that fall flights or invasions were not noted in Portotorres, Hackett (1929) subsequently called attention to movements which filled the Portotorres catching stations with mosquitoes in October and November. Missiroli (1930) summarized adult captures at Portotorres and Oschiri for the period 1925 through 1929, and while the records do not show any noteworthy increase in adults at Portotorres during the fall, an increase did occur at Oschiri. Presumably these mosquitoes came from some distance, as the three-kilometer area immediately surrounding both towns had been subjected to larviciding operations until the first of October. Pampana and Casini (1940) also reported a fall rise in adult captures at Loiri, but in their case no anti-anopheline measures had been in progress and no attempt was made to distinguish local from invading individuals.

In the cold season the females which were active apparently either restricted their movements to the shelter in which they were passing the winter or else made short flights to nearby shelters. This type of activity was evident from a study made of several farms near Uta, in the vicinity of Cagliari. Weekly inspections (with flashlights) of four farms commenced the third week of January. It was soon obvious that in spite of careful searching, all the mosquitoes were not discovered; subsequent visits produced additional females which must have hidden themselves away between roof tiles and in other inaccessible places. Following the inspection in the fourth week, two of the farms were completely sprayed by means of a pyrethrum-freon aerosol bomb in order to destroy any remaining mosquitoes. No further mosquitoes were found for five weeks in one farm and seven weeks in the other.

Meanwhile, small numbers of mosquitoes continued to be found in the other two farms. It was concluded that while a considerable amount of flying and feeding activity went on during the winter months within the farm centers themselves, there was no anopheline movement between farms. The subsequent reappearance of females at the two sprayed farms during the weeks of March 24 and April 7 meant that a new generation had developed.

During the latter half of July 1947, observations for five nights were made on the nocturnal flying activities of *labranchiae* in three different localities. One of these was in the Campidano Plain at Serramanna (near a swamp), one in the Arborea Bonification Project and the third was in the almost completely uninhabited

Picocca Valley in the Sarrabus Mountains east of Cagliari. Collections were made under bed nets using human bait and a kerosene pressure lamp as attractors. The results of these studies are summarized in figure 33.

Sylvatic nature. The only possible explanation for the widespread distribution of *labranchiae* in the island, prior to eradication activities, is that a portion of the population was capable of surviving for varying periods without close contact with man. Collections of sylvatic mosquitoes were not confined to the summer season but were obtained at various times of the year.

An examination of the adult collections made under sylvatic conditions in 1947 and 1948 showed that most were females with no signs of recent feeding or ovarian activity, hence some may have been newly emerged. On the other hand, a fair number of collections (about 20 per cent) were made from late November to early February, at a time when the species was not breeding but overwintering. During the summer months, active females were found in abandoned mine shafts in rock crevices along the Tirso River, in ancient burial caves and under bridges; these females showed every sign of recent feeding (blood, developing and mature ovaries). *Labranchiae* was at one time found throughout a 45-kilometer uninhabited tract of the upper Flumendosa River. Immature stages, including eggs, were abundant everywhere and during the one night observers spent in the heart of the area, *labranchiae* females attacked in numbers.

During 1949 the average distance of all *labranchiae* collections (both adult and aquatic stages) from village centers was about four kilometers, with maximum distances as high as 11 and 12 kilometers. In 1950, after two years of intensive eradication operations, the average distance had increased to about four and one-half kilometers, but the maximum distances remained the same as the previous year. While some isolated rural houses may have been closer, they were the exception to the rule, except possibly in the northern part of the island (Gallura) where many isolated farm houses known as *stazzi* are scattered through the countryside. Even if the *labranchiae* collections from the Gallura are excluded, the averages do not change much.

During 1947 observations were made to determine the effect DDT

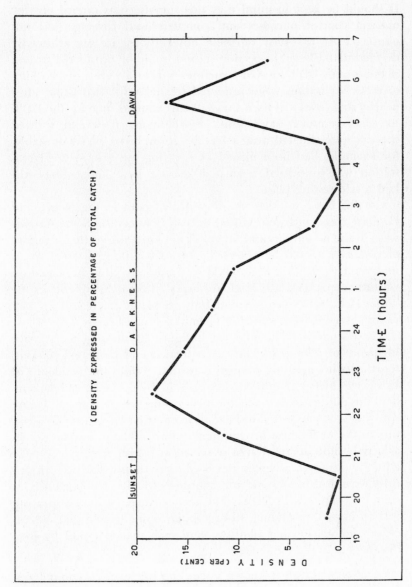

FIGURE 33. Nocturnal flight activity of female *Anopheles maculipennis* group (largely *labranchiae*) based on five nights' collections in Sardinia during July 1947.

residual spraying would have on the *labranchiae* larval population. It should be kept in mind that this spraying was carried out for malaria control purposes and complete wall coverage was not planned. At the start of these observations, it was arbitrarily decided that a larval inspection station would be considered treated if there were DDT-sprayed structures within a radius of two kilometers. No station was considered treated until two weeks after nearby structures had been sprayed; this allowed time for the DDT to affect residual anophelism. Furthermore, if several sprayed shelters were situated near a larval station, but a pigsty or stable, for example, had been missed in spraying operations, the larval station was considered untreated because local anophelines still had a safe resting place.

On this basis, stations were established both in the Nuoro and Cagliari areas, and were visited at weekly intervals. Some stations were in the mountains and others in the lowlands, so that a variety of conditions could be observed. Treated stations reverted to an untreated status after an interval of six months; this was based on wartime experience at Castel Volturno (Aitken, 1946) and in the Tiber Delta area of continental Italy (Soper *et al.*, 1947b), as well as on observed adult densities in locally sprayed houses.

These studies are summarized in figure 30, showing the relative incidence of *labranchiae* larvae in treated and untreated stations, together with monthly average densities. While the incidence of larvae was higher in untreated stations in July, August and September, the difference between the two groups was not great. House spraying alone appeared to have little effect on larval development, unlike the experience in continental Italy. There, farmhouses in a heavily built-up rural area provided attractive resting places for adult mosquitoes, whereas the Sardinian countryside was practically devoid of houses and the mosquitoes had less opportunity to come in contact with DDT. The ineffectiveness of house spraying was an important finding, since popular opinion held that *labranchiae*'s house-haunting affinities were such that it would fly long distances to find these shelters.

Longevity. Little is known about the life span of *labranchiae*. In the case of males, it is undoubtedly fairly brief, possibly a few weeks to a month in duration. This is sufficient time, however, for race propagation purposes, as once a female is fertilized she remains fertile for life. Only the females overwinter, and in the cold season their life span may encompass about four to six months. Hill (1937) reports the closely related Portuguese *atroparvus* as having an overwintering life span of at least six months. During the breeding season, the life span gradually decreases with the rise in temperature and the lower relative humidity of the air.

The life expectancy of the average *labranchiae* female under natural Sardinian conditions in the spring and early summer and in the fall is perhaps 30 days or more, but during July and August it is probably reduced to about a week. Hill (1937) states that of 150 newly emerged *atroparvus* females released in a mosquito house early in May, the last one died late in June after an existence of 44 days. Again at the end of June, 200 newly emerged females were released in the mosquito house, and the last one died 37 days afterward. Hill points out, however, that there was a high initial mortality, following which the curve flattened out.

Shute (1936) offers some interesting observations on laboratory strains of the British *atroparvus*. When kept at a constant temperature of 75° F. (24° C.) the species could live for at least two and a half months (82 days) and was capable of laying more than 2,500 fertile eggs. Under the conditions of the experiment, some females oviposited as many as 17 times. The highest eclosion rates occurred during the January to April period, the next highest in the May to July period and the lowest during the September to November period.

Swarming of males. Little information is available on this subject. During the summer of 1947 two males were seen dancing in the swarming fashion at sunset. The observations were made in a stream bed where the males were darting back and forth over a clump of bushes. Bates and Hackett (1939) reported *labranchiae* males swarming readily in small cages (one meter high by 50 centimeters wide), but only if a blue light with an intensity of almost three-foot candles (at a distance of 30 centimeters) was placed on top of the cage.

Laboratory colonization. No attempt was made to colonize the Sardinian *labranchiae*. This was perhaps unfortunate, for a study of laboratory strains could have provided additional facts pertinent to the biology of the species as well as to its reaction to insecticides under controlled conditions. Laboratory colonies are apparently not readily established; *labranchiae* males will not mate in captivity except under proper stimulus. This obstacle was overcome in the Albanian studies of Bates and Hackett (1939) by using the blue light described above (see also Bates, 1941a and b). Etherington (1944) was successful in obtaining viable eggs from laboratory-reared adults kept in a wire-mesh cage (47 × 47 × 60 centimeters) ; these adults were not exposed to artificial light and swarming of the males was not observed.

Relation to malaria. During the early nineteen thirties when the Malaria Experiment Station, under the direction of Professor Missiroli, was conducting investigations in the northern part of the island, dissections of *labranchiae* were undertaken on a number of occasions at Torpè and Posada (Missiroli and Marino, 1934; Mosna, 1934; and Mosna and Canalis, 1937). The mosquito infectivity index under normal conditions apparently ranged between 1.5 and 2.0 per cent.

During 1947, ten dissections of *labranchiae* were made in July, 101 in November and 127 in December. There were no mosquitoes with infected stomachs, but one gland infection (with normal-appearing sporozoites) was observed eight days after collection in a female taken November 21 in a pigsty at Nuraminis. These few dissections resulted in an infectivity index of 0.42 per cent.

Dissections of other anopheline species were not undertaken, primarily because the adults were rarely encountered and then usually under sylvatic conditions. The attraction of *labranchiae* for man-made shelters, plus its history of natural infections, indicated that it was the principal, if not the only, malaria vector in the island. This was borne out during the eradication campaign, for malaria declined with the elimination of *labranchiae*. Nor has the disease persisted even in areas where, for example in 1950, the incidence of other species such as *claviger* or *hispaniola* was high.

Anopheles melanoon melanoon HACKETT

Egg: Slender in appearance. In general, uniformly black, but occasionally with faint pale patches scattered over dorsum.

Floats relatively large but extending only slightly onto dorsal surface, occupying about 35 per cent of egg length and averaging about 18 ribs (costae) ; intercostal membrane smooth.

First instar larva: (see *labranchiae*) .

Fourth instar larva: Similar to *labranchiae*, but differing in that antepalmate hair of abdominal segments IV and V generally six to seven-branched (see also Bates, 1939) .

Pupa: (see *labranchiae*) .

Adult: (see *labranchiae*) .

World distribution. So far *melanoon* has been found only in Italy (Hackett and Missiroli, 1935; Del Vecchio and Del Vecchio, 1946) , Sardinia (Spanedda, 1940, and during ERLAAS campaign) , Corsica (Aitken, 1945, unpublished record) , France (Sautet, 1944; Callot and Dao Van Ty, 1945) , Algeria (Sergent, 1935) and recently in Switzerland (Büttiker, 1948) . All other published records, at least through 1940, probably refer to the variety *Anopheles melanoon subalpinus* (Bates, 1940) .

Distribution in Sardinia. The number of times *melanoon* has been collected in the island is extremely small. Spanedda (1940) reported it from the Campidano of Cagliari. During the ERLAAS campaign it was encountered in both the southern and northern portions of the island as follows: Muravera area (Sarrabus) , Monastir and Sardara (Campidano) , Senorbì (Trexenta) , Isili (Sarcidano) , Assolo and Curcuris (Marmilla) , Padria (Regione Vulcanica) , Olmedo (Nurra) and Castel Sardo (Anglona) . The highest elevation at which it was found was 438 meters.

Biology. This species was so rarely seen that little can be said about its biology. Field study was difficult since identification was restricted to the egg and fourth larval instar. These forms were positively identified only 12 times during the period 1946 to 1948, and on all but one of these occasions it was associated with *labranchiae*. Collections were made in the months of March, June, July, August and September. Aquatic habitats were ground pools, streams and water holes. During the spring *melanoon* was found in exposed situations, but in the summer its habitats tended to be shadier. Hackett and Missiroli (1935) reported the species breeding in rice fields and marshy areas in northern Italy. In Corsica, the author found it in algal mats of tiny, sunlit streams along the east coast.

Adults of the Sardinian *melanoon* were recognized, through laboratory ovipositions, on only five occasions. Four of these adults came from stables and one from a pigsty.

Anopheles claviger MEIGEN

Egg: Large and bluntly pointed. Floats large and bulbous; conspicuous against black chorion; occupying about 50 per cent of egg length and encroaching upon medial dorsal surface, thereby restricting space connecting dorsal polar areas of egg; float membrane smooth. Marginal frill interrupted by floats.

First instar larva: Subantennal hair long and bifurcate near base; about as long as antenna and apically bent inward at angle. Clypeal hairs simple; inner clypeals slightly closer to each other than to outer clypeals.

Fourth instar larva: Frontal hairs with well-developed shaft, pinnately branched. Anterior clypeal hairs simple; inner clypeals closer to each other than to outer clypeals. Inner occipital hairs simple or bifurcate at base. Subantennal hair shaft having coarse apical bifurcation bearing many small dendritic branchlets. Fronto-clypeus marked with isolated spots rather than horizontal bands. Inner prothoracic hair with slender shaft bearing three or four apical branches. Abdominal palmate hairs obtusely serrate but lacking distinct apical filament; segments IV and V with " O " hair absent or extremely minute and simple; tergal plates small (not more than three times their width).

Pupa: Lateral hair of abdominal segment VIII short and multiply branched. Lateral hair of segment VII in form of long, acutely pointed spine. Paddles with extremely minute serrations restricted to outer posterior border but not reaching terminal hair.

Adult:[1] Generally dark grayish-brown in color. Head with tuft of upright pale scales medianly and black scales laterally. Proboscis of female uniformly dark. Thorax with mesonotum having central pale stripe (not as pronounced as in *labranchiae*) and dark lateral bands; tuft of pale hair-like scales on anterior margin of mesonotum. Wings with dark scales, not forming spots.

World distribution. *Claviger* is Palearctic in distribution, extending from the British Isles to the Pamir Mountains of Turkestan and the Ob River of western Siberia. According to Beklemishev, reports of this species near the Yenisei River in central Siberia are doubtful, and it has not been recorded further eastward (Bates *et al.*, 1949). The species is found as far north as Norway, southern Sweden and the Leningrad area of Russia. In the south, *claviger* occurs in most of the Mediterranean islands, North Africa (Spanish and French Morocco, Algeria and Tunisia), Palestine, Syria, Transjordan, Iraq and Iran (Leeson *et al.*, 1950). *Anopheles habibi* Mulligan and Puri has been considered a variety of *claviger* by Russell *et al.*, (1946); if this is correct, the species' distribution has a southeastern extension as far as Quetta, Baluchistan (Puri, 1949).

Beklemishev (Bates *et al.*, 1949) reports *claviger* as occurring up to 2,800 meters in the western Pamirs of Turkestan, and Gaud *et al.* (1949) found it in Morocco at 2,500 meters.

Distribution in Sardinia. *Claviger* was found in practically every ERLAAS sector except for a few in the hot, dry Campidano Plain and some of the satellite islands. *Claviger* was found, however, in the islands of Sant'Antioco, and Maddalena and Spargi of the Maddalena Archipelago. The species was present at high altitudes in the Gennargentu, Ogliastra, Catena del Marghine and Limbara mountains, many collections being reported at 1,000 meters and above; the highest elevation at which it was recorded was about 1,300 meters in the Gennargentu Range.

---

[1] *Claviger* is difficult to distinguish from *plumbeus* in the adult stage. Marshall (1938) suggests several differences: last palpal segment of female one-half, or less, as long as penultimate in *claviger*, whereas slightly over half as long in *plumbeus*; posterior margin of scutellum in *claviger* evenly rounded, whereas irregular in outline in *plumbeus*.

Seasonal cycle. The seasonal cycle of the Sardinian *claviger* has not been satisfactorily worked out. This is partly due to the fact that adults were not commonly encountered in domestic shelters (only 18 per cent of 2,244 specimens during the period 1946 to 1950), and then always in low densities, only one or two individuals being found at a time. Also, the larval habit of diving and remaining submerged for long periods, probably more noticeable early in the year when waters are colder, may have distorted the picture of larval incidence and density.

Italian workers have considered *claviger* as largely a spring and fall species. The observations of Bates (1937) in Albania confirm this belief; stable captures near Tirana over a four-year period indicated that the species has a bimodal seasonal curve with a minor peak appearing about the first of May and a major peak the first two weeks of November.

While studying Sardinian *claviger* in a series of fixed aquatic stations during 1947, a similar bimodal curve was noted in the seasonal incidence of the larval population. The first peak occurred during June and a second larger peak in the late fall and early winter (figure 34).

In 1950, when eradication operations were directed only against *labranchiae* (in restricted areas), the frequency of *claviger* collections throughout the island dropped off gradually from May through July, and then rapidly through September when scouting operations ceased. There was thus no evidence of the bimodal distribution previously observed.

In Sardinia, adults have been found in every month of the year, the earliest collection being January 6 and the latest December 17. Pupae and first instar larvae were found in every month except January, and the latter were observed as late as December 19. Eggs were encountered from May 17 to December 1; while they were not seen during the first four months of the year, this may not be significant as first instar larvae and adults were found earlier. It would therefore seem that the Sardinian *claviger* was capable of breeding throughout the year, with the development possibly retarded in the cold months.

Further evidence supporting the suggestion that in Sardinia *claviger* overwinters in the adult as well as in the immature stages was the finding of one female with fat body in January and two

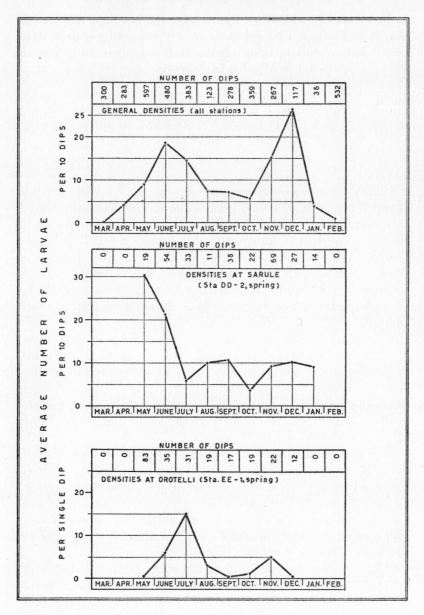

FIGURE 34. Larval densities of *Anopheles claviger* in Sardinia during 1947 and early 1948.

in December. In addition, a female with almost completely mature ovaries was collected on February 17. Overwintering females have been encountered largely in habitats such as grottoes and *nuraghi*, but one was found in a stable in February.

Larval habitats. Springs and their associated rivulets were the principal source of the 171,990 larval collections of *claviger* during the five-year period 1946 to 1950. These were followed in order by: (1) interrupted rivers and streams, (2) rivers and streams, (3) tanks and wells, (4) water holes, (5) ground pools and (6) swamps (figure 31).

Limited observations were made during 1947 on the relative attractiveness of various habitats. While larvae were encountered in springs at any season of the year, they were not particularly abundant in rivulets until the late summer and fall. Swamps, ground pools and rivers were most frequently positive during the winter months, with their attractiveness waning as the season progressed. Tanks and wells developed a certain importance during the spring and summer, and water holes during the spring, summer and fall.

The immature stages of *claviger* were always found in fresh water. The species showed a definite preference for clear, still, shaded waters containing horizontal vegetation and often overhung with dense growths of brambles and bushes. It was, however, quite frequently detected in slowly moving waters, and was not uncommonly encountered in sunny or partially sunny situations (figure 32).

During the five-year period 1946 to 1950 less than 1 per cent of the *claviger* collections were associated with other species. *Marteri* accounted for 63 per cent of these associations, followed by *algeriensis* (18 per cent) and *labranchiae* (13 per cent). Other associations were less common. On seven occasions *claviger* larvae were found with those of *plumbeus* in tanks, springs or streams, though not in tree holes, the typical habitats of *plumbeus*.

Claviger larvae are readily disturbed when the water surface of their environment is agitated. They dive and are capable of remaining submerged for long periods of time. The longest period of submersion observed by Trapido in 1950 was 14 minutes. The average submersion period in 300 trials was 67 seconds; the median was 43 seconds (range, 1 second to 14 minutes).

55. Inventory of field equipment in Cagliari depot.

56. View of the DDT mixing plant in Cagliari.

57. A typical *labranchiae* stream habitat in Sassari Province.

58. *Ranunculus aquatilis*, commonly found in spring ground pools and often associated with *labranchiae*.

59. Both *labranchiae* and *claviger* were found in sections of the Picocca River.

60. Typical *labranchiae* breeding place, indicating method of numbering.

61. *Algeriensis* habitat in Uta swamp near Cagliari.

62. A typical *algeriensis* breeding place at the base of the *Juncus* plant.

63. Spleen and parasite survey in a schoolroom in Villaputzu, Cagliari.

64. Village kitchen in Donori, Cagliari Province, with fly paper used in
fly control experiments.

65. Treating ship's hold, using DDT smoke canisters.

66. A typical courtyard in a Campidano village.

Adult habitats. Claviger adults were scarce in domestic shelters. Of 2,244 specimens collected over the five-year period, only 18 per cent were found in such structures. The great majority of the adults (56 per cent) came from grottoes, and another 23 per cent were collected from vegetation.

Claviger was rarely observed to attack man in nature and it never bit man in the laboratory on the few occasions when attempts were made to feed wild-caught females. During the 1947 studies on the nocturnal feeding and flying activities of *labranchiae* in the Picocca Valley, *claviger* adults were never seen, even though larvae were abundant in the surrounding area. The available evidence suggests that the Sardinian *claviger* is largely a sylvatic species and seldom comes in contact with man. Elsewhere, as in Palestine, the species appears to be more closely associated with man (Bates *et al.*, 1949; Weyer, 1939; Leeson *et al.*, 1950).

Nothing is known about the flight activities of *claviger* in Sardinia. The species apparently was capable of disseminating itself throughout the countryside quite rapidly; it appeared to be practically eliminated from the island at the end of the 1948 campaign, yet by the end of 1949, after eradication controls had been lifted in March, it seemed to have almost regained its former position.

Anopheles algeriensis THEOBALD

Egg: Relatively small, very narrow and sharply pointed. Shiny black. Ends of float membranes curve onto dorsal surface forming four membranous hooks resembling bicycle handle-bars; float membrane smooth. Marginal frill interrupted by floats.

First instar larva: Subantennal hair long and bifurcate near base; much longer than antenna and slightly recurved apically. Clypeal hairs simple and equidistant from each other.

Fourth instar larva: Frontal hairs with well-developed shaft pinnately branched. Anterior clypeal hairs with minute branchlets along shafts; inner clypeals closer to each other than to outer clypeals. Inner occipital hairs with about four apical branches. Fronto-clypeus marked with three dark transverse bands. Abdominal segments IV and V with well-developed " O " hair having four to five branches; tergal plates large (at least five to six times their width).

Pupa: Lateral hair of abdominal segment VIII short and multiply branched. Lateral hair of segment VII in form of long, acutely pointed spine. Paddles with minute serrations along posterior half of internal and external borders.

Adult: Brown in color. Head without tuft of pale scales. Mesonotum uniformly reddish-brown, without darker stripes laterally; no pale scales or tuft on anterior margin. Wings with dark scales, not forming spots.

World distribution. Algeriensis is essentially a Mediterranean and South Asian species. It is known in Norfolk, England (Marshall, 1938), a few localities in Germany (Weyer, 1939), the Iberian Peninsula (Romeo Viamonte, 1950) and Morocco (Gaud *et al.*, 1949). Its range extends eastward through the Mediterranean to Turkey and Palestine, Syria, Transjordan, Transcaucasia, Iraq, Iran and Turkestan, being found as far north as Tashkent in Central Asia (Leeson *et al.*, 1950; Bates *et al.*, 1949). Beklemishev (Bates *et al.*, 1949) states that in the eastern portion of its range, at least, the species has never been found above 900 meters.

Distribution in Sardinia. Formerly, *algeriensis* was widespread in Sardinia, particularly in the lowlands. At no time, however, was it as abundant as *labranchiae* or *claviger*. Occasionally it was found up to altitudes of about 800 meters in the Villanova Strisaili area. The species was also taken on the islands of Sant'Antioco and San Pietro in the southwest and Caprera in the north.

Seasonal cycle. While information regarding the seasonal cycle of *algeriensis* is far from complete, it would appear that the species develops slowly in the winter and spring and reaches a peak of abundance during late summer and early fall. August and September seem to be the months of greatest breeding activity. Monthly larval densities, as observed during 1947 and early 1948, are summarized in figure 35. The seasonal trend seems to be quite similar to subsequent experience during the eradication years. There were so few adult collections during the period 1946 to 1950 that no correlation can be made between larval and adult incidence.

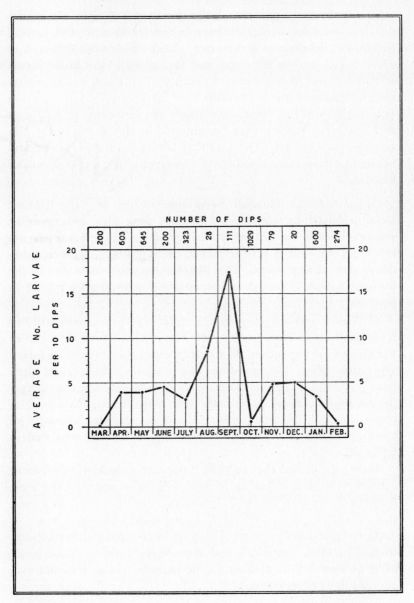

FIGURE 35. Larval densities of *Anopheles algeriensis* in Sardinia during 1947 and early 1948.

The evidence suggests that, as in the case of *claviger*, the species does not pass the winter entirely in the larval state, but instead breeds and develops at a slow rate. Adults have been collected in every month except February and September. First instar larvae were not found in January and February. This may not be significant as relatively few inspections were made early in the year. On January 20, 1947 all immature stages of *algeriensis* (except eggs and first instar larvae) were encountered in abundance in the Uta swamp near Cagliari. The fact that adults were also present and biting in considerable numbers gives weight to the theory of winter breeding.

Larval habitats. Sluggish rivers and streams were the habitats most preferred by *algeriensis*. Swamps were also an important source of larvae, but primarily during the winter; the larvae develop slowly at the base of juncus plants, cane (*Phragmites*) and other dense vertical vegetation. The 14,441 collections made during the five-year ERLAAS period are summarized according to habitat in figure 31.

Algeriensis appeared to prefer clear, fresh waters, usually still but occasionally with some movement. The species was rarely taken in the absence of vegetation. It was frequently encountered in mixed vegetation where the exposure was partially sunny rather than heavily shaded, being intermediate between *labranchiae* and *claviger* in this respect. Summer habitats were more shaded than those at other times of the year. Observations on the characteristics of the aquatic habitats of *algeriensis* during 1947 are summarized in figure 32.

During the period 1946 to 1950, 2 per cent of the 14,441 *algeriensis* collections were found in association with other species. The most frequent association was with *labranchiae*, but *claviger* was a close second. Other species were rarely encountered with *algeriensis*.

On the few occasions when diving times of *algeriensis* larvae were studied in 1950, Trapido found the average time of submergence to be 61 seconds; the median was 50 seconds (range, 1 second to 4 minutes in 31 observations).

Adult habitats. On the basis of adult collections, the Sardinian *algeriensis* appears to be more domestically inclined than *claviger*.

At least 38 per cent of the specimens collected between 1946 and 1950 were encountered in man-made shelters and 20 per cent came from natural shelters; the source of the remaining 42 per cent was unspecified. On several occasions, prior to the initiation of scouting operations, adults were encountered in large swamps where they were resting on vertical vegetation. The species apparently spends much of its time in such locations and only occasionally enters houses or domestic animal shelters.

Algeriensis in Sardinia rarely attacks man; however, the adults encountered in swamps were quite persistent biters. At such times the sky was overcast. During July 1947, ERLAAS workers spent a night in the Serramanna swamp, in the hope of gaining information about the habits of this species. Larvae were abundant in the area, but only one adult female entered the bed nets to feed (at 10 P. M.). Marshall (1938, p. 132) refers to Edwards' observations on this species in Norfolk, England, where apparently it was quite an avid feeder: " Females bit readily in the open in calm, dull weather or in sheltered spots at dusk and dawn."

Nothing much is known about the flight activities of *algeriensis* or the swarming of males. It probably is not so strong a flyer as *claviger*, because it is taking much more time to reoccupy its former domain since eradication measures have ceased. This may be due to the fact that the heavily overgrown swamps and sluggish streams preferred by *algeriensis* are less common than other habitat types favored by *claviger*.

Anopheles marteri SENEVET AND PRUNNELLE

Egg: Large and bluntly pointed. Floats large and bulbous (larger than in *claviger*); conspicuous against black chorion; occupying more than 75 per cent of egg length and encroaching on medial dorsal surface; width of float at broadest central part one and one-half times width of ventral surface of egg between floats; average of 26 ribs or costae, varying from 23 to 29 ribs per float; intercostal membrane moderately rough. (Based on Hadjinicolaou, 1938.)

First instar larva: Subantennal hair long and bifurcate near base;

much longer than antenna and strongly recurved apically. Clypeal hairs simple and equidistant from each other.

Fourth instar larva: Frontal hairs with well-developed shaft pinnately branched. Anterior clypeal hairs simple; inner clypeals closer to each other than to outer clypeals. Inner occipital hairs simple or bifurcate at base. Subantennal hair uniformly pinnately branched with no apical bifurcation of shaft and subsequent branchlets. Fronto-clypeus marked with isolated spots rather than horizontal bands. Inner anterior prothoracic hair with strongly developed shaft basally and pinnately branched, similar to but smaller than middle prothoracic hair; outer prothoracic hair simple, rising distinctly. Abdominal palmate hairs with few serrations just prior to long pseudofilaments; segments IV and V with " O " hair absent or extremely minute and simple; tergal plates small (not more than three times their width).

Pupa: Lateral hair of abdominal segment VIII short and multiply branched. Lateral hair of segment VII in form of long, acutely pointed spine. Paddles adorned with long hair-like fringe on internal and external borders.

Adult: Dark gray in color. Head with tuft of upright pale scales medianly and dark scales laterally. Proboscis of female pale apically. Thorax with mesonotum having central pale stripe (similar to *claviger*) and dark lateral bands; tuft of pale scales on anterior margin. Wings with dark scales, unspotted, except for pale apical fringe.

World distribution. Information on the distribution of *marteri* in the Mediterranean and South Asia is rather spotty, probably because little attention has been given to this epidemiologically unimportant species. It has been reported from Spain (Torres Cañamares, 1946; Romeo Viamonte, 1950), Morocco (Gaud *et al.*, 1950), Algeria (Senevet and Prunnelle, 1927), Tunisia (Sicart, 1942), Corsica (Langeron and Galliard, 1933), Albania (Bates, 1941c), Bulgaria and Greece by Shannon (Hadjinicolaou, 1938), Cyprus (Aziz, 1947), Syria, Palestine, Transjordan, Iraq, northern Iran and Tajikistan (var. *sogdianus*) (Leeson *et al.*, 1950; Bates *et al.*, 1949). Beklemishev (Bates *et al.*, 1949) says that in Tajikistan, *marteri* occurs in mountain streams of uninhabited valleys at elevations between 900 and 1,600 meters.

Distribution in Sardinia. While *marteri* was never so abundantly represented in ERLAAS collections as some of the other Sardinian species, it was not uncommon. Its principal center of distribution was in the eastern mountain mass (Barbagia, Gennargentu, Ogliastra and extending south into the Sarrabus). It was also present in the southern mountains of the Sulcis and in scattered areas of mountain terrain in the north. It never turned up in any of the satellite islands. While it was sometimes found close to sea level, it was usually encountered at higher altitudes and generally in uninhabited country. No records are available regarding the highest elevation at which it was found, but there were several collections above 1,000 meters.

Seasonal cycle. Information on the seasonal cycle of *marteri* is meager. A study of data from selected untreated sectors during 1949 and 1950 suggests that there may be two peaks in larval population densities, one in the late spring and a second in the fall. In Sardinia, females were found on one occasion (January 4) in an abandoned mine shaft in the Gennargentu Mountains at an elevation of 700 meters. Presumably these were hibernating forms. Adults of the new generation were not seen before the first week in June. Larvae (all instars) were encountered as late as September 29 and as early as March 18 (third and fourth instars).

Larval habitats. The preferred larval habitats of *marteri* were mountain streams, either flowing or interrupted, provided that the water was fairly cool and relatively well shaded. The species was also found in rivulets and springs. On a few occasions larvae were encountered in tanks and water holes, and in rare instances in swampy places and ground pools. Larvae were not always easy to find; they sometimes existed in tiny collections of water so shallow that it was necessary to collect them individually with a pipette. The 2,450 collections made during the ERLAAS campaign are summarized according to habitat in figure 31.

Larvae have been found in horizontal vegetation as well as in water devoid of green vegetation but containing fallen leaves and either completely or partially shaded by vertical vegetation or nearby trees.

Twenty-five per cent of the *marteri* collections during the period 1946 to 1950 have been mixed associations with other species. The closest relationship was with *claviger* (95 per cent of the mixed collections). It was rarely encountered with *labranchiae*, *algeriensis* or *hispaniola*.

Adult habitats. Most of the 13 adult specimens of *marteri* collected between 1948 and 1950 (none were found earlier) came from grottoes or similar natural shelters along water courses. One was found in a tree hole.

The species rarely, if ever, attacks man, restricting its biting activities to domestic and wild animals. Hadjinicolaou (1938) had great difficulty in getting *marteri* to feed on man in the laboratory. The species was never observed biting man in Sardinia. Judging from its apparent habit of remaining near its breeding places, *marteri* would not appear to be a strong flyer. No other information is available regarding its flight habits.

Anopheles plumbeus STEPHENS

Egg: Relatively large, diamond-shaped; bluntly pointed at extremities which are slightly raised; black; floats absent, replaced by well-developed marginal and prominent frill completely encircling egg.

First instar larva: Subantennal hair extremely short, bifurcate apically. Anterior clypeal hairs approximately equidistant, adorned with tiny branchlets.

Fourth instar larva: Frontal hairs extremely small and simple. Anterior clypeal hairs approximately equidistant, adorned with tiny branches. Subantennal hair very short, with two to three apical branches. Abdominal segments I to VI with lateral hairs pinnately branched; tergal plates small (about one to two times their width).

Pupa: Lateral hair of abdominal segment VIII long, slender and unbranched. Paddles with minute serrations along outer posterior border, but not reaching terminal hair.

Adult: Dark gray in color. Head with tuft of upright white scales medianly and black scales laterally. Proboscis of female uniformly dark. Thorax with mesonotum having central pale stripe and dark lateral bands; tuft of white hair-like scales on anterior margin of mesonotum.

World distribution. The range of *plumbeus* extends from the British Isles through western Europe, including Scandinavia, to southern Russia (Kiev, Kharkov) and the Caucasus (Krasnodar, Terek Valley); from there it extends into northern Iran (Elburz Mountains) and the Kopet Dagh Mountains of Southern Transcaspia. The closely related *Anopheles barianensis*, a possible subspecies of *plumbeus*, is found further east in Tajikistan (elevations of 1,000 to 1,600 meters) and the western Himalayas (elevations of 1,500 to 2,400 meters). *Plumbeus* has also been reported from Algeria and Corsica (Bates *et al.*, 1949; Puri, 1949).

Distribution in Sardinia. While never abundant, *plumbeus* has been found throughout the island, in the plains as well as in the mountains wherever trees with rot holes occur.

Seasonal cycle. Inasmuch as the larval habitats of *plumbeus* (primarily rot holes of trees) were not routinely inspected, information regarding the seasonal abundance of the species is scanty. Between 1948 and 1950, 618 collections of *plumbeus* were made, the greatest number being found during the months of March, June and July.

Larvae were found in every month of the year except January, a month when few, if any, inspections of tree holes were made. First instar larvae were encountered from March through December. Pupae had a similar incidence, except in the latter month. Adults were captured in April, May, June, July and September. Presumably the species overwinters in the larval stage.

Larval habitats. The immature stages of *plumbeus* are usually found developing in water accumulations in tree holes. Of the 618 collections made between 1948 and 1950, 82 per cent came from such sources. In the course of the large number of inspections made by a field force of several thousand scouts, *plumbeus* was occasionally encountered in other habitats such as tanks, springs, streams, ground pools and, on one occasion, a swampy place. Some of these records are dubious, as tree hole species are rather fastidious in their preference. Inasmuch as *plumbeus* larvae are easily identified, records are included which indicate that the species may occasionally (during very dry summers, for example) continue its life cycle in places other than its normal surroundings.

The only mixed collections of *plumbeus* have been associated with *claviger*, and then only rarely—twice each in streams, interrupted streams and springs, and once in a tank.

Adult habitats. Only 19 specimens of *plumbeus* were collected during the period 1947 to 1950. Most of these were found in sparsely inhabited regions. Nine came from tree holes, five from grottoes, two from a well and one each from a *nuraghe*, a spring niche and a hen house. The latter specimen laid one egg in the laboratory which served for the above description.

Anopheles hispaniola (THEOBALD)

Egg: Relatively small; dark bluish-gray in color. Bluntly rounded at enlarged micropylar end and more pointed at the other; curved somewhat like a banana. Exochorion consisting of hexagonal pattern, completely covering egg except for rosette-shaped black area around micropyle. No floats. Marginal frill reduced to small oval-shaped spot adjacent to and touching micropylar area; appressed rather than upturned as in *Anopheles pseudopunctipennis franciscanus*.

First instar larva: Subantennal hair long and bifurcate near base; about as long as antenna; slightly recurved apically. Clypeal hairs simple; inner clypeals slightly closer to outer clypeals than to each other.

Fourth instar larva: Inner frontal hairs normally with well-developed shaft basally with six or more branches; all branches arising near base of shaft. Anterior clypeal hairs simple; inner clypeals widely separated, closer to outer clypeals than to each other; posterior clypeals as long as inner clypeals. Inner anterior prothoracic hair with strongly developed shaft and pinnately branched, similar to but smaller than middle prothoracic hair. Mesopleural hairs (No. 9 and 10) branched. Abdominal palmate hairs present in segments II to VII, those of segment II with fewer leaflets; palmate hair leaflets with short terminal filaments; lateral hairs of segments IV to VI rather weakly pinnately branched.

Pupa: Lateral hair of abdominal segment VIII short and multiply branched. Lateral hair of segment VII in form of long, acutely pointed spine. Paddles edged with row of robust teeth occupying more than half of outer posterior border; short row of fine hairs apically between teeth and apical hair.

Adult: Pale gray in color. Head with tuft of pale upright scales medianly and dark scales laterally. Palpus of female with three pale rings and dark apex. Wing with pale and dark scales grouped to form spotted areas, with five pale areas along anterior margin; base of costa dark.

World distribution. The distribution of *hispaniola* is confused with that of *Anopheles turkhudi* because many authors have considered the two synonymous. While material on *turkhudi* has not been available for comparison, the distinguishing characteristics of *hispaniola* noted by Mattingly (1947) have been verified in Sardinian specimens; hence, the specific name *hispaniola* is retained in this report. The species apparently occurs in the following regions: Rio de Oro, French and Spanish Morocco (as *turkhudi*, Gaud et al., 1950), Canary Islands and Spain (Romeo Viamonte, 1950), Algeria and Sahara (Senevet, 1935), Tunisia and Tripolitania (Callot, 1938), Libya (Ghidini, 1934), southern Italy (as *italicus*, Raffaele, 1928) and Transjordan (Leeson et al., 1950). Romeo Viamonte (1950) considers *Anopheles rifenus* of Spanish Morocco the same as *hispaniola*. Gaud et al. (1950) report the species occurring in Morocco from sea level up to elevations of 2,500 meters.

Distribution in Sardinia. Like *marteri*, *hispaniola* appears to have a restricted distribution in Sardinia, being confined largely to the southeastern mountain mass and littoral from the lower slopes of the Gennargentu Range south to the Sarrabus. It turned up occasionally in the Sulcis Mountains and a few other localities but was rarely encountered in the north. The species was never detected in any of the satellite islands. It was taken at elevations of at least 800 meters in the Villanova Strisaili area.

Seasonal cycle. Hispaniola is largely a late summer and fall species. The collections made during the early years of ERLAAS were not sufficient for a satisfactory study of the seasonal cycle. Larval collection data from certain untreated sectors are available for 1949 and 1950 and give some idea of seasonal trends. The incidence of the species appeared to reach its peak during August and early September. Larvae were not found before late May (all instars and pupae), and adults were not found before the first week in June. First instar larvae were collected as late as October 2 and other instars until October 25. Adults were captured as late as November 11. Presumably the species overwinters in the adult state.

Larval habitats. Observations were made on the occurrence of eggs in natural habitats during September 1950. Prior to this, eggs had not been encountered despite diligent search. Neither had it been possible to obtain eggs from females on the few occasions when the latter were collected.

The eggs of *hispaniola* were observed in mats of spirogyra growing over bits of gravel in very shallow water of an exposed stream bed. The majority of the eggs rested vertically, enmeshed among the algal strands, but even those resting in the horizontal position had the enlarged micropylar end in contact with the surface. Except for those lying horizontally, the eggs were very difficult to find as only the minute dark micropylar end could be seen clearly. When touched, the eggs slipped below the surface, so presumably the algal filaments act as a support to hold them in their customary position. Eggs were scattered throughout the algal patches, either singly or in groups of two to six, indicating that the female oviposited in more than one spot. From the position of the eggs it would seem that the female actually tucked them into the mats from a standing position.

The preferred larval habitats of the Sardinian *hispaniola* were gravelly stream beds well exposed to the sun during the greater portion of the day. Larvae were usually found in mats of spirogyra, but occasionally they were seen in water cress or in clear water around pebbles. The water was frequently very shallow. As a result, the larvae could not always be easily collected with a dipper or dip net unless quantities of gravel were scooped up. Kneeling and collecting the larvae directly with a pipette permitted close observation of the water surface; only then was it possible to appreciate the heavy densities frequently present.

Larvae and pupae occurred in slowly moving water in the algal mats, or free around stones, or else in rapidly running water among water cress. They were most abundant in the first habitat, suggesting that it was only the disturbed strays which were found in sheltered spots where the current was greater.

Hispaniola was also encountered in intermittent streams and to a much lesser extent in springs, rivulets, swampy places along streams, water holes, tanks and ground pools. Some of these sources are doubtful as the species appeared to have definite preferences for clear, well-aerated water. The 2,582 aquatic collections of *hispaniola* for the period 1947 to 1950 (none encountered in 1946) are classified according to habitat in figure 31.

Larvae and pupae were extremely susceptible to outside disturbance, diving immediately into the spirogyra mats and remaining there for long periods. Observations made by Trapido in 1950 indicated that the species was capable of remaining submerged for as long as 35 minutes; in 258 observations the average time spent below was 87 seconds; the median was 38 seconds (range, 1 second to 35 minutes). This reaction is remarkable for an active larva such as *hispaniola*, which occupies an aquatic environment with temperatures comparable to those preferred by *labranchiae* (23° C. to 25° C.). *Claviger* also is capable of remaining submerged for long periods, but it is a much less energetic larva, living in cool, shaded waters with temperatures averaging about 18° C.

Hispaniola's capacity for lengthy submersion may be due to the highly oxygenated state of the spirogyra mats, which are exposed to the sun for long periods of time. In addition, the algae give off bubbles of oxygen, many of which are trapped among the strands. The submersion phenomenon may be an explanation for *hispaniola*'s resistance to larviciding operations, particularly in flowing water, during 1948 and 1949.

Only 3 per cent of the 2,582 *hispaniola* collections were mixed associations with other species. Seventy-one per cent of these were with *claviger* and 19 per cent with *labranchiae*, the remainder with *algeriensis* and *marteri*. The association with *labranchiae* would undoubtedly have been much greater had eradication measures not been in operation.

Despite numerous attempts to find *hispaniola* and *superpictus* during 1946, neither was encountered. In 1947 the former was collected on a number of occasions with *labranchiae*. Thereafter *labranchiae* disappeared under the action of larvicides and residual sprays, but *hispaniola* took over the habitats and multiplied. It would seem therefore that *labranchiae* was the more generalized species, dominating the environment and keeping *hispaniola* down to such small numbers that it was very difficult to find.

Adult habitats. Since only 148 adult specimens were collected during the period 1947 to 1950, little information is available concerning the resting places. About 49 per cent of the specimens came from domestic shelters; the remainder were collected in the open, in abandoned mine shafts, grottoes, vegetation, and on two occasions biting man. Numerous attempts were made to locate adults in domestic shelters along river valleys where the larvae abounded, but most of these were unsuccessful. At no time were adults found, even in natural shelters near the breeding places, in numbers which were at all commensurate with the nearby larval population. Because of their pale color, adults were hard to distinguish against the background of their resting places and may easily have been overlooked in locations such as densely vegetated banks of streams.

Little information is available on the feeding habits of this species in Sardinia. As mentioned previously, it was taken only twice in the act of biting man. During 1947, in the course of observations on the nocturnal habits of *labranchiae* in the Picocca Valley, *hispaniola* was never taken in the collections; an occasional specimen was found in a pigsty one to two kilometers away and larvae were subsequently encountered in a nearby stream. Repeated attempts to get the species to feed on man in the laboratory were unsuccessful.

BIOLOGICAL CONSIDERATIONS

HAROLD TRAPIDO

The striking success in the elimination of *Anopheles gambiae* from Brazil has focused attention on the feasibility of the total eradication of a population of a disease vector. On the completion of this project Soper and Wilson (1943) remarked that, " Many workers in the control of mosquito-borne disease have been more than reluctant to accept the idea that man has it in his power to eradicate any mosquito anywhere, no matter what the effort made. . . . The traditional ingrained philosophy that species eradication is impossible, that a species is something sacred and eternal in spite of the dodo, the passenger pigeon and the dinosaur to the contrary, and that when species disappear they do so in response to ' cosmic' or ' biological' rather than man-made factors, is most persistent." Despite this somewhat pessimistic view of the inertia to be overcome by the eradication concept, in the decade since this was written, a number of efforts have been made to extend the principle of total eradication to other situations, and the ERLAAS project for the eradication of *Anopheles labranchiae labranchiae* from Sardinia has been one such effort.

We might first consider the position of the biologist in this matter. The biologist does not insist that species are either " sacred " or " eternal." Quite the contrary, a primary tenet of evolutionary theory is that species are limited in the dimension of time as well as space. Thus Simpson (1944) has devoted a book, *Tempo and Mode in Evolution*, to a study of the life span of species in geological time. The causes of the decline and extinction of species are many and complex. In recent times, geologically speaking, the species which have been most subject to extermination or near extermination by the activities of man exhibit certain special characteristics. First, they may be economically useful to man (for food and clothing). Second, they may be conspicuously easy to find. Third, they may have a low reproductive potential. Fourth, they may be in poor adjustment to their environment at the time that man is added as a burden to an already unfavorable situation. That is, they may have a very limited range of habits and lack the ability is added as a burden to an already unfavorable situation. That survival of a species may be endangered by any one, any combination or all of these situations. The passenger pigeon, the heath hen, the ivory-billed woodpecker, the bison in America, the wisent in Europe and the dodo have all become extinct or are in danger of extinction because they have suffered from some combination of these characteristics.

Let us examine the mosquitoes which interest us because of their unfavorable effect on human activity as transmitters of disease, in the light of these characteristics which may affect their survival.

While it is true that mosquitoes are subject to pressure from man and the diminution of their numbers or eradication would be favorable to man, there is no daily economic gain apparent to the lay human population, so that man as a species does not exert continuous pressure. When herds of bison roamed the Great Plains of the western United States, the economic gain to be derived by going on a bison hunt for meat, tallow and hides did not have to be explained in schools or at public meetings, nor was it necessary that the hunts be undertaken by some governmental agency for want of interest by the lay public. To say that the organization of people to similarly set about the hunting of a mosquito species would be less spontaneous is a gross understatement.

The conspicuousness of such unfortunate creatures as the passenger pigeon, the heath hen and the bison, as contrasted with the inconspicuous nature of the breeding and resting places of mosquitoes need hardly be commented upon. It is well to point out, however, that when species, or strains of species, of mosquitoes are what we speak of as "domestic" they are, relatively at least, more conspicuous because they are in close proximity to man. A domestic species, or a domestic strain of a species, thus approaches the condition of conspicuousness and thereby becomes vulnerable. The domestic strains of *Anopheles gambiae* and *Aedes aegypti* which invaded the Americas carried this fatal failing with them.

The reproductive potential of mosquitoes is high, not only because of the relatively large number of eggs laid, but also because

67. District headquarters in Lodè, Nuoro Province.

68. District office in hill country, Cagliari Province.

69. Ditching foreman, Cagliari Province.

70. Division chief, Nuoro Province.

71. Ollasta Simaxis swamp near Oristano, showing difficulties
of both scouting and treatment.

72. Cutting vegetation in a *labranchiae*-positive area in the
Colostrai swamp near Muravera.

the time required to mature is short. This permits a rapid recovery of populations following unfavorable environmental conditions, whether these conditions be cold (winter), desiccation (dry season in the tropics) or attack by man. The low reproductive rate of mammals and birds is in extreme contrast.

From this we can appreciate how the biologist on the one hand entertains no mystic belief in the immortality of species in geological time, while on the other hand he may believe that a species in good adjustment with its environment is very likely to continue to survive so long as there is no major change in the environment nor a change in its habit pattern which brings it into major conflict with that environment through the sort of limiting factors we have so briefly outlined. It is unfortunate for man that the mosquitoes which interest him as disease vectors are, in the regions where they are vectors, for the most part well adjusted to their environment.

With the understanding that there is nothing immortal about species, we come to our main purpose which is to explore and contrast, from the biologists' point of view, the fundamental differences between the introduced populations of *Anopheles gambiae* and *Aedes aegypti* attacked in Brazil, and the indigenous population of *Anopheles l. labranchiae* in Sardinia; to gather the evidence indicating that the population of the latter mosquito is indeed indigenous in Sardinia; and to give some basis for an appreciation of how the outcome of the ERLAAS project in Sardinia may have thereby been affected. We will attempt to show how terminological confusion may have brought about the concept of a closer parallel between the situations in Brazil and Sardinia than the biological nature of the mosquito populations would justify.

It has been appreciated from the first that the populations of *Aedes aegypti* and *Anopheles gambiae* in the New World were introduced by human agency, in the case of *Aedes aegypti* probably several centuries ago at the time of the conquest of the New World, and in the case of *Anopheles gambiae* about a decade before the eradication effort against it was begun. This had led to discussion of the differences between introduced and indigenous mosquito populations, there being some awareness that mosquito populations which have been attributed to one species might have a limited range of habits in an environment into which they have been introduced, as in the case of *Aedes aegypti* and *Anopheles gambiae* in the Americas, but more diverse habits in the region of their natural occurrence in Africa (Soper and Wilson, 1943 and Soper, 1948). It would appear, however, that the biological basis of these differences, which is of profound significance in evaluating the possibilities of success of eradication schemes elsewhere, has not been adequately brought to light. The importance of throwing light on this phase of the problem will be appreciated when it is recalled that the mystery of " anophelism without malaria," a classical problem in the epidemiology of malaria in Europe, was not understood until the *maculipennis* anophelines were sorted, by various ingenious means, into the several taxonomic categories comprising what had at first appeared to be a homogeneous population.

Even in the face of the meager knowledge we presently possess of the behavior and genetic composition of mosquito population units, it is now possible to demonstrate tangible biological differences between indigenous and introduced mosquito populations. In large measure the difficulty in comprehending the nature of the population units involved has been one of semantics. The taxonomist has applied a formal system of nomenclature to the naturally occurring mosquito populations in the laudable attempt to provide a set of file boxes into which the information on the morphology, physiology, behavior and genetics of these organisms may be sorted, stored and organized for most efficient use. The nomenclatorial system is necessarily somewhat complicated if it is to express in universal terms the complex and intricate relationships between populations and the place of individual organisms in a particular population. We must, therefore, at the outset define our terms, for certain of these which are in common usage have relatively strict meanings in technical taxonomy. The precision with which these definitions may be formed is unfortunately limited, since the exact meanings of these terms are, and will continue to be, points of controversy among taxonomists as the understanding of the nature of populations grows.

We must first concern ourselves with the biologists' definition of " species." The species concept does not envision a group of organisms as a naturally occurring genotypically pure line. For a working definition we can take the statement of Emerson (1938) quoted in Bates (1949), that species are, " genetically distinctive, reproductively isolated, natural populations." It is often an intricate and difficult process to measure a population by these criteria, and for the most part biologists accept as a working approximation the thesis that populations with distinctive morphology, physiology and behavior are separate species, and name them as such without applying the genetical test. All too often, for practical reasons, morphological similarity alone is used as the basis for species definitions. The taxonomist working in a museum with a group of insects on pins or a collection of skins and skulls of mammals, is in no position to inquire into the behavior in nature of the organisms with which he is dealing, or their possible interfertility or intersterility. He merely sorts them into groups as best he can on the basis of distinctive morphology or coloration, and names these groups as species.

We must interest ourselves also in a second category recognized by the International Rules of Zoological Nomenclature since the mosquito population which concerns us most in Sardinia is often called by the taxonomist *Anopheles labranchiae labranchiae*—a trinomial involving the term "subspecies." This term has formal nomenclatorial status, and for it we may select the definition of Mayr (1942) : "The subspecies, or geographic race, is a geographically localized subdivision of the species, which differs genetically and taxonomically from other subdivisions of the species." Where the ranges of the subspecies of a particular species are contiguous, the subspecies interbreed. The reason for dignifying these infra-specific variations exhibiting geographic integrity with the formal nomenclatorial status of "subspecies" has been expressed by Bates (1940) : ". . . it is only through geographic separation that a single animal population can become divided into two or more populations sufficiently isolated from one another to permit divergent evolutionary trends to set in." At present the often, though not universally, accepted interpretation of the relationships within the *maculipennis* complex places the mosquito which interests us in Sardinia in the subspecies *labranchiae* of the species *Anopheles labranchiae* (Bates, 1940). The distribution of this subspecies aside from Sardinia includes the adjacent island of Corsica, central and southern Italy, Sicily, North Africa and southeastern Spain. The second subspecies of *Anopheles labranchiae*, in this view, is *atroparvus* which replaces subspecies *labranchiae* to the north and is widely distributed on the continent of Europe.

Finally, there are the trivial variations which exist throughout populations, without geographic correlation or evident survival value, which have no formal nomenclatorial status but are referred to by the nontechnical terms " variety," " strain," " form," " group," " breed," etc.

The International Rules of Zoological Nomenclature, since they seek to apply universal rules to cover the naming of all organisms in the animal kingdom, deal only with the main units of animal populations, i. e., categories of the magnitude of subspecies or larger. The terms " variety," " strain," " breed," etc., are colloquial and are not recognized under the formal code. Thus genetical variations within a species or subspecies which are not marked by morphological differences, but which may be of importance in disease transmission, go unrecognized insofar as designation by formal names is concerned. With this much understanding of the nature of the population units with which we are concerned, we may now consider the main problem of interest to us.

It has been remarked that if mosquitoes or sand flies were as large as dogs, or even mice, we would know a great deal more about their classifications because they would be so much easier to observe, describe and manipulate. To illustrate the fundamental difference between an introduced and an indigenous mosquito it is also much easier to consider by analogy some species we know more about, such as *Canis familiaris*, the dog. A basic difference between dogs and any mosquito species we might choose to discuss is the fact that dogs have been domesticated and their breeding manipulated for several thousand years, while mosquitoes have, in the main, been subject only to the chance selection of nature.

Keeping this difference in mind, however, we can now appreciate that within the concept of a single species may be such diverse creatures as the dachshund and the great Dane, as well as both pointers and setters. These breeds or " strains " of the species *Canis familiaris* are strikingly different in both their appearance and characteristic behavior patterns, but as they are freely inter-fertile they are of only one species. Our understanding of a species tends to be colored by our special interest in that species. In the case of coon dogs we are interested primarily in the particular traits that enable the breed to rapidly and successfully track down raccoons. In the case of most anopheline mosquitoes, the aspect of the behavior in which we have been most interested, and about which we know the most, are those characteristics which make a particular population either a successful or unsuccessful vector of malaria.

It is at once apparent that a Pekingese would be of no possible use in hunting foxes. If this breed (or strain) were turned loose it is doubtful if it could long survive by its own efforts. A mongrel dog of the same species would in all probability make out well enough under these circumstances. The Pekingese has been selectively bred for characteristics which enhance its value as a lap dog but which have little or no survival value in nature. There was a time when primitive *Canis familiaris* lived by its own efforts, and the mongrel of today retains many of these characteristics of survival value, untampered with by man.

In the case chosen as an illustration, the strains are marked by both morphological and behavioristic differences, i. e., the coon dog and the Pekingese look different and also act differently. But it is also possible for strains of a species to have the same morphological appearance, but act differently, i. e., two coon dogs may look alike but one will be a good hunter while another with the same training will not. Differences in behavior alone are of course more subtle, and often difficult to define.

Unlike the numerous clearly defined breeds of *Canis familiaris*, the populations of which mosquito species are comprised are still in the wild "mongrel" state. Exceptions to this general rule are colonies of these insects which have been bred in the laboratory for such purposes as experiments in the transmission of malaria, or for studies in resistance to certain toxicants. Such inbred laboratory standardized populations are usually referred to as "strains" of a particular species. A mosquito species as it occurs in nature must be considered as "mongrel" since there is free opportunity for interchange of all the genetic material of which it is comprised.

The work of Huff (1931) can be used to illustrate this point. This author was able to show that the ability of *Culex pipiens* to transmit infections of *Plasmodium cathemerium* to birds behaved as a simple recessive Mendelian character. By selective breeding he was able to produce one group of *Culex pipiens* which was relatively susceptible to *Plasmodium cathemerium* and another group refractory to infection with this parasite. It would appear that, had his experiments been carried further, he would have been able to produce two strains of *Culex pipiens*, the one completely susceptible, the other completely refractory. (One strain would be a homozygous dominant for infectivity, the other a homozygous recessive which was refractory to infection.) Since this very important characteristic of this mosquito species appears, as these experiments would indicate, controlled by only one gene, there is no reason to suppose that any other morphological, physiological or behavioristic character of these strains would be concurrently affected. We would then have the anomalous situation in which we would say with equal accuracy either that, " *Culex pipiens* has been shown to be an effective transmitter of *Plasmodium cathemerium* " or " *Culex pipiens* has been shown to be incapable of transmitting *Plasmodium cathemerium*." Both statements would be correct as far as they went but neither would be the whole truth. The truth of the matter is that our nomenclatorial system is too coarse a tool to deal with this situation. To express the situation accurately we must resort to some such colloquial term as " strain " and say: " There is one strain of *Culex pipiens* which is an effective vector of *Plasmodium cathemerium* and another strain which is incapable of transmitting this parasite, but the whole unselected natural population of this species is composed of a mixture of both strains, and is in consequence intermediate in its ability to transmit."

It is possible for man to exercise selection of strains in the field, without conscious effort. We unfortunately have no information on the genetical composition of *Aedes aegypti* or *Anopheles gambiae*, either concerning the African populations, or those which invaded the New World. But we do know that in Brazil the populations of both these species exhibited the kind of behavior we associate with the term " domestic," while in Africa, in addition to domestic behavior, both also demonstrate what we call " nondomestic " or " sylvan " behavior. The consistency over a period of time with which the wide range of habits has been observed in Africa, and the more limited domestic habit found in the Americas, clearly indicates the heritable genetic basis of behavior in the strain imported into the New World.

Considering *Aedes aegypti* first, we know that in Africa it is very generally associated with man, breeding in a great variety of artificial receptacles close to dwellings. But, like the other members of the subgenus *Stegomyia* to which it belongs, it also breeds in Africa in small accumulations of water in tree holes, coconut hulls and leaf axils. In Bwamba County, Uganda, Haddow (1945) found that while it was true that the species occurred in domestic receptacles, it was more often found breeding in tree holes, sometimes in virgin rain forest, and that in Bwamba it is essentially a sylvan and zoophilous species. Garnham, Harper and Highton (1946) working in Kenya found larvae a mile or more inside the forest.

Populations of this species have been introduced by human agency throughout almost all of the tropical, subtropical and portions of the temperate regions of the world. Such populations have been widespread in the New World, though eradication efforts in recent years have restricted their range in many places. The critical point to be noted in the New World is that, with only very rare exceptions, what has been called the " species," but what is in fact only a " strain," is always associated with human habitations, breeding in artificial containers, and nowhere can be considered sylvan in habit.

The *Aedes aegypti* of Kenya and Uganda are populations of the same species as that now occurring in the New World, as well as can be established by morphological comparisons, and this could be confirmed, no doubt, by the test of interfertility. But man has selected, without conscious effort, a strain of *aegypti* for importation to the New World. The strain was accidentally chosen for the characteristics of space preference and favored site for egg deposition, etc., which add up to what we call "domesticity." The individual *Aedes aegypti* that were accidentally brought by man from the Old World to the New, were in all probability those that were breeding in the water containers he carried with him. The portion of the *Aedes aegypti* population living and breeding in the African forest would not be subject to chance transportation overseas. This represents as careful a choice of strain as we exercise in selective breeding in the laboratory.

A similar situation may be observed in the case of the behavior of *Anopheles gambiae* in Africa, in comparison with the accounts of the population of this species which was imported to Brazil. In Brazil it was shown that the population of *Anopheles gambiae* was highly domestic, biting only indoors (Causey, Deane and Deane, 1943) . " Even when captures were attempted with animal and human bait right outside of houses teeming with *gambiae*, it was never possible to catch *gambiae* outdoors." (Soper and Wilson, 1943). While *Anopheles gambiae* in Africa is also considered in the main to be domestic, there are a number of reports of other behavior. De Meillon (1947) found " that when *gambiae* entered an area on the Transvaal highveld from which it is normally absent adults did not enter human habitations." At Freetown, Blacklock and Wilson (1941) report *gambiae* resting in the open on hedges and on young oil-palms. Symes found *gambiae* in an uninhabited area and considered " that it subsists mainly on animal blood until human settlement brings about a permanent increase in numbers " (quotation from Haddow, 1945, based on Symes, 1931). De Meillon has summarized the situation by pointing out that *gambiae* may (first) be almost entirely domestic, (second) may remain indoors at night only, or (third) may not enter human habitations at all.

Soper and Wilson (1943) conclude that the introduction of *Anopheles gambiae* into Brazil at Natal was probably effected by the transport of an adult or a few adults on fast mail-carrying French destroyers from Dakar. The population of *gambiae* in Brazil would thus be the progeny of one or a very few mosquitoes, with a limited genetic complement, selected for characteristics of domesticity by the circumstance of their boarding a ship in the harbor at Dakar.

It follows from this evidence that we would be in error if we concluded from the results obtained in eradicating strains of these two species in the Americas that a similar sort of effort would produce the same end result if applied against the whole genetic potential of these species in their native environment in Africa; just as we would be in error if we concluded from trials in the transmission of *Plasmodium cathemerium* with a laboratory selected strain of *Culex pipiens* refractory to this parasite, that the species *Culex pipiens* as a whole, in nature, was incapable of transmitting the infection. To put the situation accurately we can only make the qualified statement that strains of *Anopheles gambiae* and *Aedes aegypti*, characterized by domesticity, were eradicated—it was not the species *Anopheles gambiae* and *Aedes aegypti* with their full complement of genetic material enabling them to successfully weather periodic unfavorable conditions, whether natural or brought about by man, which were eliminated.

In Sardinia the ERLAAS project was concerned with a portion of a mosquito population which is widespread and successful in the western Mediterranean on both the continental shores and the islands encompassed by them. It is of importance to determine if the population of *Anopheles l. labranchiae* on Sardinia may properly be considered as indigenous there. If we could satisfy ourselves on this point we would have some basis for the belief that the population included the full scope of genetic material of a species or subspecies, from which we could expect some diversity in various of its characteristics. On the other hand, if we found evidence that *labranchiae* on Sardinia is a relatively recent introduction, since the advent of man, with the limited genetic material of a selected strain, we would be in some measure justified in making the analogy between the status of *labranchiae* in Sardinia and the condition and events illustrated by the introduction of domestic strains of *Anopheles gambiae* and *Aedes aegypti* into the Americas. It is also necessary to take some measure of just how domestic was the population of *labranchiae* on Sardinia.

The success of the original plan in the eradication of *labranchiae* in Sardinia depended, to a considerable extent, on whether it could survive on being denied the artificial shelters and the blood of man and his domestic animals (which is essentially what effective residual spraying over a period of years would have done).

This is a difficult point on which to gather direct evidence. The experience of Professor Missiroli and his associates in Latina has given rise to the hope that, in limited areas under intensive cultivation, where complete residual spraying of all human and domestic animal shelters is possible, the apparent absence of *labranchiae* larvae and adults may indicate eradication or near eradication. It should be noted, however, that this is a highly specialized situation. The bonification of the Pontine Marshes, with the radical change it brought about in the ecology of the area, must have seriously changed the native mammalian fauna. The pre-existing mosquito—native mammal relationship was modified some years before the advent of residual spraying, which then secondarily denied human and domestic mammal blood and artificial shelter to the *labranchiae* population.

In other places, where the vector of malaria has been a species with habits somewhat similar to those of *labranchiae*, as in the case of *A. quadrimaculatus* in Arkansas and *A. pseudopunctipennis* in Morelos, Mexico (Gahan and Payne, 1947), residual spraying of human and domestic animal shelters has been reflected in a significant reduction of adults in the area (of the order of 50% to 85%) but no approach to eradication or even good control of larvae. In Panama, where the vector is *A. albimanus*, a species which invades artificial structures sheltering man and domestic animals only during the active feeding period at night, no significant modification of the mosquito population of the area outside the houses was observed, except for the brief period of two or three weeks following each spraying, although excellent malaria control was obtained (Trapido, 1946).

To deal with the problem of whether *labranchiae*, or for that matter any other mosquito requiring a blood meal for oviposition, can survive in the absence of man and domestic animals, we might look into the history of the relationship. Because the studies of anopheline mosquitoes have been motivated by the interest in the group as vectors of disease, the tendency has been to work most on those aspects of the biology of these insects related to disease transmission, in this case, malaria. A fresh view of the anopheline—human relationship, quite aside from the malaria relationship involved, would undoubtedly prove profitable.

Setting aside malaria for the moment, how could we determine if the species *A. labranchiae* could survive in the absence of man and his dependent domestic animals? Obviously by removing all traces of the structures built by man and by removing man himself and his domestic animals—then observing if the mosquito survives. This is not feasible. Another way of going about the same thing would be to establish if *labranchiae* existed in Sardinia before the advent of man, and before the development of agriculture and animal husbandry as instruments of increasing and concentrating human populations. This line of investigation quickly leads us back into prehistory and a certain amount of speculation, although such information as may be deduced from prehistorical evidence can be as accurate or more accurate than a good many written records.

Prehistory is the era before the appearance of written records, and until recently it has provided us only with a relative chronology based on stratigraphy. Now, however, we are able more and more, through the application of the methods of geochronology, to translate the evidence provided by prehistory into an absolute time scale. Geochronology may be defined as " the science of dating in terms of years those periods of the past to which the human historical calender does not apply. It covers human prehistory as well as the whole of the geological past." (Zeuner, 1951) .

What we are now specifically interested in establishing is whether or not *labranchiae* existed in Sardinia before the advent of man. The record with regard to man seems fairly clear. The means of establishing the early presence of man in an area is usually that of searching for the artifacts of relatively imperishable stone or pottery he left behind. One of the prime criteria for determining that an anthropoid type was a man is the test of whether or not he made and used tools. The presence of stones which were modified into tools of one sort or another is accepted evidence of the presence of man. Archeologists also accept the premise that the mode of manufacturing these tools underwent a kind of evolution just as did man himself. Tools made by chipping stones are most primitive, while those showing grinding or polishing are more advanced. Cultures characterized by the presence of chipped stone tools are spoken of as being paleolithic, those of polished stone as neolithic. The working of metal came later, first copper or bronze and then iron, and the cultures characterized by these materials are termed the bronze or the iron age. The evolution of man through these steps to his present state occurred at different times in different places, and in some cases intermediate steps may be missing, as in the case of the South Seas where the arrival of Europeans brought the iron age to a stone age culture without the intervening bronze age. The absolute dating of these ages must be worked out separately for each locality.

It would appear that there is no record of the finding of paleolithic artifacts in Sardinia. Childe (1925) , in referring to Sardinia, states, " In paleolithic times the island was uninhabited." In his maps showing the distribution of human cultures in Europe, the first culture indicated for Sardinia is in the second half of the third millennium B. C. The *nuraghi*, which so characteristically dot the Sardinian landscape, Childe attributes to the late bronze age which would be of the order of 1000 B. C. Zeuner (1951) , who has gathered and evaluated evidence related to geochronology

from a great number of sources, presents a table (his figure 30),
based on European data, which places the beginning of the neolithic
age at about 3500 B. C., the beginning of the bronze age from about
2000 to 1500 B. C. and the beginning of the iron age at about 600 B. C.

The account of prehistoric man in Sardinia by Kendrick (1929)
is also of interest here. " No trace of paleolithic man is recorded in
Sardinia, and the earliest evidence of human occupation dates from
the time when metal was first coming into use in the Western
Mediterranean. There are, it is true, a few coastal stations in the
south of the island that have yielded purely lithic industries, but
in the greater number of the simple cave-dwellings wherein the
earliest civilization is to be recognized, there are abundant copper
implements together with the usual stone and obsidian tools.
Indeed, it was probably the natural richness of the island in copper
and lead that was responsible for the first settlements therein. The
first civilization is, in a sense, the only prehistoric civilization of
the island, for it continued without any remarkable alteration not
only until the advent of the Greeks and the Carthaginians, but
even until the coming of the Romans." Thus we see that Kendrick
would date the first human culture on Sardinia as being of the
bronze age.

In addition to attempting to date the appearance of man in
Sardinia and relate it to the time of arrival of the mosquito, we
are also interested in when man took on the way of life which
characterizes him now in most parts of the world, i. e., the living
in concentrated groups made possible by his discovery of agriculture and the domestication of wild mammals and fowl providing
a continuous food source which could be stored between growing
seasons in the case of grains, or which could be butchered as needed
in the case of domestic animals. A further requirement for the
agglomeration of human population is an adequate and continuous
supply of water. In temperate regions, with an annual cold period,
there would also be need for cover extensive enough to shelter the
entire group, i. e., either extensive natural caves, or shelters of wood,
hides, stone or earth, made by man himself. All of the basic necessities for the beginning of the social existence which characterizes
man today, favor in equal measure what we speak of as " domestic "
mosquitoes. The clustering of man himself, together with the
animals he domesticated, provided an abundant and continuously

available source of blood meals requisite to the maturation of eggs in anopheline mosquitoes; man's location near a dependable source of water established in advance that the mosquito maturing eggs after a blood meal would find a place to deposit them close at hand. Finally, the shelter required by man for protection from the adverse winter season served in equal measure as a resting place for the hibernation and diurnal retreat of adult mosquitoes.

Thus if we can date the time that man took up agriculture and animal husbandry we will have the date of the earliest time at which the man-domestic animal-mosquito relationship can have been established; for prior to this, even if an early man and the mosquito co-existed in the same area, man lived in no larger than family groups, and must of necessity have moved about in a ceaseless search for food. Zeuner (1951, figure 30) applying the methods of geochronology to the data on European man has placed the nature of the economy on a dated time scale. The paleolithic is characterized by hunters, fishermen and food collectors, while it is not until the neolithic (3500 B. C) that the food producers (agriculturists) are found.

We may now consider the age of the mosquito population. The paleontological evidence with regard to the *Culicidae* has been discussed by Edwards (1923), who states: " Since we have reason for believing that the order *Diptera* arose not later than the Triassic period, and since the *Culicidae* are certainly one of the more primitive families of the order, it is highly probable that members of this family existed during the Jurassic period, before the age of mammals; the fact that many *Culex* at the present day attack lizards and frogs, suggests that even the blood-sucking habit may have been developed at this early period." Zeuner (1951) in his figure 83 dates the Triassic at 152 to 182 million years ago, and the Jurassic at 127 to 152 million years ago. Fossil mosquitoes of a modern genus (*Culex*) are known from the Eocene (approximately 50 million years ago), and Edwards says further that, " In the Oligocene rocks of the Isle of Wight and Germany remains of *Culicidae* are numerous, but the species hardly differ from those of the present day; all the three subfamilies are represented, as well as the genera *Dixa*, *Chaoborus*, *Mochlonyx*, *Culex*, *Aedes*, and perhaps *Theobaldia*, *Mansonia* and *Megarhinus*." (The Oligocene dates back about 30 million years.) With regard to the anophelines which are of particular interest to us we have the additional statement by Edwards (1923), "Although no fossil *Anopheles* has yet been found, there can be no doubt from its morphology that it is an old genus, most probably older than any culicine form; its nonoccurrence in the fossil state can be accounted for by supposing that it has always been, as it is now, less abundant than the *Culicinae*." It has also been pointed out that the scarcity of fossil mosquitoes in general is a reflection of their unsuitability for preservation as fossils rather than any lack of them in remote geological time.

In attempting to piece together the picture of the relationship of the anopheline mosquito *A. labranchiae* and *Homo sapiens* as an agriculturist and herdsman in Sardinia, we have thus far only established the fact that mosquitoes similar to if not identical to modern species existed millions of years ago, while the record of man in Sardinia is relatively brief, i. e., extending back only about 5,500 years from the present. It will be recognized that the information with regard to man is quite specific, while that for *labranchiae* is rather general, since there are no records of fossil anophelines. How then can we tie down the status of *labranchiae* in more specific terms? Recent work on the life of species in terms of geological time can help us on this point. Zeuner (1951) points out that some species have persisted without apparent alteration for as much as 30 million years, while others have evolved during periods of only half to one million years. The following generalizations are made by Zeuner based on his own work and that of others.

(1)   "There appears to be a fastest rate of evolution of species of the animal kingdom under natural conditions, namely about 500,000 years per species-step."

(2)   "In evolution the number of generations appear to be less significant than absolute time." That is to say, the fact that a mosquito may have several generations a year, while man may have only several in a century, does not necessarily mean that the mosquito will evolve more rapidly than man.

(3)   "Every species passes through an episode of rapid evolution but may become stabilized thereafter and persist unaltered for a long time."

Our knowledge of the great antiquity of the *Culicidae* would lead us to the conclusion that the group passed through its episode of rapid evolution many millions of years ago, and is now relatively stable. But, in any event, we could reasonably expect *labranchiae* to be not less than 500,000 years old.

With this much background we may now examine in more detail the relationship of *labranchiae* to man and to the native fauna in Sardinia, and evaluate the two propositions: the one, that this mosquito is dependent on man for its existence; the other, that the species has in the past, and can at the present, get along very well in the absence of man.

1. An examination of a map of Europe and the Mediterranean basin during Pleistocene times (i. e., within the past one million years) shows that at the time of the greatest extension of land, Sardinia and Corsica were connected with northwestern Italy (figure 14 in MacCurdy, 1924). There would have been at that time no water obstacle to the free passage of *labranchiae* from the mainland to these land masses. From what we know about the probable antiquity of the anopheline species in the area, it is also likely that *labranchiae* was on the scene at that time, and quite capable of inhabiting this peninsula, as well as what was then the Italian isthmus connecting Europe to North Africa, where the species also occurs today. There is abundant evidence that during the interglacial epochs Europe had a much milder climate than at present, as proved by the fossil remains there of such mammals characteristic of warm regions as the hippopotamus, rhinoceros, hyena, etc.

2. Kendrick (1929) in discussing the archaeological reconstruction of the prehistory of man in Sardinian states: "The first habitations were perhaps cave dwellings, but it was not long before stone-built huts were erected. Many villages of such huts are known, one of the best examples being that of Gonessa in the southwest of the island. The little houses themselves were mostly round, and about 20 feet in diameter; inside they were furnished with benches, stalls for animals, and an altar near the entrance. In a strategic position near the huts were dwellings of grander character, perhaps the residences of chief-

tains, but fortified so that they might serve as watch-tower, refuge and defense for the whole village in times of danger. These are the *nuraghi*, double-storeyed towers in the shape of a truncated cone and built of large stones laid in regular horizontal courses sometimes with the aid of a clay mortar."

We are struck at once by this evidence that the first human habitations on the island were caves, with stone-built huts being erected later. To place the horse in proper relation to the cart we can only conclude that at the time of the geologically recent introduction of man to the island, it was he who invaded the habitation of the mosquitoes, rather than the converse. As man prospered through his exploitation of agriculture and animal husbandry, he increased and undertook the construction of stone huts to provide shelter for his greater numbers. This activity provided additional facilities for mosquitoes, and no doubt the mosquitoes increased also.

3. If we hesitate to accept the thesis that *labranchiae* was a resident of Sardinia at the time that island was connected with the European mainland, or that man invaded the mosquito habitat rather than the converse, we might next look into the possibility of the introduction of *labranchiae* onto this land mass by natural agency before the advent of man. The path of the seasonal flight of migratory birds follows an ancient pattern. In the present instance we are interested in waterfowl which feed in what is also a favored *labranchiae* habitat—fresh-water swamps with surface vegetation. Corsica and Sardinia are along the flyway of a number of species of waterfowl which winter in North Africa and summer in Europe. Dr. Alexander Wetmore, Secretary of the Smithsonian Institution, has kindly provided a partial list of species of ducks migrant between Europe and northern Africa which have also been recorded from Sardinia. This list excludes several species of rare, casual or accidental occurrence.

> *Tadorna tadorna* (Linnaeus). Shelduck
> *Anas platyrhynchos platyrhynchos* Linnaeus. Mallard
> *Anas strepera* Linnaeus. Gadwall.
> *Anas acuta acuta* Linnaeus. Eurasian Pintail
> *Anas querquedula* Linnaeus. Garganey
> *Anas crecca crecca* Linnaeus. Teal

Spatula clypeata (Linnaeus). Shoveler
Mareca penelope (Linnaeus). Wigeon
Netta rufina (Pallas). Red-crested Pochard
Nyroca ferina ferina (Linnaeus). Common Pochard
Nyroca fuligula (Linnaeus). Tufted Duck
Mergus albellus Linnaeus. Smew

That such waterfowl are capable of transporting the eggs of mosquitoes adhering to their feet, legs and feathers is strongly supported by the unpublished observations of Dr. Herbert C. Clark and Lawrence H. Dunn who, while examining ducks shot by members of a hunting club at the La Jagua swamps in Panama for ectoparasites, also found the eggs of several species of mosquitoes, which hatched out in the laboratory. While anopheline eggs are not known to withstand prolonged desiccation, they might be expected to remain viable for the few hours flight from either Corsica or North Africa to Sardinia.

In the light of this information we might digress a moment to suggest that migrating waterfowl may reintroduce *labranchiae* into Sardinia, either from North Africa to the south, or Corsica to the north. The quarantine of ships, boats and aircraft, no matter how thorough or effective, will not block this means of reintroduction.

4. Evidence of the north or southward extensions of the ranges of mosquitoes within the separate hemispheres is lacking. The impression is strong that these ranges are well established, and have been determined by natural agencies before the advent of man, though of course they are frequently locally modified by man's alteration of the hydrology. A case illustrating this point very clearly is that of the status of *Anopheles albimanus* in Florida. The species is the common and abundant malaria vector in Cuba, and on a number of occasions specimens have been taken in the Florida Keys only a few miles to the north and in southern Florida itself. On several such occasions alarm has been expressed over the possibility that the species might become established as a malaria vector in Florida, but, whether control measures were taken or not, the species remains a rare curiosity, apparently being at the natural limit of its range to the north, with man serving neither to extend nor restrict its range.

Such introductions as have been spectacularly successful (from the point of view of the mosquitoes) have been made by man himself along lines of equal latitude from one continent to another (*Aedes aegypti* and *Anopheles gambiae*), natural agencies before the advent of man having failed to bridge the vast oceanic gap to a suitable habitat of like latitude on another continent.

5. One is struck at once in Sardinia by the fact that the conspicuous native mammalian fauna of the island includes wild boar, moufflon and rabbits, whose domestic counterparts, pigs, sheep and rabbits were, by all accounts, before the advent of ERLAAS, hosts of *labranchiae*. While *labranchiae* is considered a very domestic species, Hackett (1937) reports that " in southern Italy and Sardinia, where *labranchiae* prevails, from 10 to 20 per cent live on human blood." We see then that the bulk of these mosquitoes feed on other animals and the implication is clear that the species could get along very well without man, and indeed with only the wild counterparts of man's aggregations of domestic animals.

6. It is very much more difficult to search natural resting places of mosquitoes than the conveniently accessible structures built by man to shelter himself and his domestic animals, but Dr. T. H. G. Aitken has accumulated a number of records of *labranchiae* resting in such places during the summer and hibernating in winter. It has been suggested that *labranchiae* is never found more than five kilometers from some structure made by man, and reasoned from this that the species is completely dependent on man. But if circles five kilometers in radius were drawn about every such structure below the 1000 meter level on Sardinia it is likely that little, if any, part of the island below this level would not be covered. This observation, therefore, can only be taken as a statement of the evident fact that man-made structures are widely dispersed on most of the island. A more useful method of judging how closely *labranchiae* may be bound to man would be that of reviewing positives in relation to *centers* of human population. Dr. Aitken has had this done, with interesting results. Of all *labranchiae* positives found during 1950 only 8.2 per cent were less than one kilometer from a

village center, while 33.3 per cent were more than five kilometers distant. The comparable figures given by him for 1949 are 8.6 per cent and 21.5 per cent (ERLAAS memoranda from Dr. Aitken, dated January 15, 1951 and January 27, 1951). It might be explained that the small proportion of positives near villages is a result of attrition following the residual spraying of dwellings, but this in no way diminishes the significance of the fact that a substantial number of such positives as were found, were more than five kilometers distant from these centers of population, and in several cases were as much as 11 to 12 kilometers distant.

The great weight of all this evidence indicates that *labranchiae* antedated man, the agriculturist and herdsman, on Sardinia by a vast period of time, maintaining itself on the native mammal population. It is unlikely that it would have abandoned this relationship in its entirety during a period so brief in the geological lifespan of a species as five or six thousand years.

This conclusion is of considerable significance in the eradication effort on Sardinia. *Anopheles labranchiae* as a long-time native resident of Sardinia may be expected to have the full genetic complement of that species. It is not a selected strain of the species, accidentally chosen for its domestic characteristics, and is therefore not bound to man for its survival. It may be expected to demonstrate the resilience of species in their native environment to adverse conditions, whether natural or man-made. On being denied access to man and his domestic animals it might be expected to survive through the portion of the population which maintains its original relationship with the native mammal fauna and original natural resting places. The experience of ERLAAS during the 1949 and 1950 seasons would appear to demonstrate that *Anopheles labranchiae* has by this means fulfilled the biological potential of an indigenous population with a high reproductive rate and a good adjustment with its environment. In just what way or ways *labranchiae* expressed this biological potential in avoiding complete destruction, we unfortunately cannot be sure.

It has recently been suggested by Soper (1951) that if indeed the ERLAAS program has been effective in eliminating the portion of the *labranchiae* population on Sardinia bound to man, then:

" Are the few remaining *labranchiae* in Sardinia direct descendants of the *labranchiae* of thousands of years before adaptation to life with man occurred and, therefore, incapable of building up the heavy infestation responsible for the previous highly malarious state of the island? " To expect such an outcome, we would have to assume that the behavior characteristics which we sum up with the term " domesticity " are controlled by a very few genes, and that the ERLAAS program had completely eliminated the portion of the *labranchiae* population with these genes which bind it to man's activities, leaving a residual population homozygous for the characteristics which relate it only to the native fauna, and completely dissociate it from man. That the selective action on the *labranchiae* population has been so drastic and complete (as, for example, in the converse case of the selection of a very few domestic individuals of the species *Anopheles gambiae* and *Aedes aegypti* for introduction into the New World) is unlikely, since, despite the continuous attrition produced by the residual spraying program in Sardinia, some of the positives of the last year of the ERLAAS operation were found in domestic situations. We may also recall that since *labranchiae* invaded the habitat of man when he settled on the island in prehistoric times, as would appear from the evidence assembled earlier in this paper, the residual population of *labranchiae* will retain sufficient plasticity to do so again.

THE ERLAAS DECREE
OFFICIAL GAZETTE
OF
THE KINGDOM OF ITALY

HUMBERT OF SAVOY

In virtue of the authority delegated to Us;

In view of decree law of June 25, 1944 No. 151;

In view of the decision of the Council of Ministers;

As proposed by the President of the Council of Ministers, the Prime Minister, Secretary of State, and Minister of Foreign Affairs, and in accord with the Ministers of Finance, Public Instruction, Public Works, Agriculture and Forests;

We have approved and promulgated the following:

Article 1

There is created with headquarters in Cagliari, a para-governmental entity to be known as the *"Ente Regionale per la Lotta Anti-Anofelica in Sardegna"* (ERLAAS).

The above mentioned Service is placed under the supervision of the High Commissioner for Hygiene and Public Health.

Article 2

ERLAAS has as its objective the elimination of anophelines from all of Sardinia.

ERLAAS will also:

a—Conduct investigations on anophelines;

b—Give its opinion regarding projects connected with drainage and land improvements;

c—Report to the sanitary authorities all hygienic defects which could maintain or aggravate malaria;

d—Arrange for the coordination by the local sanitary authorities of the activities of other institutions or services, which are interested in anti-anopheline measures, with its own activities;

e—Take all the action deemed necessary, under existing legislation, to ensure that all necessary measures for the elimination of anophelines are carried out.

ERLAAS is authorized to take over, in whole or in part, the activities of any other local agency or institution which is engaged in similar activities.

Article 3

ERLAAS, in order to carry out its work, is provided:

a) With a contribution of 300,000,000 lire from the UNRRA Assistance and Reconstruction fund;

b) With the equipment and supplies donated for this purpose by UNRRA; and

c) With any other subsidies and contributions which may be made by organizations interested in the antimalaria campaign.

Article 4

ERLAAS is to be directed by a Superintendent who is an expert in anopheline eradication work, appointed by the High Commissioner for Hygiene and Public Health in agreement with the representative of The Rockefeller Foundation for the Mediterranean Region.

In the same manner a Vice-Superintendent will be appointed.

The Superintendent and the Vice-Superintendent may be non-Italian.

Article 5

The Superintendent will legally represent and administer the Service; arrange for the employment of personnel; make agreements with public and private agencies; draw up the regulations regarding accounting, personnel, and working conditions; and will be generally responsible for all matters connected with the Service.

The budget and the accounts of the Service will be subject to the approval of the High Commissioner for Hygiene and Public Health, as well as the regulations referred to in the preceding paragraph.

In case of absence or disability, the Superintendent will be substituted by the Vice-Superintendent.

Article 6

The Superintendent of the Service will be assisted by a Committee composed of the following members:

—A member appointed by the High Commissioner for Hygiene and Public Health;

—A member appointed by the Ministry of the Treasury;

—A member appointed by the Ministry of Agriculture and Forests;

—A member appointed by the Ministry of Public Works;

—A member appointed by the Italian Government Delegation for Relations with UNRRA;

—A member appointed by the UNRRA Italian Mission;

—A member appointed by the High Commissioner for Sardinia;

—A representative of the *Consorzi di Bonifica* (Reclamation Bureau) of Sardinia;

—The Provincial Health Officer of Cagliari;

—The Provincial Health Officer of Sassari;

—The Provincial Health Officer of Nuoro;

—The Director of the Institute of Hygiene of the University of Cagliari;

—The Chief Engineer of the Public Works Department of the Province of Cagliari.

The functions of secretary will be carried out by one of the members of the Committee.

Article 7

The Committee will be convoked by and presided over by the Superintendent and will give opinions on the following:

a) Accounts and budgets of the Service and the regulations governing accounting, personnel, and working conditions;

b) On all other matters which are brought to its attention.

Article 8

The members of the Committee who reside in the *comune* in which the Committee meets will be paid an attendance honorarium;

other members will have the right to reimbursement for traveling and living expenses.

In the case of Committee members who are not government employees the honorarium and other allowances mentioned in the preceding paragraph will be paid on the scale specified for government employees of grade 5.

Article 9

The Superintendent of the Service may grant special allowances to members of the Committee for special duties of a permanent nature.

Article 10

The fiscal year of the Service will start on January 1 and end on December 31.

In November of each year the Superintendent will prepare the budget for the ensuing year.

The Superintendent will have the power, within the limits of the budget and without any special formalities, to make all payments; except that he must justify them in accounts submitted to the Office of the High Commissioner for Hygiene and Public Health for approval not later than March 31 of each year.

Article 11

At the beginning, and until the Service is in a position to prepare its budget, funds will be advanced to the Service on authorization of the High Commissioner for Hygiene and Public Health.

Article 12

The High Commissioner for Hygiene and Public Health is authorized to make inspections of the offices and work of the Service.

Article 13

Once the objective for which the Service has been created has been attained, the High Commissioner for Hygiene and Public Health, in agreement with the Ministry of Treasury, by means of a decree of the President of the Council of Ministers, will dissolve the Service and dispose of its assets.

Any remaining resources will be allotted to the antimalaria work of the High Commission for Hygiene and Public Health.

Article 14

The present decree will be in effect the day following its publication in the Official Gazette.

We order that the present decree, stamped with the Seal of State, be placed in the official file of laws and decrees of the Kingdom of Italy, charging everybody to observe it, and require others to observe it, as a law of the State.

Dated: Rome, April 12, 1946.

HUMBERT OF SAVOY

De Gasperi—Corbino
Molè—Cattani—Gullo

" Seen: " Keeper of the Seal—Togliatti

Registered in the *Corte dei Conti,* April 19, 1946.

Government Documents Register No. 9—page No. 150—Frasca.

UNRRA
ESTIMATE OF PROPOSED PROGRAM
FOR MALARIA ERADICATION–SARDINIA
NOVEMBER 1945

(Summarized)

Total population	1,119,109
Total area of island	9,250 sq. miles

Larviciding

Assume larviciding for one season of six months with weekly dusting using Paris green with 0.5 per cent of the area to be treated; 46.25 sq. miles. Assume 1.0 pounds Paris green per acre and that one larvicider can cover 4 acres per day.

1,225 larviciders	6 jeeps
175 foremen	385 tons Paris green
50 area supervisors	200 hand dusters
6 region chiefs	3,000 buckets
50 weapons carriers	150 larvae dippers

(The use of a PT-17 airplane may be desirable.)

Minor drainage

250 laborers	1 engineer assistant
25 foremen	25 weapons carriers
1 jeep	

Adult control

Assume 66 grams of DDT per person for 1,119,109 people plus 25 per cent additional for respraying. Using 5 per cent DDT in kerosene, an eight-man crew sprays 100 gallons of solution daily. Work to be done in a four-month period during one winter.

350 laborers	10 jeeps
50 foremen	500 sprayers
10 supervisors	100 tons DDT
50 weapons carriers	500,000 gallons of kerosene

Cost

	Personnel	Trans-portation	Supplies + Freight	Subtotal
Larviciding program	$911,760	$108,400	$202,975	$1,233,135
Minor drainage	102,300	51,400	3,218	156,918
Adult control	372,670	139,000	238,165	749,835
General office	14,280		23,563	37,843
General & repair shop			5,185	5,185
Rent				3,400
Freight				43,500
Additional UNRRA expense				
Freight (supplies)				50,000
Bicycles		4,000		4,000
Standby weapons carriers		20,000		20,000
Standby jeeps		11,200		11,200
Totals	$1,401,010	$324,000	$473,106	$2,305,016
20 per cent Contingent Fund				461,003
Total estimated cost of project				$2,766,019

PERSONNEL

STAFF

Superintendent

	Period of Service		
J. H. Bauer, M. D. (Interim)	Sept.	1949–Feb.	1950
J. A. Kerr, M. D.	Sept.	1946–Sept.	1947
John A. Logan	Oct.	1947–Sept.	1949
	Feb.	1950–July	1951
D. B. Wilson, M. D. (Interim)	May	1946–Sept.	1946

Vice-Superintendent

Thomas H. G. Aitken (Interim)	May	1946–Sept.	1946
Frederick W. Knipe	Sept.	1946–July	1951

Operations

Thomas H. G. Aitken	May	1946–July	1951
Beneviene Barachini	Oct.	1947–Oct.	1950
Guido Casini, M. D.	May	1946–July	1951
Eric Holder	Mar.	1947–July	1951
Ezio Mosna, M. D.	Mar.	1949–Oct.	1950
Ronald S. Stapley	Feb.	1947–Oct.	1950
Gordon Sutherland	April	1947–Oct.	1950

Epidemiology

John Maier, M. D.	Sept.	1950–July	1951
Athol J. Patterson, M. D.	Jan.	1949–Sept.	1950
Osler L. Peterson, M. D.	Nov.	1947–June	1948
Luigi F. Spano, M. D.	Jan.	1947–May	1951

Public Relations

Kellow R. Chesney	Nov.	1946–Dec.	1948
Stella Dunn	Dec.	1947–July	1951

Administrative Services

Vincenzo Amat	Nov.	1946–Feb.	1949

Fernando Aru	Feb.	1947–July	1951
Paolo Carta	Sept.	1946–July	1951
Ettore Chirico	April	1947–July	1951
Fred Collins	Feb.	1947–Dec.	1950
Igino Costi	Oct.	1947–Aug.	1949
Francesco Falqui	Dec.	1946–Aug.	1949
Salvatore Marocco	Mar.	1947–Dec.	1950
Ernesto Pacchiarotti	Oct.	1946–April	1949

Administrative Assistants

Salvatore Cabras	Mar.	1947–Nov.	1950
Giuseppe Canalis	Mar.	1946–Jan.	1950
Andrea Chessa	June	1946–July	1951
Ernesto Collu	Feb.	1947–July	1951
Giovanni Deidda	Jan.	1947–July	1951
Angelina Fornari	Oct.	1949–July	1951
John Gaias	April	1947–July	1951
Irma A. Hilton	Dec.	1946–June	1947
Marion Isay	July	1947–Aug.	1949
Loris Melis	Nov.	1946–July	1951
Bernardo Murgia	Dec.	1946–Dec.	1950
Mario Pelaghi	July	1947–Mar.	1949
Leopoldo Ruffi	Jan.	1947–Oct.	1949
Giovanni Russo	April	1947–July	1951
Nellie C. Valenti	Oct.	1946–Dec.	1950

Special Services

Stefano Achenza	Feb.	1948–April	1950
Rolando Bugli	Mar.	1948–Oct.	1950
Giuseppe Collu	Jan.	1947–Oct.	1950
Emilio Gario	April	1950–Sept.	1950
Luigi Mamberti	April	1947–Oct.	1950
Luigi Mioligi	May	1946–Nov.	1946
Achille Petrocchi	Mar.	1949–June	1951
Antonio Porcu	Nov.	1946–Mar.	1951
Franco Rosas	May	1947–Dec.	1950
Adolfo Secchi	Oct.	1946–July	1951
Paolo Serra	Jan.	1947–Oct.	1950
Giovanni Tocco	Jan.	1947–Dec.	1950
James Wright	Sept.	1946–Feb.	1949

Division Chiefs

Italo Aru	May	1947–Feb.	1951
Vito Asaro	Feb.	1948–Feb.	1951
Massimo Cadeddu	Jan.	1948–Sept.	1950
Alfredo Callegari	Mar.	1947–Dec.	1950
Mario Corongiu	Aug.	1947–Feb.	1951
Ettore Dettori	Feb.	1947–Sept.	1950
Leonardo Faedda	Mar.	1947–Aug.	1950
Carmine Ferullo	June	1947–Feb.	1951
Giovanni Fois	June	1947–Feb.	1951
Eraldo Innocenti	Jan.	1948–Aug.	1950
Antonio Lanero	Feb.	1947–Jan.	1951
Alessandro Lupo	Jan.	1947–July	1951
Ernesto Marongiu	Nov.	1946–Feb.	1951
Paolo Masia	Dec.	1946–Nov.	1948
Bruno Piredda	Jan.	1947–Feb.	1951
Raimondo Orrù	July	1947–Feb.	1949
Giovanni A. Scanu	Oct.	1947–Jan.	1951
Baldassarre Sebastiani	Jan.	1947–Oct.	1950
Giovanni Sechi	Nov.	1947–Feb.	1951
Angelo Sulas	Mar.	1947–Feb.	1951
Nicolò Ventura	Feb.	1947–Dec.	1949
Adriano Venturini	Jan.	1947–Dec.	1948

ERLAAS ADVISORY COUNCIL

Ing. Ruggero de Angelis
Dr. Aristide Arrighi
H. E. Professor Gino Bergami
H. E. Professor Giuseppe Brotzu
H. E. Prefect Stanislao Caboni
Dr. Prof. Antonino Canalis
Dr. Felice Cipolla
Dr. Luigi Cosco Marzucca
Ing. Terenzio Congiu
Ing. Salvatore De Maria
Dr. Aldo Duce
Ing. Faustino Martelli
Professor Alberto Missiroli

Gr. Uff. Rag. Odoardo Mola
Dr. Ezio Mosna
Dr. Michele Muzzetto
Avv. Luigi Oggiano
Professor Francesco Passino
Professor Tommaso Patrissi
H. E. General Pietro Pinna
Ing. Adolfo Sciavicco
Senator Aldo Spallicci

TEMPORARY INVESTIGATORS

M. H. M. Abdulcader, M. D.
Professor Maria E. Alessandrini
Sergio Bettini, M. D.
Francesco Boselli
Lord John Boyd-Orr
James R. Busvine
Antonio Ciocco
Ralph Gander
G. Garrett-Jones
Hendrijk Kraan
Antonio Medda
Ezio Mosna, M. D.
J. F. Newman
Professor Giuseppe Pegreffi
Diego Pitruzzella
H. Pirie
Harold Trapido
Giuseppe Saccà, M. D.

LEGAL REPRESENTATIVE

On. Avv. Antonio Maxia

INSECTICIDE MIXING PLANT

During the 1947 campaign the larvicide was mixed by hand. Measured amounts of DDT, Triton X-100 and Diesel oil were added to standard 220-liter metal drums, and then placed in the sun. The drums were rolled or tipped for a few minutes each hour until solution took place, usually within one and a half to three days. This was too slow to cope with the demand and the system was replaced with one whereby agitation was provided in individual barrels by a hand pump which kept the mixture circulating rapidly.

While these temporary processes were employed throughout 1947, it was realized that the expanded program in 1948 would require a much faster and more flexible system in order to turn out large quantities of larvicide without interruption. It was also necessary to make provision for preparing bulk lots of DDT-kerosene solution for use, in conjunction with DDT emulsion, for residual spray operations.

The Italian State Railways agreed to let ERLAAS have the use of a spur track and an adjacent plot of ground on which mixing operations could be carried out. They also loaned two water-tank cars (having a total capacity of 24,500 liters) and an empty box car. The former were used for the actual mixing and the latter served as an office and pump house. Electrical lines were extended to the site for light and power. Three electrically driven pumps of 14 h.p., 2.5 h.p. and 1.5 h.p. were borrowed and used to recirculate the contents of the tanks. Storage was provided by the use of three steel storage tanks, two of 10,000 and one of 50,000-liter capacity, loaned by the Italian Air Force.

The two tank cars were interconnected by two-inch and three-inch pipes to the storage tanks and the pumps in such a way that each of the tank cars could fill or draw from any of the storage tanks independently. The two tank cars operated separately, one normally being connected to the 14 h.p. pump and the second to the 2.5 h.p. one. The 1.5 h.p. pump was for reserve use only. The flow diagram is shown in figure 36.

386

73. Airplane view of the Colostrai swamp near Muravera.

74. Growth of aquatic vegetation in a previously cleared
collector canal near Cagliari.

75. Clearing a typical mountain stream in Muravera division.

76. Effect of stream training, using Martin ditcher,
Padrongiano River near Olbia.

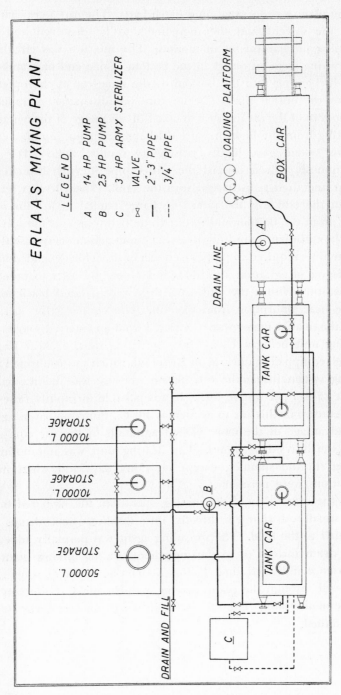

FIGURE 36. Schematic layout of insecticide mixing plant.

The plant was operated on a batch basis. The cars were charged with the solvent and the ingredients to be dissolved and the pumping mechanism set in motion. The mixture was circulated by drawing from an outlet in the bottom of one end of a tank car and discharging into the bottom of the same car at the opposite end to the outlet pipe. The mixture was discharged parallel to the bottom of the car in order to take full advantage of the agitation resulting from the high pressure discharge from the pump.

This system gave highly satisfactory results. Solid DDT was continuously driven toward the outlet pipe, drawn through the pump and then redischarged into the tank. The currents set up within the tanks by the pump discharge tended to lift the solid DDT from the bottom and to distribute it throughout the solvent, and the turbulence resulting from the pump action delayed settling.

The time required to prepare a batch of larvicide depended upon the degree of agitation and the temperature. In order to raise the temperature within the tank cars, they were painted black to increase heat absorption from the sun. The tank usually operated with the smaller motor was also heated from an external source, the heating unit being a U. S. Army sterilizing unit, Cleaver Brooks Model, equipped to operate on Diesel oil, which was connected to a piping system inside the car. Steam pressure was maintained at about 25 lbs. per square inch. It was possible to rapidly raise the temperature in this car to as high as 40° C., thus compensating for the advantage of the more violent agitation in the car equipped with the heavy-duty pump. The heating unit was not normally needed in the summer, except on rainy days and when night operations were necessary.

At the conclusion of the mixing operation, the prepared batch was usually discharged directly into 220-liter steel drums for dispatch to the field. The spreading agent was normally added to each drum instead of to the ingredients in the mixing plant, as experience indicated that Triton X-100 was liable to congeal as it passed through the plant, leaving a thick, sticky residue on the inside of the tank. The reason for this reaction was never clearly determined.

Whenever it was possible to prepare larvicide in advance, it was stored in one of the three reserve tanks. Usually, however, at least two of these were used for the storage of solvents.

The mixing unit was placed in operation in October 1947 and continued to function until October 1950. Two or three brief shutdowns for general overhauls took place, but no time was lost because of breakdowns. When operated at full capacity, the plant was capable of turning out a total of 73,500 liters per day, equivalent to three batches per tank per 24-hour period. During the three years of operation, a total of 5,186.6 metric tons of ingredients were mixed, producing approximately 5,700,000 liters of insecticide.

RECOMMENDATIONS TO THE ITALIAN GOVERNMENT

On the conclusion of operations in the fall of 1950, even though it appeared that ERLAAS had failed in its primary objective of eradicating *Anopheles labranchiae* from Sardinia, the all-out attempt originally approved by The Rockefeller Foundation Health Commission had been made. In the process, ERLAAS had amassed a great deal of data and experience which most certainly would be of value in the fields of malariology and public health. Malaria transmission had been stopped and Sardinia, for the first time, was in a position to exploit more fully the island's economic and social resources.

Regardless of any considerations on the relative merits of the species eradication technique as a method of malaria control, the benefits from ERLAAS more than justified the cost of the project and it was desirable that adequate provision be made to protect these gains. In preparing a recommendation to the Italian Government concerning post-ERLAAS activities, the following possibilities were considered:

(a) A continuation of the eradication program by means of selective scouting and larviciding for a period of five years in an attempt to assure the total elimination of *labranchiae* from the island.

(b) The termination of all control and eradication operations, maintaining only a combined entomological-epidemiological scouting service. In the event of renewed malaria transmission, a suitable program of control could then be initiated.

(c) A limited DDT residual spray campaign directed against those sections of the island still considered dangerous from an entomological point of view.

(d) An annual island-wide DDT residual spray campaign

390

similar to that being carried out in the malarious regions of Italy.

It was estimated that the eradication program (a) could be continued at an annual cost of not more than 400,000,000 lire, that is, an amount equivalent to that necessary for an island-wide DDT residual spray campaign (d). The completion of eradication would have the great advantage of not requiring in perpetuity the large annual expenditures necessitated by the residual spray type of control. Either the (b) or (c) method would entail annual savings for an indefinite period of time, but at the end of that time it would probably be necessary to reinitiate island-wide control.

After a careful review, the following recommendation was forwarded to the Italian High Commissioner for Hygiene and Public Health.

January 31, 1951

Professor Mario Cottellessa
Alto Commissario per l'Igiene
e la Sanità Pubblica
Palazzo Viminale
Roma

Your Excellency:

The ERLAAS project, established by legislative decree on April 12, 1946, is now in the final stages of completion. All field operations have terminated and all supplies and equipment have been returned to Cagliari. We are now engaged in closing the accounts and in preparing a Final Report. This report will not be ready until about July of this year. Our Annual Report, which has now been completed in English, is being translated into Italian and should be ready to turn over to you in February.

These reports will show that malaria transmission appears to have been eliminated from Sardinia, and there is no reason to expect that it will return, provided that adequate precautions are maintained. No mosquito transmission has been verified by ERLAAS during 1950 and the number of relapses has been reduced to a very low figure. I am attaching herewith a table showing the number of cases of malaria officially reported, by province and by year, from 1936 to 1950.

As regards the original objective of eliminating the malaria vector *Anopheles labranchiae* from the island, it is still too early for a final evaluation of the results obtained, but it is not likely that island-wide eradication has been achieved. *Labranchiae*, however, appears to have been eliminated from the great majority of the known infested areas and probably the only remaining members of the species are scattered in a relatively few isolated areas. Should your office decide that eradication is advisable, for either scientific or practical purposes, it now appears possible and could be obtained with a selective scouting and larviciding program carried out over the next few years. I am attaching herewith a sector map showing the sectors found positive after July 1, 1950 which indicates the very limited areas found to have been most recently occupied by the species. However, intensive eradication measures have been carried out in these areas and presumably most of them were eliminated by October 31.

The evidence which we have indicates that residual spraying alone has no major effect on the sylvatic *labranchiae* populations in Sardinia. Because of this capacity to survive in sparsely inhabited areas, it can be expected that any malaria control program based on residual spray operations will permit the *labranchiae* population to increase and eventually reoccupy much of its former territory.

While the evidence from practically every part of the world has shown that the use of DDT residual spraying has stopped malaria transmission, regardless of its effect on the vector population, certain other limitations in the use of residual spraying should be considered:

(a) Due to the world situation the price of DDT is mounting rapidly and its availability is becoming increasingly uncertain. In addition, Sardinia, because of its insular location, would be particularly vulnerable to any dislocation of normal shipping or trade.

(b) The use of DDT residual spraying in Italy has been facilitated by its concomitant fly control. In Sardinia, at the present time, there is no residual insecticide or combination of residual insecticides known to us which will control flies. The future use of DDT residual spraying is going to be seriously hindered by this fact and the resulting lack of cooperation on the part of the public.

(c) The partially sylvatic nature of Sardinian *labranchiae*, combined with the necessity for people to work long distances from their villages, would make it possible for a certain amount of transmission to continue regardless of residual spraying.

As malaria has been reduced to such an extremely low level, the chain of malaria transmission may already have been broken. Even if it has not been broken it is also true that, if all control methods were abandoned, malaria would not be a problem in Sardinia for several years to come. However, it is evident that the present situation as regards *labranchiae* density cannot be maintained except by a continuation of a larviciding program. This could be confined to those areas still considered dangerous plus scouting operations carried out as a preventive measure in the rest of the island. The costs for a program of this type would probably not exceed those necessary for an island-wide residual spraying program.

It must be pointed out that a program of the kind recommended would be more difficult to organize than a residual spray program. To carry it out, a good deal of flexibility would be necessary in the organization. Also, although we have made considerable advances, many of the scientific problems in connection with the eradication of an indigenous species are still unsolved and it would be necessary that such a program have additional skilled technical staff available.

Nevertheless, it is the opinion of the ERLAAS staff that the proposed island-wide residual spraying be replaced by a limited but carefully planned scouting and larviciding program aiming at eventual eradication. This would be followed by quarantine measures to prevent the reintroduction of the vector species, when eradicated. The goal of complete eradication is at hand and if this can be attained, the high cost of annual residual spraying campaigns can be eliminated. If, at some future date, it is found that residual spraying is advisable because of new developments in the field of insecticides, it can then be undertaken.

As our 1950 and Final Reports will indicate, it is felt that the

ERLAAS project has been a useful experiment. Although the eradication of *labranchiae* from the entire island may not have been accomplished the value of the experiment, both to Italy and to the world, far exceeds the cost of the project. In addition, as a rehabilitation measure, ERLAAS has drained and improved considerable areas of land which can now be farmed, it has made it possible for anyone to live and work anywhere in Sardinia without fear of malaria and has given Sardinia a new hope and a tremendous opportunity for the future.

I would be pleased to discuss the details of this general recommendation with you or representatives of your Department at any time. With best personal regards, I am,

Yours very truly,

JOHN A. LOGAN

Superintendent of ERLAAS

The contents of this letter were discussed at a special meeting called by the High Commissioner in Rome on February 22, 1951. The conference was attended by representatives of the Office of the High Commissioner and of ERLAAS, by Professor Alberto Missiroli of the Istituto Superiore di Sanità and by Dr. P. F. Russell of The Rockefeller Foundation. Details of the proposed plan were presented and a map (figure 37) was used to indicate those areas which should continue under treatment and those which should receive intensive or routine scouting.

The sylvatic nature of *labranchiae* in Sardinia was emphasized. It was agreed that while there was no danger of malaria transmission in Sardinia for the next few years regardless of the type of control used, a residual spray program would eventually have to take into account the sylvatic aspects of the problem. This would add to the difficulty of residual spraying in Sardinia and would increase its cost. Although this did not present any unusual difficulties, it did necessitate special consideration as to methods and costs and made it impossible to duplicate in Sardinia the type of program carried out on the mainland of Italy. There seemed to be no doubt that a carefully supervised residual spray program would control malaria, but a partial or poorly executed program would eventually permit the return of *labranchiae*, particularly in rural areas, with the consequent danger of renewed malaria transmission.

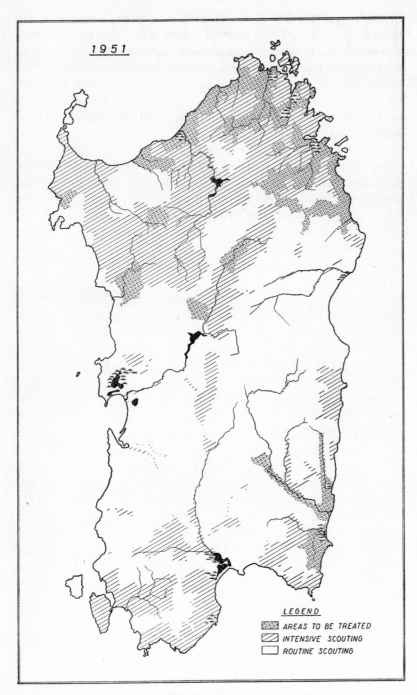

FIGURE 37. Proposed subdivision for future eradication measures.

The representatives of the High Commissioner concluded that the effectiveness of DDT residual spraying in other parts of Italy was ample guarantee of the success of a similar plan in Sardinia. As there was no apparent scientific reason for the continuation of eradication activities, they preferred to include Sardinia under the national program. Their decision was to proceed with plans for an island-wide DDT residual spray program for Sardinia in 1951 and in succeeding years.

With regard to the achievements of ERLAAS in the field of rehabilitation, no opportunity was lost to impress on both the Regional and Central Governments the fact that the project, although the most important effort up to that time, was only the first step in the development of Sardinia. It was suggested that an unbiased scientific survey should follow to investigate the island's social and economic resources, its principal problems and its opportunities. On the basis of this survey, a systematic plan of development could be evolved.

Both governments had previously recognized this principle; in fact, Article 13 of the Sardinian constitution provides for inter-governmental cooperation in formulating a unified program of development. ERLAAS has been at least partially responsible for activating this agreement, and early in 1951 a joint Italian-Sardinian Study Commission was established to plan the "rebirth of Sardinia." With the initiation of this new project, the considerable investment both in time and in money which ERLAAS represents will begin to pay dividends.

BIBLIOGRAPHY

ADAM, N. K.
  1945 A rapid method for assessing the spreading power of anti-
        malarial oils. Bull. Ent. Res., 36:269-272
AITKEN, T. H. G.
  1945 Unpublished record.
  1946 A study of winter DDT house-spraying and its con-
        comitant effect on anophelines and malaria in an
        endemic area. J. Nat. Mal. Soc., 5:169-187
  1948 Recovery of anopheline eggs from natural habitats, an
        aid to rapid survey work. Ann. Ent. Soc. Am., 41:327-
        329
ALESSANDRINI, M. E.
  1948 Metodo rapido per svelare piccole quantità di DDT su
        superfici spruzzate; nota preliminare. Rendic. Ist.
        Super. di San., 11:518-520
ALLIED MILITARY GOVERNMENT
  1943 Sardinia: People and Administration. Western Central
        District Office, London, Handbook No. 2, Part I, 42 pp.
AZIZ, M.
  1947 Report on the *Anopheles* (malaria) eradication scheme,
        Karpas-Cyprus 1946. Cyprus Govt. Print. Office,
        Nicosia, 67 pp., 35 figs. (see Trop. Dis. Bull., 45:152-
        154, 1948)
  1948 Interim report on island-wide *Anopheles* (malaria) eradi-
        cation programme for the year 1947, Nicosia, Cyprus.
        Ann. Med. and San. Rept., Appendix F, pp. 18-32
  1949 Report on the *Anopheles* (malaria) eradication pro-
        gramme for the year 1948, Nicosia, Cyprus. Ann. Med.
        and San. Rept., Appendix I, pp. 24-35
BARBIERI, V.
  1946 Notes on larviciding procedures in Dougherty County,
        Georgia. (Unpublished report to the Italian High Com-
        missioner for Hygiene and Public Health)

BATES, M.

1937 The seasonal distribution of anopheline mosquitoes in the vicinity of Tirana, Albania. Riv. di Malariol. 16:253-264

1939 Variation in the antipalmate hairs of larvae of the *Anopheles maculipennis* complex. Riv. di Malariol. 18:299-312

1940 The nomenclature and taxonomic status of the mosquitoes of the *Anopheles maculipennis* complex. Ann. Ent. Soc. Am., 33:343-356

1941a Studies in the technique of raising anopheline larvae. Am. J. Trop. Med., 21:103-122

1941b Laboratory observations on the sexual behavior of anopheline mosquitoes. J. Exper. Zool., 86:153-173

1941c Field studies of the anopheline mosquitoes of Albania. Proc. Ent. Soc. Wash., 43:37-58

1949 The Natural History of Mosquitoes. The Macmillan Company, New York, xv, 379 pp., 9 figs., 16 plates

1950 The Nature of Natural History. Charles Scribner's Sons, New York, 309 pp.

BATES, M. and HACKETT, L. W.

1939 The distinguishing characteristics of the populations of *Anopheles maculipennis* found in southern Europe. Verhandlungen des VII Internationalen Kongresses für Entomologie, 1938, Weimar, 3:1555-1569

BATES, M., BEKLEMISHEV, W. N. and LA FACE, L.

1949 Anophelines of the Palearctic Region, pp. 419-442. In: Malariology, edited by M. F. Boyd, W. B. Saunders Co., Philadelphia and London, Vol. I, 787 pp.

BLACKLOCK, D. B. and WILSON, C.

1941 Notes on *Anopheles gambiae* and *A. gambiae* var. *melas* in Freetown and its vicinity. Ann. Trop. Med. & Parasit., 35:37-42

BOYD, M. F.

1949a Epidemiology of malaria: factors related to the intermediate host, pp. 551-607. In: Malariology, edited by M. F. Boyd, W. B. Saunders Co., Philadelphia and London, Vol. I, 787 pp.

1949b Epidemiology of malaria: factors related to the definitive host, pp. 608-697. In: Malariology, edited by M. F. Boyd, W. B. Saunders Co., Philadelphia and London, Vol. I, 787 pp.

BROTZU, G.
1935 Relazione sulla campagna antimalarica in provincia di Cagliari nel 1934, pp. 3-93. Comitato Antimalarico Provinciale di Cagliari, Tipografia Valdès, Cagliari

BRUCE, W. N. and DECKER, G. C.
1950 Housefly tolerance for insecticides. Soap and Sanitary Chemicals, 26:122-125

BUSVINE, J. R.
1951 Mechanism of resistance to insecticide in houseflies. Nature, 168:193-195

BÜTTIKER, W.
1948 Beitrag zur Kenntnis der Biologie und Verbreitung einiger Stechmückenarten in der Schweiz. Mitt. Schweiz. Ent. Ges., 21:1-148 (see Rev. Appl. Ent., B, 38:168, 1950)

CALLOT, J.
1938 Contribution à l'étude des moustiques de Tunisie et en particulier du sud de la Régence. Arch. Inst. Pasteur Tunis, 27:133-183

CALLOT, J. and DAO VAN TY
1945 Contribution à l'étude des moustiques français. Culicides de Richelieu (Indre-et-Loire). Ann. Parasit. Hum. et Comp., 20:43-66

CANALIS, A., FADDA, M. and SANNA, A.
1950 La malaria in provincia di Sassari prima e dopo la campagna anti-anofelica dell'ERLAAS. L'Igiene Moderna, 43:17

CASINI, P.
1949 Il gruppo elettrico Sardo e gli impianti dell'alto Flumendosa. Società Elettrica Sarda, Rome, 191 pp., 6 maps, 31 figs.

CAUSEY, O. R., DEANE, L. M. and DEANE, M. P.
1943 Ecology of *Anopheles gambiae* in Brazil. Am. J. Trop. Med., 23:73-94

CHILDE, V. GORDON
1925 The Dawn of European Civilization. Alfred A. Knopf, New York, xvi, 328 pp.

COMMISSION FOR THE STUDY OF THE REORGANIZATION OF THE HEALTH CARE SERVICES
1949 Reports of the Consultants. Alto commissariato per l'igiene e la sanità pubblica, Rome, Vol. 2, 271 pp., 4 maps

CORRADETTI, A.
1931 Alcune osservazioni sulla biologia dell' *Anopheles maculipennis.* Riv. di Malariol., 10:689-702
1934 Ricerche sulla biologia delle diverse razze di "*Anopheles maculipennis.*" Riv. di Malariol. 13:182-190

DEL VECCHIO, G. and DEL VECCHIO, V.
1946 Prime osservazioni sull'anofelismo in provincia di Salerno. Boll. Soc. Ital. Biol. Sper., 22:7-8 (see Rev. Appl. Ent., B, 36:109, 1948)

DE MEILLON, BOTHA
1947 The Anophelini of the Ethiopian geographical region. Pub. South African Inst. Med. Res., Johannesburg, 10:1-272

DEONIER, C. C. and GILBERT, I. H.
1950 Resistance of salt-marsh mosquitoes to DDT and other insecticides. Mosq. News, 10:138-143

DEONIER, C. C., RAUN, E. S., PEEK, E. H., DAVIS, A. N., JR., and NOTTINGHAM, E.
1949 A comparison of DDT and other new insecticides for mosquito control. Mosq. News, 9:150-152

EARLE, W. C., PÉREZ, M., DEL RIO, J., and ARZOLA, C.
1939 Observations on the course of naturally acquired malaria in Puerto Rico. Puerto Rico J. Pub. Health & Trop. Med., 14:391-406

EDWARDS, F. W.
1923 Oligocene mosquitoes in the British Museum: with a summary of our present knowledge concerning fossil Culicidae. Quart. J. Geolog. Soc., 79:139-155

ETHERINGTON, D.
1944 Fertilization of *A. maculipennis* var. *labranchiae* in the laboratory. Nature, London, 154:608

FALLERONI, D.
1926   Fauna anofelica italiana e suo "habitat" (paludi, risaie, canali). Metodi di lotta contro la malaria. Riv. di Malariol., 5:553-593

FERMI, C.
1934   Regioni malariche, decadenze, risanamento e spesa, "Sardegna." Tipografia Editrice di Roma, S. A., Rome, Vol. I, 344 pp.

FERMI, C. and TONSINI, C.
1902   La profilassi della malaria e la distribuzione delle zanzare nell'Isola dell'Asinara. Studi Sassaresi, 2:141

FLORIS, M.
1948   Relazione sulla campagna antimalarica 1947 nella provincia di Cagliari. Riv. di Malariol., 27:29-40

FREEBORN, S. B.
1932   The seasonal life history of *Anopheles maculipennis* with reference to humidity requirements and "hibernation." Am. J. Hyg., 16:215-223

GAHAN, J. B. and PAYNE, G. C.
1947   Control of *Anopheles pseudopunctipennis* in Mexico with DDT residual sprays applied in buildings. Am. J. Hyg., 45:123-132

GARNHAM, P. C. C., HARPER, J. O. and HIGHTON, R. B.
1946   The mosquitoes of the Kaimosi forest, Kenya Colony, with special reference to yellow fever. Bull. Ent. Res., 36:473-496

GAUD, J., FAURE, J. and MAURICE, A.
1949   Biogéographie des espèces anophéliennes au Maroc. Bull. Inst. Hyg. Maroc, 9:145-164

GAZZETTA UFFICIALE DELLA REPUBBLICA ITALIANA
1948   Maritime Health Order No. 3 and Aeronautical Health Order No. 3A, February 18

GHIDINI, G. M.
1934   Contributo alla conoscenza dei culicidi della Libia. Boll. Soc. Ent. Italiana, 66:32-34

HACKETT, L. W.
1929   Malaria control through anti-mosquito measures in Italy. Trans. Roy. Soc. Trop. Med. & Hyg., 22:477-499

1935   Races of *Anopheles maculipennis*. Riv. di Malariol., (suppl.) , 14:48-57

1937   Malaria in Europe. Oxford University Press, Humphrey Milford, London, xvi, 336 pp., 60 figs.

1944   Spleen measurements in malaria. J. Nat. Mal. Soc., 3:121-133

1949   Conspectus of malaria incidence in northern Europe, the Mediterranean Region and the Near East, pp. 788-799. In: Malariology, edited by M. F. Boyd, W. B. Saunders Co., Philadelphia and London, Vol. II, pp. 788-1643

HACKETT, L. W. and MISSIROLI, A.

1930   Field studies on the causes of the natural disappearance of malaria in certain regions of Europe. Comptes Rendus 2me Cong. Internat. du Paludisme (Alger) , 1:322-347

1935   The varieties of *Anopheles maculipennis* and their relation to the distribution of malaria in Europe. Riv. di Malariol., 14:45-109

HADDOW, A. J.

1945   On the mosquitoes of Bwamba County, Uganda: I. Description of Bwamba with special reference to mosquito ecology. Proc. Zool. Soc., London, 115 (pts. I-II) : 1-13

HADJINICOLAOU, J.

1938   Observations on *Anopheles marteri*, S & P. Riv. di Malariol., 17:44-50

HILL, R. B.

1937   The length of life of *Anopheles maculipennis*, var. *atroparvus*. South. Med. J., 30:952-953

HUFF, CLAY G.

1931   The inheritance of natural immunity to *Plasmodium cathemerium* in two species of *Culex*. J. Prev. Med., 5:249-259

INTER-SERVICE INFORMATION SERIES (ISIS)

1942   Report on Sardinia, History, Geography and Medical. Inter-Service Topographical Department, London, C. B. 4096 G (1) , Parts I, II and III, 142 pp.

ISTITUTO CENTRALE DI STATISTICA
  1950a Compendio Statistico Italiano, 1949-50. Istituto Poli-
        grafico dello Stato, Rome, 279 pp.
  1950b Annuario Statistico Italiano, 1949-50. Istituto Poli-
        grafico dello Stato, Rome, xxvii, 489 pp.

ISTITUTO NAZIONALE DI ECONOMIA AGRARIA
  1947a La Distribuzione della Proprietà Fondiaria in Italia—
        Sardegna. Edizioni Italiane, Rome, 105 pp.
  1947b L'Economia Agraria della Sardegna. Edited by Enzo
        Pampaloni, Edizioni Italiane, Rome, 273 pp.

ISTITUTO SUPERIORE DI SANITÀ
  1946 Andamento nel 1940 delle malattie infettive e diffusive
        soggette a denunzia obbligatoria. Istituto Poligrafico
        dello Stato, Rome
  1950 Andamento nel 1946 delle malattie infettive e diffusive
        soggette a denunzia obbligatoria in Italia. Istituto
        Poligrafico dello Stato, Rome

KENDRICK, T. D.
  1929 Archaeology (Sardinia). Encyclopaedia Britannica, 14th
        edition, 19:995-996

KRUSÉ, C. W. and METCALF, R. L.
  1946 An analysis of the design and performance of airplane
        exhaust generators for the production of DDT aerosols
        for the control of Anopheles quadrimaculatus. Pub.
        Health Rep., 61:1171-1184

LA FACE, L.
  1931 Sull'esistenza di razze diverse di Anopheles maculipennis.
        Riv. di Malariol., 10:673-683
  1933 Contributo allo studio della biologia delle diverse razze
        di Anopheles maculipennis. Riv. di Malariol., 12:1069-
        1114

LANGERON, M. and GALLIARD, H.
  1933 Deux types de larves d'anophèles nouveaux pour la Corse.
        Ann. Parasit. Hum. et Comp., 11:93-95

LAVEN, H.
  1950 Der Schuppenindex als Unterscheidungsmerkmal der
        Arten in der Anopheles maculipennis-Gruppe. Zeitschr.
        f. Tropenmed. u. Parasit., 2:111-124

LEESON, H. S., LUMSDEN, W. H. R., YOFE, J., and MACAN, T. T.

1950 Anopheles and Malaria in the Near East. London School
Hyg. & Trop. Med., Memoir No. 7, H. K. Lewis & Co.
Ltd., London, xii, 223 pp., 73 figs.

LEWIS, D. J.

1939 The seasonal and geographical distribution of *Anopheles
maculipennis* in Albania. Riv. di Malariol., 18:237-248

1949 The extermination of *Anopheles gambiae* in the Wadi
Halfa area. Trans. Roy. Soc. Trop. Med. & Hyg., 42:
393-402

MACCURDY, G. G.

1924 Human Origins; a manual of prehistory. Vol. II—The
new stone age and the ages of bronze and iron. D.
Appleton and Co., New York, xvi, 516 pp.

MACDONALD, G.

1950a Notes on a visit to ERLAAS, August 1950. (Unpublished)

1950b The analysis of infection rates in diseases in which superinfection occurs. Trop. Dis. Bull., 47:907-915

MADWAR, S. and SHAWARBY, EL.

1950 A short report on the eradication of *Anopheles sergenti*
from the oases in Egypt—1946-1948. WHO Expert
Comm. on Malaria, WHO/Mal/39

MARCH, R. B. and METCALF, R. L.

1949 Development of resistance to organic insecticides other
than DDT by houseflies. J. Econ. Ent., 42:990

MARSHALL, J. F.

1938 The British Mosquitoes. The British Museum (Natural
History), William Clowes and Sons, Ltd., London, x,
341 pp. 172 figs., 20 pls.

MATTINGLY, P. F.

1947 Notes on the early stages of certain Ethiopian mosquitoes,
with some locality records from British West Africa.
Ann. Trop. Med. & Parasit., 41:239-252

MAYR, ERNST

1942 Systematics and the Origin of Species. Columbia Univ.
Press, New York, xiv, 334 pp., 29 figs.

BIBLIOGRAPHY

MEIGEN, J. W.

1804 Klassifikazion und Beschreibung der europäischen zwei-
flügeligen Insekten (Diptera). Karl Reichard, Braun-
schweig, Germany, 1:4

MINISTERO DELL'INTERNO (ISTITUTO DI SANITÀ PUBBLICA)

1941 Andamento nel 1939 delle malattie infettive e sociali
soggette a denunzia obbligatoria. Istituto Poligrafico
dello Stato, Rome

MISSIROLI, A.

1927 La prevenzione della malaria nel campo pratico. Riv.
di Malariol., 6:501-572

1928 La prevenzione della malaria nel campo pratico. II
Relazione. Riv. di Malariol., 7:413-455

1930 La prevenzione della malaria nel campo pratico. III
Relazione (1928-1929). Riv. di Malariol., 9:667-705

1932 Tipi epidemici delle febbri malariche. Riv. di Malariol.,
11:1-24

1939 The varieties of *Anopheles maculipennis* and the malaria
problem in Italy. Verhandlungen des VII Internationalen Kongresses für Entomologie, 1938, Weimar,
3:1619-1640

1944 La malaria nel 1944 e misure profilattiche previste per il
1945. Rendic. Ist. Super. di San., Rome, 7:616-641

1946 La malaria nel 1945 e previsioni per il 1945. Conferenza
tenuta presso l'Istituto Superiore di Sanità, Rome,
Gennaio 1946. (Unpublished report)

1947 Riduzione o eradicazione degli anofeli? Riv. di Parassit.,
8:141-169

MISSIROLI, A. and MARINO, P.

1934 Anwendung des Chinoplasmin zur Malariasanierung.
Archiv. f. Schiffs-u. Tropenhyg., 38:1-16

MOSNA, E.

1934 La chinoplasma usata nella profilassi della malaria. Riv.
" Croce Rossa," Rome, 9:1-15

MOSNA, E. and CANALIS, A.

1937 Profilassi e terapia della malaria coi prodotti sintetici
(esperienze coordinate dai Comitato d'Igiene della
S. d. N.). Riv. di Malariol. (suppl.), 16:1-74

PAMPANA, E. J.
1944 Epidemiologia della malaria. Studi di Medicina e
Biologia, Editrice Nazionale, Rome, 403 pp., 92 figs.
PAMPANA, E. J. and CASINI, G.
1940 Studi di epidemiologia malarica in Sardegna. Riv. di
Malariol., 19:273-289
PATRISSI, T.
1949 L'impiego del DDT nella lotta antimalarica. Ann. Sanità
Pubblica, Rome, 10:3-93
PURI, I. M.
1949 Anophelines of the Oriental Region, pp. 483-505. In:
Malariology, edited by M. F. Boyd, W. B. Saunders Co.,
Philadelphia and London, Vol. I, 787 pp.
PUTNAM, P. and HACKETT, L. W.
1946 An appraisal of the malaria endemic in protected and
comparison areas of Sardinia in the years 1925-34.
J. Nat. Mal. Soc., 5:13-37
RAFFAELE, G.
1928 Una nuova specie di *Anopheles*. Riv. di Malariol.,
7:11-17
REGIONAL LAW OF SARDINIA
1950 Regional Law No. 2 of February 3
THE ROCKEFELLER FOUNDATION HEALTH COMMISSION
1945 Minutes of Meeting of the Board of Scientific Directors,
October 26.
ROMEO VIAMONTE, J. M.
1950 Los anofelinos de España y de la zona española del
Protectorado de Marruecos. Su relación con la difusión
del paludismo. Rev. San. e Hig. Púb., Madrid, 24:213-
295
RUSSELL, P. F., WEST, L. S. and MANWELL, R. D.
1946 Practical Malariology. W. B. Saunders Co., Philadelphia
& London, xx, 684 pp., 238 figs.
SAUTET, J.
1944 Etat actuel du paludisme et de l'anophélisme dans la
région méditerranéenne. Rec. Travaux Inst. Nat. Hyg.,
Paris, 1:176-196. (see Trop. Dis. Bull., 46:1103-1104,
1949)

SCUDDER, H. I.
1947   A new technique for sampling the density of housefly populations. Pub. Health Rep., 62:681-686

SENEVET, G.
1935   Les anophèles de la France et de ses colonies. Iʳᵉ partie, France, Corse, Afrique, Madagascar, La Réunion. Encyclopédie Entomologique, Ser. A, XIX, Paul Lechevalier, Paris, 361 pp., 144 figs., 34 pl.

SENEVET, G. and PRUNNELLE, M.
1927   Une nouvelle espèce d'anophèle en Algérie, Anopheles marteri, n. sp. Arch. Inst. Pasteur Algérie, 5:529-533

SENIOR WHITE, R.
1948   Malaria transmission in the light of modern evolutionary theory applied to malaria-carrying mosquitoes. Indian J. Mal., 2:13-33

SERGENT, ED.
1935   La prémunition dans le paludisme. Riv. di Malariol., (suppl. to no. 3), 14:5-25

SHOUSHA, A. T.
1948   Species-eradication. The eradication of Anopheles gambiae from Upper Egypt, 1942-1945. Bull. World Health Organ., 1:309-352

SHUTE, P. G.
1936   A study of laboratory-bred Anopheles maculipennis var. atroparvus, with special reference to egg-laying. Ann. Trop. Med. & Parasit., 30:11-16

SICART, M.
1942   Contribution à l'étude des Anophèles de Tunisie. Présence de Anopheles (A.) marteri (Senevet et Prunnelle, 1927) Arch. Inst. Pasteur Tunis, 31:132-134

SIMPSON, G. G.
1944   Tempo and Mode in Evolution. Columbia Univ. Press, New York, xviii, 237 pp.

SOPER, FRED L.
1948   Species sanitation as applied to the eradication of (A) an invading or (B) an indigenous species. Proc. 4th Internat. Cong. Trop. Med. & Malaria, Washington, 1:850-857

1951 Nation-wide malaria eradication projects in the Americas. V. General Principles of the Eradication Programs in the Western Hemisphere. J. Nat. Mal. Soc., 10:183-194

SOPER, F. L. and WILSON, D. B.

1942 Species eradication; practical goal of species reduction in control of mosquito-borne disease. J. Nat. Mal. Soc., 1:5-24

1943 *Anopheles gambiae* in Brazil, 1930 to 1940. The Rockefeller Foundation, New York, xviii, 262 pp., 75 figs.

SOPER, F. L., WILSON, D. B., LIMA, S. and SÁ ANTUNES, W.

1943 The Organization of Permanent Nation-Wide Anti-*Aedes aegypti* Measures in Brazil. The Rockefeller Foundation, New York, ix, 137 pp., 27 figs.

SOPER, F. L., DAVIS, W. A., MARKHAM, F. S. and RIEHL, L. A.

1947a Typhus fever in Italy, 1943-1945, and its control with louse powder. Am. J. Hyg., 45:305-334

SOPER, F. L., KNIPE, F. W., CASINI, G., RIEHL, L. A. and RUBINO, A.

1947b Reduction of *Anopheles* density effected by the preseason spraying of building interiors with DDT in kerosene, at Castel Volturno, Italy, in 1944-1945 and in the Tiber Delta in 1945. Am. J. Trop. Med., 27:177-200

SPANEDDA, A.

1940 Tipi di anofelini esistenti in Provincia di Cagliari. Rassegna Medica Sarda, Cagliari, 42:1-5

STAGE, H. H.

1950 Petroleum oils used in mosquito control. Joint symposium on the agricultural applications of petroleum products. Am. Chem. Assn., Chicago, Ill., September 3-8, pp. 53-68

STEPHENS, J. F.

1828 Art. LIV. Note on the foregoing paper, with a description of a new species of *Anopheles*. Zool. J., 3:502-504

SVENSSON, R.

1940 A Handbook of Malaria Control. The Shell Group of Oil Companies, London, vii, 77 pp., 13 figs., 20 pls.

SYMES, C. B.

1931 Report on anophelines and malaria in the Trans-Nzoia district. Kenya E. Afr. Med. Jour., 8:64-77, 108-121

THEOBALD, F. V.

1903 A Monograph of the Culicidae or Mosquitoes. The British Museum (Natural History), London, Vol. III, xviii, 359 pp., 193 figs., 17 pls.

TORRES CAÑAMARES, F.

1944 Contribución al conocimiento del *Anopheles claviger*, Mg. de España (Dip. Cul.). Eos, 20:233-245

1946 Nuevos datos sobre el *Anopheles marteri* Sen. y Pru. en España. ¿Sé trata de una variedad?, (Dip. Cul.). Eos, 22:47-59

TRAPIDO, HAROLD

1946 The residual spraying of dwellings with DDT in the control of malaria transmission in Panama, with special reference to *Anopheles albimanus*. Am. J. Trop. Med., 26:383-415

1951a The toxicity of DDT to *Anopheles claviger* (Meigen) in Sardinia and on the Italian mainland. J. Nat. Mal. Soc., 10:266-271

1951b Factors influencing the search for anopheline larvae in Sardinia. J. Nat. Mal. Soc., 10:318-326

UNGUREANU, E. and SHUTE, P. G.

1947 The value of the wing scales as an aid to the taxonomy of adult *Anopheles maculipennis*. Proc. Roy. Ent. Soc., London, B, 16:79-85

UNITED NATIONS RELIEF AND REHABILITATION ADMINISTRATION

1945 Estimate of proposed program for malaria eradication. (Unpublished inter-office correspondence)

UNITED STATES PUBLIC HEALTH SERVICE

1946 Larviciding. Communicable Disease Center, Atlanta, Ga., 62 pp.

VAN THIEL, P. H.

1938 On zoöphilism and anthropophilism of *Anopheles* biotypes and species. Acta Convent. Tertii de Trop. Atque Malar. Morbis, Amsterdam, 2:142-151

WEYER, F.

1939 Die Malaria-Überträger (Eine Zusammenstellung der wichtigen *Anopheles*-Arten mit Angaben über Verbreitung, Brutgewohnheiten, Lebensweise und praktische Bedeutung). George Thieme, Leipzig, 141 pp., 15 figs.

WORLD HEALTH ORGANIZATION

1948a Doc. S. 19, Report on the Second Session of the Expert
Committee on Malaria of the Interim Commission
Off. Rec. WHO, 11:43-61

1948b Doc. a/69, Second Report of the Committee on Programme of the First World Health Assembly, July 16,
1948. Off. Rec. WHO, 13:301-302

1950a Report on the First Session of the Expert Committee on
Insecticides. Technical Report Series No. 4, Geneva

1950b Report on the Second Session of the Expert Committee
on Insecticides. Technical Report Series No. 34, Geneva

ZEUNER, F. E.

1951 Dating the Past. An Introduction to Geochronology.
Longmans, Green and Co., New York, xviii, 474 pp.

INDEX

Accounting department: 215–16
Aedes aegypti: 3, 354, 355, 360–62, 363
Aitken, T. H. G.: 5, 28, 372, 382
Alarm reactions: 100–101
Allied Military Government: 5, 6; Allied (Control) Commission, 5, 6; Public Health Sub-Commission, 6
Anopheles: *albimanus*, 364, 371; *algeriensis*, adult habitats, 342–43, description, 178, 305, 339–40, distribution, 29, 171, 180, 257, 303, 307, 340, larval habitats, 342, reaction to larvicides, 97, seasonal cycle, 340–42, species association, 321; *atroparvus*, 99, 180, 303, 304, 316, 320, 321, 325, 331; *claviger*, adult habitats, 339, description, 305, 334–35, distribution, 29, 53, 54, 153, 171, 180, 303, 306–307, 332, 335, larval habitats, 338, 351, reaction to larvicide, 60, 97, 99–101, seasonal cycle, 336–38, species association, 321; *culicifacies*, 65; *freeborni*, 314; *gambiae*, 3, 4, 28, 49, 65, 84, 141–42, 279, 353, 354, 355, 361–62, 363; *hispaniola*, adult habitats, 352, description, 348-49, distribution, 153, 171, 180, 303–304, 323, 332, 349, larval habitats, 350–52, seasonal cycle, 350; *labranchiae*, vii, ix, x, 6, 8, 157, 392–93, adult habitats, 323–32, 370, 372–74, breeding places, 25–26, 295–96, description, 307–308, feeding habits, 325–26, flight activities, 326–28, geographic distribution, 29, 35–36, 43, 84, 196–97, 204, 251, 291, 293, 297–98, 303–305, 308–309, 357, incidence, 153, 163, 167, 171, 175, 355, 363, laboratory colonization, 331–32, larval habitats, 317–21, 351, longevity, 296, 330–31, 1946–47 campaign, 30–37, 1947–48 campaign, 37–49, 283, 285, 1949 campaign, 49–55, 129, 147–48, 284, 1950 campaign, 55–62, 85, 129, 149–50, 152, 1951 campaign, 63–64, reaction to insecticides, 95–97, 100–101, relation to malaria, 178–82, 332, relation to man, 365, 368, 373, residual spraying against, 39, 66–68, 288, seasonal cycle, 309–17, seasonal distribution, 182–85, 189, species association, 321–23, swarming of males, 331, sylvatic nature, 328–30; *maculipennis*, 25, 26, 178, 296, 303, 304–306, 313, 314, 357; *marteri*, adult habitats, 346, description, 343-44, distribution, 29, 171, 180, 303, 307, 323, 344–45, larval habitats, 345–46, seasonal cycle, 345; *melanoon*, biology, 333–34, description, 332–33, distribution, 29, 171, 180, 288, 321, 323, 325; *messeae*, 180, 288, 304, 320, 321, 325; *plumbeus*, 147, adult habitats, 348, description, 335, 346-47, distribution, 180, 303, 347, larval habitats, 347–48, seasonal cycle, 347; *pseudopunctipennis*, 364; *quadrimaculatus*, 364; *sacharovi*, 26, 35, 178, 180, 288, 304, 320, 325; *superpictus*, 26, 35, 180, 303
Arrighi, Aristide: xxviii, 384
Atzeni, Euco: xxvii

Bacchiani, Augusto: xxvii
Banditry: 46, 232
Bastianelli, G.: 49
Bates, Marston: xi
Benedetti, Gian Battista: xxviii

411